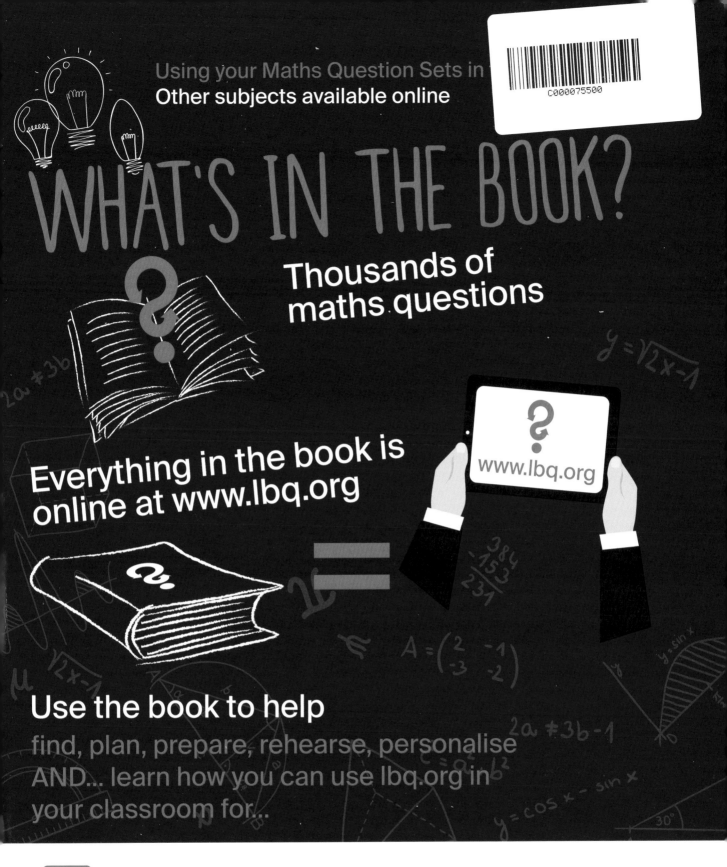

Using your Maths Question Sets in
Other subjects available online

C000075500

WHAT'S IN THE BOOK?

Thousands of maths questions

Everything in the book is online at www.lbq.org

www.lbq.org

Use the book to help

find, plan, prepare, rehearse, personalise
AND... learn how you can use lbq.org in
your classroom for...

Whole Class Teaching
Teach mode turns any question into a slide - ideal for whiteboard or touchscreen display

Ad hoc Questioning
Instantly create and send questions to your class

Self Paced Tasks
Set Questions Sets for your class to work through at their own pace.

Teach

If you've got a whiteboard or touch screen you can turn any question into a whole class teaching resource

Wherever you see the 'Teach' symbol you're one click away from turning a question or Question Set into a teaching resource.

TEACH ICON

Each question can be an ideal teaching point

Annotate to explain, model and work as an example

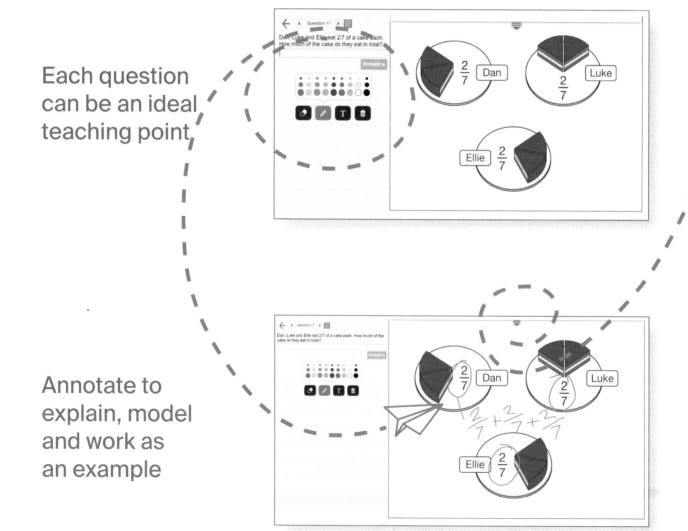

Use the pull down pad to construct your own questions

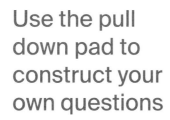

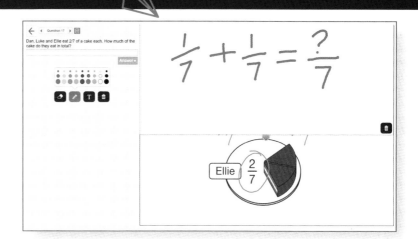

Work through multiple questions like a slide show

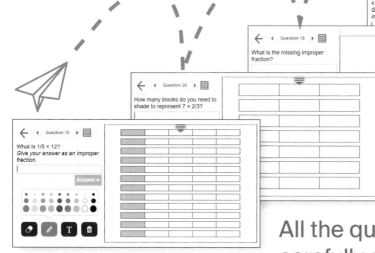

All the questions are grouped into carefully scaffolded sets and provide great support for progression from simple practice to mastery

TEACH MODE IS **FREE** TO ALL REGISTERED USERS

Register FREE at lbq.org

USE THE BOOK TO HELP FIND, ORGANISE AND REHEARSE QUESTIONS TO INCLUDE IN YOUR LESSONS

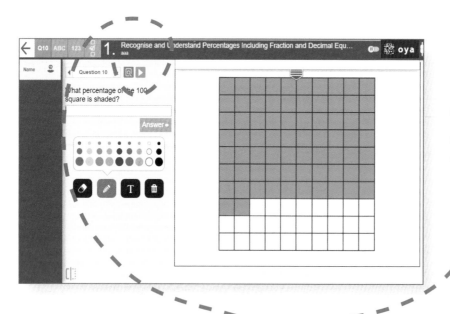

Want to build on an existing lbq.org question?

Annotate to explain, model, modify and extend...

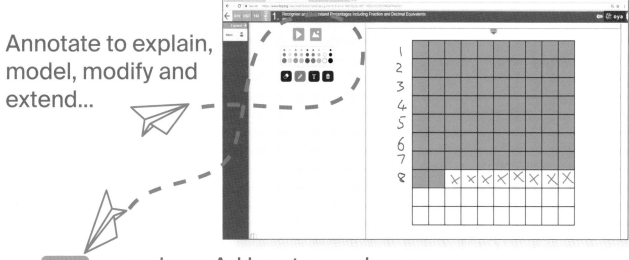

...and use Ad hoc to send as a new question to your class.

Or just make your own questions on the fly?

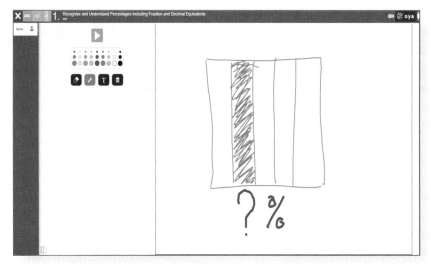

Use our teach tools to create the right question at the right time.

Write a question, draw a question or just ask a question...

... and forget **'hands up'.**   With Ad hoc questioning everyone answers, every question, every time!

USE THE BOOK TO CHOOSE, ORGANISE AND REHEARSE QUESTIONS TO TEACH IN YOUR CLASSES

Self Paced Tasks*

Lbq.org is built on tens of 1000's of questions - questions grouped into carefully scaffolded sets to provide structured support for learning and to help pin point problems.

When you click the 'Start' button you're opening the door for your class to start answering questions

START BUTTON

Pupils connect with a simple code and start receiving questions straight away.

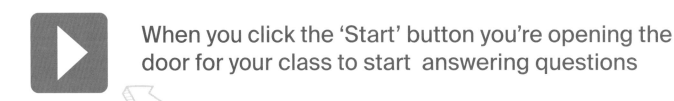

Enter your code

6 l d

using LbQ Tasks

App Store   Google play   Get it from Microsoft

Connect using:
QR Code

Learning by Questions

*Subscription required for self-paced and ad hoc tasks after initial trial. Teach mode remains free.

Register FREE at lbq.org

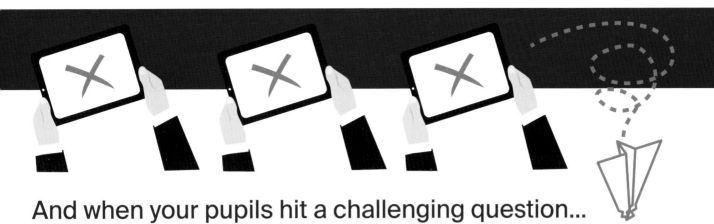

And when your pupils hit a challenging question...

... you'll know about it.

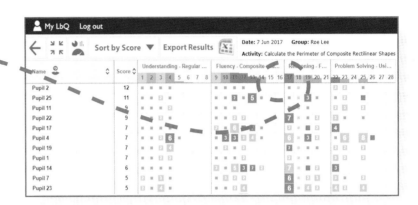

So drill down to see every answer - be right on top of every misconception.

Then pause, intervene, explore, explain, model with the 'Teach' features.

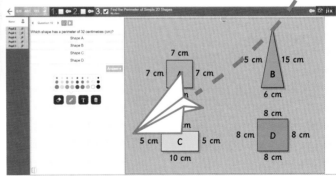

And try the question again with ad hoc questioning.

Everything in this book is online at www.lbq.org

USE THE BOOK TO PICK THE RIGHT TASKS FOR YOUR CLASS AND BE READY FOR INTERVENTION OPPORTUNITIES.

Other titles in the series

Learning by Questions

PRIMARY KS2	SECONDARY KS3
Maths Year 3 Mathematics Primary Question Sets Year 4 Mathematics Primary Question Sets Year 5 Mathematics Primary Question Sets Year 6 Mathematics Primary Question Sets **Science** Years 3&4 Science Lower KS2 Question Sets* Years 5&6 Science Upper KS2 Question Sets* **English** Years 3&4 English Lower KS2 Question Sets* Years 5&6 English Upper KS2 Question Sets*	**Maths** Year 7 Mathematics Primary Question Sets* Year 8 Mathematics Primary Question Sets* Year 9 Mathematics Primary Question Sets* **Biology** KS3 Biology Question Sets* **Chemistry** KS3 Chemistry Question Sets* **Physics** KS3 Physics Question Sets* **English** KS3 English Question Sets*
US Math Grades 4&5 Mathematics Question Sets**	**US Math** Grades 6&7 Mathematics Question Sets**

* Available January 2019
** Available summer 2019

See www.lbq.org/books for title availability

Understanding a question set

Question set title

Topic & sub topic

Curriculum objective

Quick Search Reference number

Default feedback to students

Block number & title

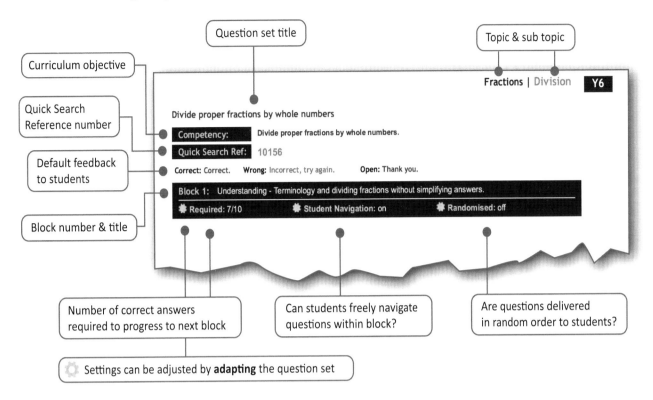

Number of correct answers required to progress to next block

Can students freely navigate questions within block?

Are questions delivered in random order to students?

⚙ Settings can be adjusted by **adapting** the question set

Understanding a question

Question

Answer options, green for correct.

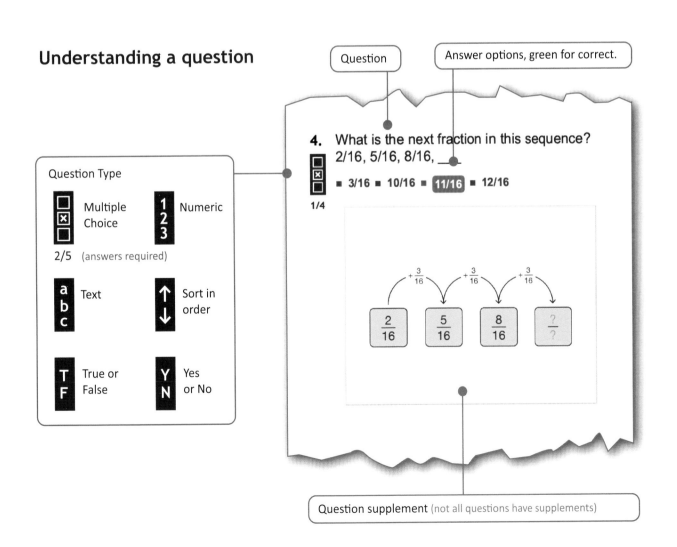

Question supplement (not all questions have supplements)

Finding a Question set from this book on the LbQ Platform

The **year group, topic** and **sub topic** classifications used in this book relate directly to those used on the LbQ platform. The fastest way to find a specific question set on lbq.org is via the **Quick Search Reference Number** (e.g. 10654). To further refine a search select a distinctive **keyword** from the question set title or competency.

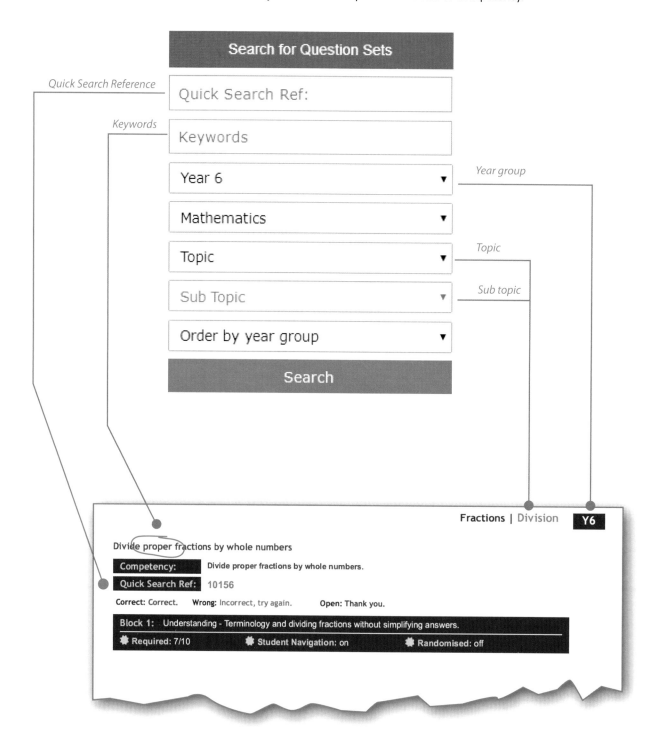

Note: The question sets detailed in this book are correct at time of compilation (July 2018) and correspond directly to the question sets as published on www.lbq.org.

Owing to the nature of www.lbq.org we will from time to time extend, update or modify the question sets published there, which will give rise to discrepancies between this book and the online resources.

Topic Directory   `Y5`

Mathematics

Y5

Place Value

Counting

Compare and Order

Read and Write

Negative Numbers

Rounding and Estimation

Roman Numerals

Count in steps of powers of 10 up to 1,000,000

Competency: Count forwards or backwards in steps of powers of 10.

Quick Search Ref: 10104

Correct: Correct.   **Wrong:** Incorrect, try again.   **Open:** Thank you.

Level 1:   Understanding - Understand and count in powers of ten.

✿ **Required:** 7/10   ✿ **Student Navigation:** on   ✿ **Randomised:** off

1. Count back 10 from 4,562. What is the answer?

 ▪ 3,562 ▪ 4,561 ▪ **4,552** ▪ 4,572 ▪ 4,462

1/5

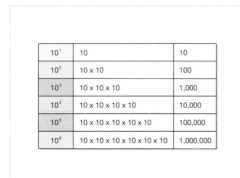

2. What is a power of 10?

 ▪ Any number that results in a whole number when it's divided by 10. For example, 70 ÷ 10 = 7.

1/3 ▪ **The number 10 multiplied by itself a number of times. For example, $10^3 = 10 \times 10 \times 10 = 1,000$.**

▪ Any number that 10 can be divided by equally. For example, 10 ÷ 2 = 5.

10^1	10	10
10^2	10 x 10	100
10^3	10 x 10 x 10	1,000
10^4	10 x 10 x 10 x 10	10,000
10^5	10 x 10 x 10 x 10 x 10	100,000
10^6	10 x 10 x 10 x 10 x 10 x 10	1,000,000

3. What is 63,137 + 100?

 ▪ **63237** ▪ **63,237**

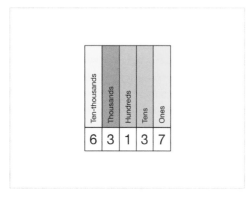

4. $10^2 = $ __.

 ▪ 20 ▪ **100** ▪ 12 ▪ 8 ▪ 5

1/5

5. Count back 1,000 from 847,925. What is the answer?

 ▪ **846,925** ▪ **846925**

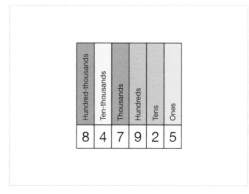

6. Select the 4 numbers that are powers of 10.

 ▪ **10** ▪ 50 ▪ 1,010 ▪ **100** ▪ 101 ▪ **1,000** ▪ **100,000**

4/7

7. Count backwards 10,000 from 359,761. What is the answer?

 ▪ **349,761** ▪ **349761**

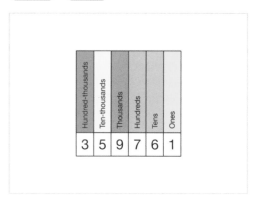

8. What is 10^3?

 ▪ **1,000** ▪ 30 ▪ 13 ▪ 7 ▪ 10,000

1/5

Level 1: *cont.*

9. Count forwards 10 from 6,826. What is the
answer?

■ 6836 ■ 6,836

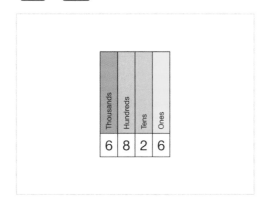

10. Which of the following numbers are **not** powers of
10?

4/7

■ 10 ■ 50 ■ 1,010 ■ 100 ■ 301 ■ 8,117 ■ 100,000

Level 2: Fluency - Calculations and sequences
involving powers of ten.

✿ **Required:** 7/10   ✿ **Student Navigation:** on
✿ **Randomised:** off

11. What number comes next in the sequence?

a
b
c

1,200; 1,300; 1,400; 1,500; _____.

■ 1,600 ■ 1600

12. Kostas has represented a number on the place
value chart. If he subtracts 6 thousands, what
number will he have?

a
b
c

■ 52137 ■ 52,137

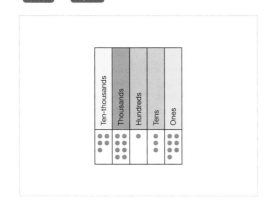

13. What number is missing from the sequence?

a
b
c

28,370; 27,370; _____; 25,370; 24,370.

■ 26,370 ■ 26370

14. What is the pattern in the following sequence?

1/6

59,211; 59,111; 59,011; 58,911; 58,811; 58,711;
58,611.

■ Increasing by 100.   ■ Decreasing by 10.
■ Decreasing by 100.   ■ Increasing by 1,000.
■ Decreasing by 1,000. ■ Increasing by 10.

15. What is 10,000 more than 95,038?

a
b
c

■ 105038 ■ 105,038

16. Jermaine has made a number using base-ten
blocks. If he adds 7 hundreds, what number will he
have?

1
2
3

■ 946

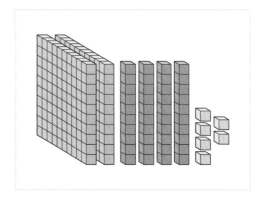

Level 2: cont.

17. What is 1,000 less than 30,563?

a
b
c
 • 29,563 • 29563

18. Jimmy counts back 1,000 from 67,159. What number does he end up with?

a
b
c
 • 66159 • 66,159

19. Add **10,000** to 245,683.

a
b
c
 • 255,683 • 255683

20. What number comes next in the sequence?

a
b
c
43,110; 43,120; 43,130; 43,140; _____.

 • 43,150 • 43150

Level 3: Reasoning - Working with sequences to find missing numbers.

✱ **Required:** 5/7   ✱ **Student Navigation:** on
✱ **Randomised:** off

21. Maya has written a sequence, but the last number is incorrect. What should the last number be?

a
b
c
869,429; 879,429; 889,429; 899,429; 900,429.

 • 909429 • 909,429

22. If you count forwards in 10s from 0, which **four** of these numbers will you say?

☐
☒
☐
 • 1,230 • 10,005 • 60 • 197,520 • 190 • 1
4/7 • 80,008

23. Tim counts forward in 100s:

a
b
c
42,600; 42,700; 42,800; 42,900; 43,100; 43,200.

Can you explain Tim's mistake?

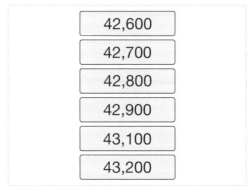

24. Larnea counts forwards in 10s from 8,109. Which of the following numbers will she count?

☐
☒
☐
 • 8,169 • 4,109 • 10,447 • 18,190 • 8,195
3/7 • 13,729 • 189,119

25. What is the value of *x* on the number line?

a
b
c
 • 43,700 • 43700

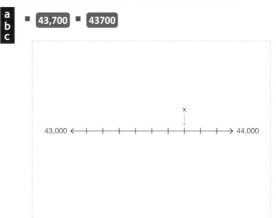

26. Sofia writes a sequence of numbers. What number is missing?

a
b
c
21,800; 21,900; 22,100; 22,200; 22,300.

 • 22000 • 22,000

27. Ashraf says, "If I count forwards in 1,000s from 0, I will say the number 42,100".

a
b
c
Is Ashraf correct? Explain how you know.

Level 4:   Problem Solving - Using knowledge of counting in steps of powers to answer contextual questions.

✹ **Required:** 6/6   ✹ **Student Navigation:** on
✹ **Randomised:** off

28. What is the **answer** to the next number sentence
a
b   in the sequence?
c   492,000 - 10,000 = 482,000
    482,000 - 1,000 = 481,000
    472,000 - 100 = 471,900
    _____ - _____ = ?

   ▪ 461,990 ▪ 461990

29. If a bus company sold 187,422 tickets in 2010,
a   how many tickets did they sell in 2014?
b   In 2011, they sold 1,000 more tickets than 2010.
c   In 2012, they sold 10 fewer tickets than 2011.
    In 2013, they sold 100 fewer tickets than 2012.
    In 2014, they sold 10,000 more tickets than 2013.

   ▪ 198312 ▪ 198,312

30. Liam uses base-ten blocks to make the number
1   shown. Starting with this number, he counts
2   forwards in 100s. How many numbers will he
3   count before he says a number **greater
    than** 3,000?

   ▪ 16

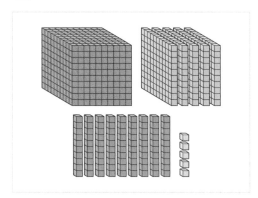

31. Fill in the blanks to make the number sentence
a   true.
b   _ 6, 8 _ 3 - 1,000 + 100 = **7** _, _ **4** _
c   What is the answer to the calculation?

   ▪ 75,943 ▪ 75943

32. Find the value of *a* and then count back in 1,000s
a   five times. What number do you get?
b
c   ▪ 235000 ▪ 235,000

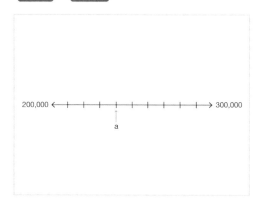

33. Andie sells her car for £3,480. She then wins £100
a   in a competition and decides to spend £10 on a
b   new book and £1,000 on a motorbike. How much
c   money does she have **left**?
    Include the £ sign in your answer.

   ▪ £2,570 ▪ £2570

Read, write, order and compare numbers to at least 1,000,000

Competency: Read, write, order and compare numbers to at least 1,000,000 and determine the value of each digit.

Quick Search Ref: 10279

Correct: Correct.   Wrong: Incorrect, try again.   Open: Thank you.

Level 1:   Understanding - Read, write, order and compare numbers using place value.

✿ Required: 7/10   ✿ Student Navigation: on   ✿ Randomised: off

---

1. What is 3,452 written in words?

1/5
- Three thousand, five hundred and forty-two
- Thirty-four thousand and fifty-two
- Three thousand, four hundred and fifty-two
- Thirty-four hundred and fifty-two
- Three thousand, four hundred and twenty-five

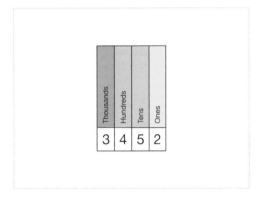

2. Write ninety-four thousand one hundred and twenty-nine in digits.

a b c
- 94,129 ■ 94129

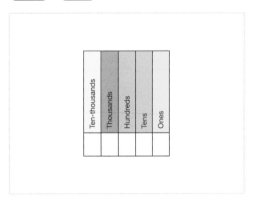

3. What is the value of the digit in the **hundreds column** in the number 345,826?

1/5
- 600 ■ 800 ■ 500 ■ 200 ■ 8

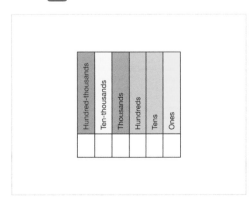

4. Which number is **larger**, 6,812 or 6,598?

1/2
- 6,812 ■ 6,598

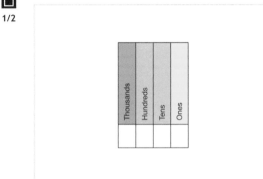

5. Order these numbers from smallest to largest:

 ■ 29,650 ■ 30,270 ■ 30,560 ■ 31,080 ■ 31,700
■ 31,720

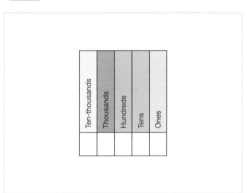

6. Write seven hundred and eighty thousand, four hundred and four in digits.

a b c
- 780,404 ■ 780404

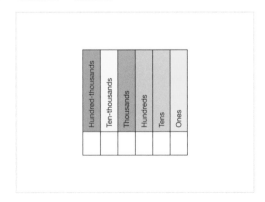

Level 1: *cont.*

7. How many **ten-thousands** are in the number 134,567?

■ 1 ■ 4 ■ 5 ■ **3** ■ 6

1/5

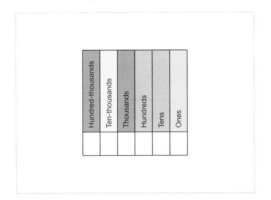

8. What is the value of the digit in the **ten-thousands column** in the number 784,619?

■ 10,000 ■ 40,000 ■ 60,000 ■ 70,000 ■ **80,000**

1/5

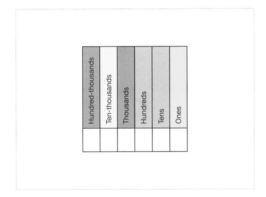

9. What is 599,214 written in words?

■ Five hundred and ninety-nine, two hundred and fourteen
■ **Five hundred and ninety-nine thousand, two hundred and fourteen.**
■ Five million, ninety-nine thousand, two hundred and fourteen.

1/3

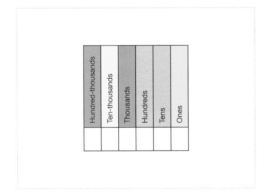

10. Write eighty-one thousand and sixty-seven in digits.

a
b
c

■ **81067** ■ **81,067**

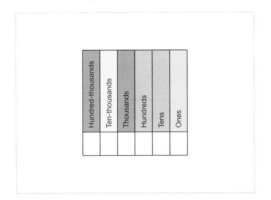

Level 2: Fluency - Place value including decimals and converting between place.

❋ **Required:** 6/9   ❋ **Student Navigation:** on
❋ **Randomised:** off

11. How many **tens** are there in 462 in total?

1
2
3
■ **46**

12. The base-ten blocks represent thousands, hundreds, tens and ones. What number is represented?

a
b
c

■ **1359** ■ **1,359**

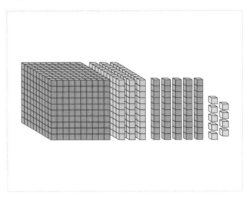

13. What is the value of the 8 in the number 628.714?

1
2
3
■ **8**

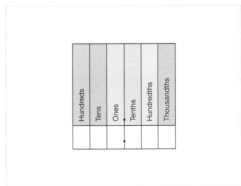

Level 2: cont.

14. What is the value of 2 in the number 402,381? Choose two correct answers.

2/6

- two hundred ■ **two thousand**
- two thousand, three hundred and eighty-one ■ 200
- **2,000** ■ 2,381

number	place value of 2
3,842	2 or two ones
27,839	20,000 or twenty thousand
402,381	
1,516,219	200 or two hundred

15. What digit represents **hundredths** in the number 6,132.895?

1
2
3

- **9**

16. Arrange these numbers in **descending** order:

↑
↓

- **732,970** ■ **729,764** ■ **727,355** ■ **726,010**
- **720,736** ■ **711,499**

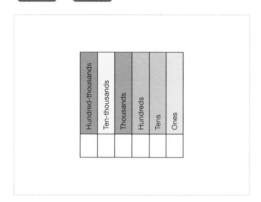

17. What is the value of the digit in the **ten-thousands** column in the number 846,513?

a
b
c

- **40000** ■ **40,000**

18. How many **hundreds** are in 90 tens?

1/5

- 0.9 ■ **9** ■ 900 ■ 9000 ■ 0

19. What is **ten-thousand** more than 261,378?

a
b
c

- **271,378** ■ **271378**

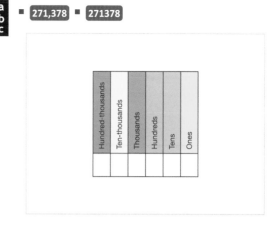

Level 3: Reasoning - Interpreting and comparing place value.

⚙ **Required:** 4/6   ⚙ **Student Navigation:** on
⚙ **Randomised:** off

20. Which symbol makes the statement true?
64,231 ____ 64,099

1/3

- < ■ **>** ■ =

21. The table shows UK rainfall in millimetres (mm) for each year from 2009 to 2015. Which year had the most rainfall?

1/7

- 2015 ■ **2014** ■ 2013 ■ 2012 ■ 2011 ■ 2010 ■ 2009

year	rainfall in mm
2015	1,309.1
2014	1,330.7
2013	1,086.2
2012	1,179.2
2011	1,200.3
2010	1,295.0
2009	1,213.3

22. Using each digit card once, make the largest number possible.

a
b
c

- **977,421** ■ **977421**

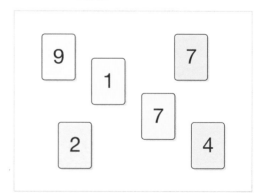

Level 3: *cont.*

23. Harriet says she can order these numbers by looking at only the first four digits in each number. Is she correct? Explain your answer.

a
b
c

1,532,786
1,534,826
1,603,221
1,537,123
1,534,776
1,689,332

24. Sara has written **3,900,466** in words as thirty nine thousand, four hundred and sixty-six, which is **incorrect**. Select the correct way of writing the number **and** the reason why.

2/6

- Thirty-nine hundred, four hundred and sixty-six
- **Three million, nine hundred-thousand, four hundred and sixty-six**
- Three million, nine thousand, four hundred and sixty-six
- There are two zeros after the 3 and 9, which makes thirty-nine thousand
- The digit 9 represents thousands.
- **The digit 3 represents millions.**

25. Daniel says that when he orders these numbers from smallest to largest, the third number will be 353,013. Is he correct? Explain how you know.

a
b
c

353,015
335,015
353,013
335,033
355,555

✿ **Required:** 6/6   ✿ **Student Navigation:** on
✿ **Randomised:** off

26. Using each digit card once, make the closest possible number to 200,000.

a
b
c

■ 201489 ■ 201,489

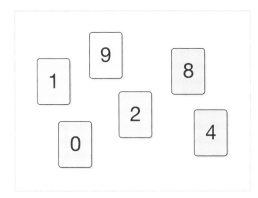

27. The table shows the approximate populations in six European countries, but some of the values are missing. What is the population of Iceland?

a
b
c

The population of Spain is 8,000,000 more than the population of Poland.
The population of Malta is 100 times smaller then the population of Spain.
The population of Iceland is 131,000 less than the population of Malta.

■ 334,000 ■ 334000

country	population
Spain	
Poland	38,500,000
Malta	
Croatia	4,200,000
Iceland	?
Italy	59,700,000

Level 4: *cont.*

28. Omar has written down four numbers containing only the digits 2, 4, 6 and 8. He has represented each digit as a letter. What is the value of **AABCA**?

DDBAC is the largest number.
The sum of the digits in **BDBCD** equals 32.
The sum of the digits in **CCCCC** equals 20.

▪ 22642 ▪ 22,642

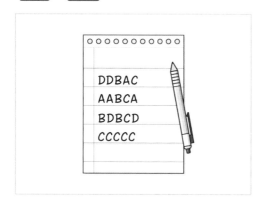

29. What 6-digit number is Chet thinking of?

There is a 2 in the thousands column.
The ones column contains the smallest possible odd number.
The number is larger than 370,000.
The tens column has no value.
The number is smaller than 400,000.
The digit in the ten-thousands column is even.
The hundreds column is equal to 40 divided by 10.

▪ 382401 ▪ 382,401

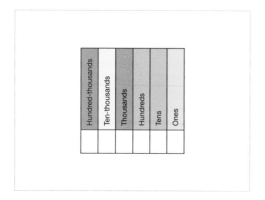

30. Using each digit card once, make the **smallest possible even number**.

▪ 234,798 ▪ 234798

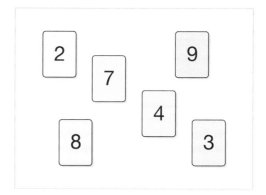

31. Katy is thinking of a number. The number is greater than 8,300 and smaller than 8,600. All of the digits are **even**. How many possible numbers could Katy be thinking of?

▪ 25

Interpret negative numbers

Competency: Interpret negative numbers in context, count forwards and backwards with positive and negative numbers including through zero.

Quick Search Ref: 10024

Correct: Correct.   Wrong: Incorrect, try again.   Open: Thank you.

Level 1: Understanding - Identifying greatest and lowest value and sorting.

❖ **Required:** 7/10   ❖ **Student Navigation:** on   ❖ **Randomised:** off

1. What is a **negative** number?

- ■ A number less than zero. ■ A number greater than zero.
- ■ A number equal to zero.

1/3

2. Which of the following are **negative numbers**?

■ 7 ■ 0 ■ 9 ■ -2 ■ -567 ■ 23 ■ -77

3/7

3. What is a **positive** number?

- ■ A number less than zero. ■ A number greater than zero.
- ■ A number equal to zero.

1/3

4. Sort the numbers in order, starting with the **highest value number**.

■ 3 ■ 2 ■ 1 ■ 0 ■ -1 ■ -2 ■ -3

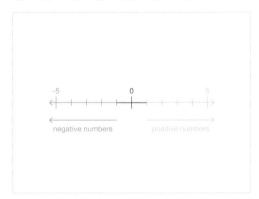

5. Which of the following numbers are **less than zero**?

■ 0 ■ -876 ■ 20 ■ -6 ■ 345 ■ 91 ■ -76

3/7

6. Which number has the **lowest** value?

■ 0 ■ 7 ■ 101 ■ -872 ■ -2 ■ 10,000

1/6

7. Which number has the **greatest** value?

■ -3,543 ■ 0 ■ 182 ■ 28 ■ -56 ■ -1

1/6

8. Sort the numbers in **ascending** order (smallest at the top).

 ■ -4 ■ -2 ■ 0 ■ 2 ■ 4 ■ 6 ■ 8

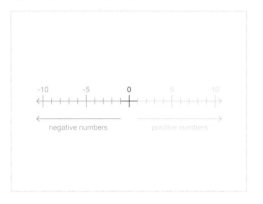

9. Which statement best describes zero?

- ■ Zero is a positive number. ■ Zero is a negative number.
- ■ Zero has no value.

1/3

10. If you count backwards from zero, will the number you stop on be positive or negative?

■ Positive ■ Negative

1/2

Level 2: Fluency - Counting through zero.

❖ **Required:** 7/10   ❖ **Student Navigation:** on
❖ **Randomised:** off

11. What is the missing number in this sequence?

1
2
3

3, 2, 1, 0, -1, ___, -3, -4

■ -2

Level 2: *cont.*

12. According to the table, what is the **difference** in temperature between the coldest month and the warmest month?

1 2 3

- 42

month	temp (°C)
January	-22
February	-18
March	-10
April	0
May	9
June	15
July	17
August	14
September	8
October	-4
November	-17
December	-25

13. If the temperature this morning was -3°C and now it is 7°C warmer, what is the current temperature in °C? *Don't include the units in your answer.*

1 2 3

- 4

14. What is 5 **less than** 2?

1 2 3

- -3

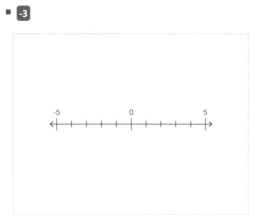

15. Count back 22 from 12. What number do you get?

1 2 3

- -10

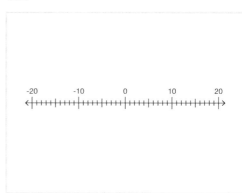

16. What is -7 + 12?

1 2 3

- 5

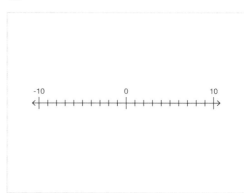

17. What is the value of Y shown on the number line?

1 2 3

- -3

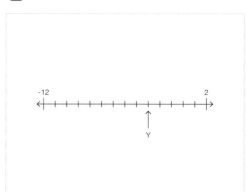

18. Arrange the numbers in **ascending** order (smallest first).

↑ ↓

- -59 ▪ -22 ▪ -11 ▪ -1 ▪ 27 ▪ 40 ▪ 68

Level 2: *cont.*

19. What number is missing from the sequence?

-15, -12, -9, -6, ___, 0, 3, 6, 9

▪ -3

20. Count forwards 11 from -7. What number do you get?

▪ 4

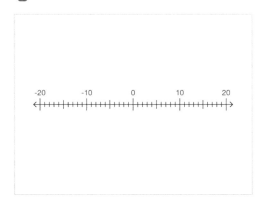

Level 3: Reasoning - Counting in steps greater than one.

✿ **Required:** 5/5   ✿ **Student Navigation:** on
✿ **Randomised:** off

21. Scott counts backwards in 2s. The first number he says is 4. What is the sixth number he says?

▪ -6

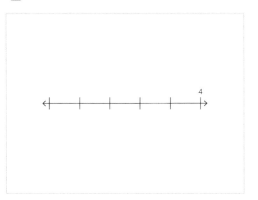

22. According to the table, what was the **difference** in temperature (°C) between Tuesday and Friday? *Don't include the units in your answer.*

▪ 9

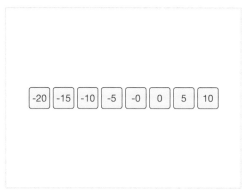

day	temp (°C)
Monday	4
Tuesday	7
Wednesday	3
Thursday	1
Friday	-2
Saturday	3
Sunday	11

23. There is a mistake in the number sequence. Explain what it is.

a
b
c

-20, -15, -10, -5, -0, 0, 5, 10

24. Sabrina writes down a sequence which increases in 3s. The first number in the sequence is -15. What is the 8th number in the sequence?

▪ 6

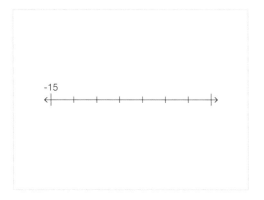

25.

If the temperature on Monday was 9°C and every day the temperature gets 2°C colder, will the temperature on Saturday be below 0°C? Explain how you know.

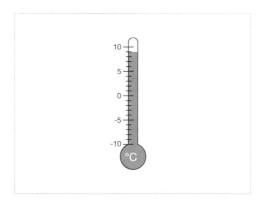

Level 4: Problem Solving - Counting through zero and finding the difference in real life contexts.

✱ **Required:** 5/5   ✱ **Student Navigation:** on
✱ **Randomised:** off

26.

In a quiz, 2 points are given for a correct answer and 1 point is deducted for a wrong answer. A team needs a score of 10 or more to win and they currently have -7 points. How many correct answers do they need to win the quiz?

▪ **9**

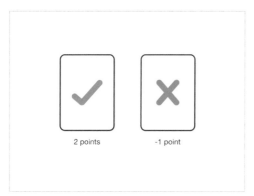

2 points   -1 point

27.
1
2
3
Colin works in a skyscraper. His office is on the 14th floor and the car park is on the -2nd floor. How many floors does he travel to get from his car to his office?

▪ **16**

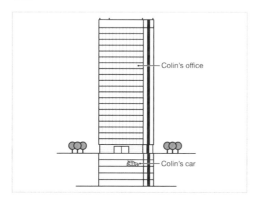

— Colin's office

— Colin's car

28.
1
2
3
If the average temperature in Manchester is 4°C, what is the average temperature (°C) in **Glasgow**?
London is 7°C warmer than Manchester.
Newcastle is 10°C colder than London.
Cardiff is 4°C warmer than Newcastle.
Glasgow is 6° colder than Cardiff.
Don't include the units in your answer.

▪ **-1**

city	temp (°C)
London	
Manchester	4
Cardiff	
Newcastle	
Glasgow	

29.
1
2
3
In a maths test, 1 mark is awarded for a correct answer and 1 mark is deducted for an incorrect answer. If Sofia gets 9 questions correct and 11 questions incorrect, what is her score?

▪ **-2**

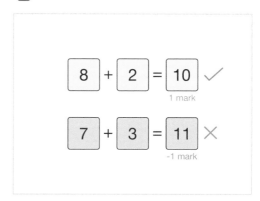

8 + 2 = 10 ✓
1 mark

7 + 3 = 11 ✗
-1 mark

30.
1
2
3
Jessica and her mum are getting out of the swimming pool. To reach the top step, how many steps do they need to take in total?

▪ **11**

Round numbers up to 1,000,000

Competency: Rounding to the nearest 10, 100, 1,000, 10,000 and 100,000.

Quick Search Ref: 10124

Correct: Correct.   Wrong: Incorrect, try again.   Open: Thank you.

Level 1: Understanding - Understanding of rounding, including which columns determine whether to round up or down.

✿ **Required:** 7/10   ✿ **Student Navigation:** on   ✿ **Randomised:** off

1. When rounding a number to the nearest 10, if the digit in the ones column is **5 or above**, would you round up or down?

   1/2
   ▪ round up   ▪ round down

2. What is 75 rounded to the nearest **10**?

   1/2
   ▪ 70   ▪ 80

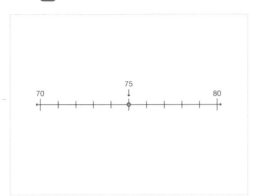

3. What is 152 rounded to the nearest **100**?

   1/2
   ▪ 100   ▪ 200

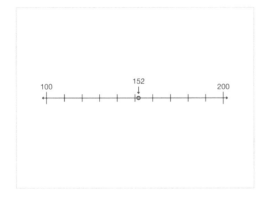

4. When rounding 13,453 to the nearest **1,000**, which column determines whether you round up or down?

   1/6
   ▪ thousands ▪ tens ▪ ten-thousands ▪ ones
   ▪ hundreds ▪ hundred-thousands

5. When rounding 67,429 to the nearest **10,000**, which column determines whether you round up or down?

   1/6
   ▪ tens ▪ thousands ▪ ones ▪ ten-thousands
   ▪ hundreds ▪ hundred-thousands

Level 1: *cont.*

6. When rounding 298,147 to the nearest **100,000**, which column determines whether you round up or down?

1/6 ■ tens ■ ones ■ hundred-thousands ■ thousands
■ hundreds ■ ten-thousands

7. What is 49,997 rounded to the nearest **10**?

1/4 ■ 50,000 ■ 49,990 ■ 49,900 ■ 49,000

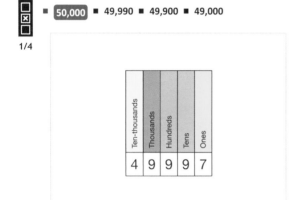

8. When rounding to the nearest **10**, which of the following numbers **round up**?

4/7 ■ 23 ■ 18 ■ 45 ■ 9 ■ 31 ■ 77 ■ 94

9. What is 680 rounded to the nearest **100**?

1
2
3
■ 700

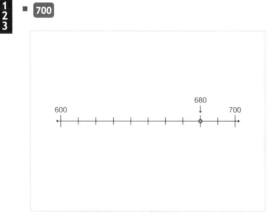

10. What is 84,502 rounded to the nearest **1,000**?

a
b
c
■ 85000 ■ 85,000

Level 2: Fluency - Rounding to powers of ten including misconceptions when rounding.

✿ Required: 7/10   ✿ Student Navigation: on
✿ Randomised: off

11. What is 21,871 rounded to the nearest **100**?

a
b
c
■ 21,900 ■ 21900

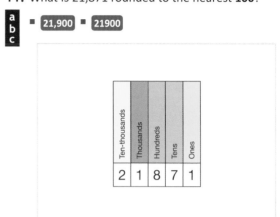

12. When rounding to the nearest 100, which **two** numbers would **not** round to **500**?

2/7 ■ 512 ■ 550 ■ 470 ■ 539 ■ 458 ■ 449 ■ 504

13. A school has 1,642 pupils. How many pupils does it have to the nearest **1,000**?

a
b
c
■ 2,000 ■ 2000

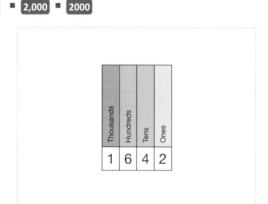

14. There are 12,105 spectators at a volleyball game. What is this to the nearest **10,000**?

a
b
c
■ 10,000 ■ 10000

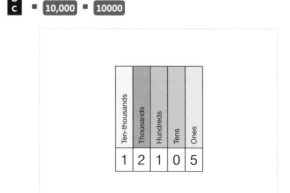

Level 2: *cont.*

15. The population of Luxembourg is 576,243. What is
 this to the nearest **100,000**?

■ 600000 ■ 600,000

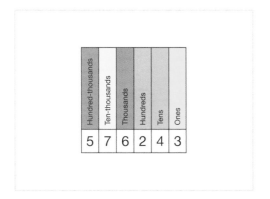

16. What is 999,950 rounded to the nearest **100,000**?

 ■ 1000000 ■ 1,000,000

17. When rounding to the nearest **10,000**, which
three numbers **round down**?

 ■ 13,233 ■ 76,022 ■ 90,277 ■ 129,039 ■ 544,987
3/6 ■ 776,086

18. What is 5,387,102 to the nearest **100,000**?

■ 5400000 ■ 5,400,000

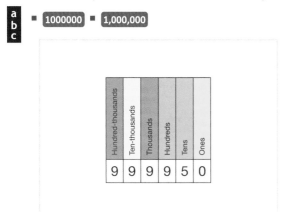

19. What is 168,342 rounded to the nearest **1,000**?

 ■ 168000 ■ 168,000

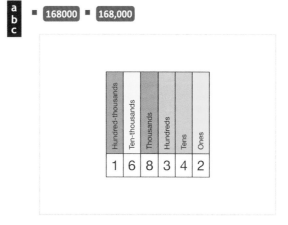

20. There are 8,276 seashells on a beach. What is this
rounded to the nearest **1,000?**

■ 8,000 ■ 8000

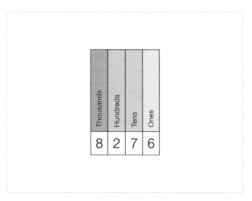

Level 3: Reasoning - Using knowledge of rounding to compare numbers.

✱ **Required:** 5/7   ✱ **Student Navigation:** on
✱ **Randomised:** off

21. A number rounded to the nearest **100** is 23,400.
What is the **largest** possible number that it
can be?

■ 23,449 ■ 23449

22. Amber says, "When I round 24,498 to the nearest
1,000, the number will be 25,000".
Is she correct? Explain your answer.

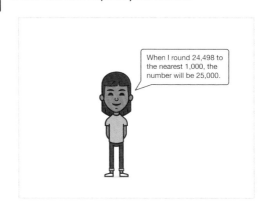

Level 3: cont.

23. Which symbol makes the statement true?
153,646 to the nearest 100,000 __ 192,999 to the nearest 10,000.

1/3   ■ > ■ = ■ <

24. A number rounded to the nearest **10,000** is 480,000. What is the **smallest** possible number that it can be?

■ 475,000   ■ 475000

25. Round the numbers 25,692 and 67,104 to the nearest 10,000 and add the values together.
Add 25,692 to 67,104 and round the answer to the nearest 10,000.

1/3   Which gives the most **accurate** answer?

   ■ Rounding both numbers then adding.
   ■ Adding the numbers then rounding.
   ■ They are both the same.

26. A train breaks down 598 miles into a 1,000 mile journey. Is it closer to its starting point or its destination?
Explain your answer.

27. Select **all** of the numbers that round to 400,000 when rounded to the nearest **100,000**.

   ■ 463,000 ■ 405,789 ■ 349,002 ■ 390,000 ■ 402,609

3/5

Level 4: Problem Solving - Using knowledge of rounding to solve problems.

✱ **Required: 6/6**   ✱ **Student Navigation:** on
✱ **Randomised:** off

28. The table shows how many miles Becky travels each year in her car. Round each value to the nearest **1,000** first to find her **approximate** total mileage.

   ■ 42000   ■ 42,000

year	mileage
2011	9,482
2012	6,201
2013	11,853
2014	14,790
total	

29. William is thinking of a 5-digit number. When rounded to the nearest 10,000 his number is 50,000. All the digits in the number are different odd numbers. What is the **largest** possible number William could be thinking of?

   ■ 53,971   ■ 53971

30. In a year, a shop sells 138,211 pairs of men's shoes, 52,694 pairs of women's shoes and 92,042 pairs of children's shoes.
Round each value to the nearest 10,000 first to find the **approximate** total number of pairs of shoes sold.

   ■ 280000   ■ 280,000

last year's sale figures	
men's shoes	138,211
women's shoes	52,694
children's shoes	92,042

31. A number has a different digit in each column. When rounded to the nearest 1,000 it equals 49,000. What is the **largest** possible number it can be?

   ■ 49,387   ■ 49387

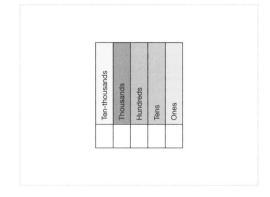

Ten-thousands	Thousands	Hundreds	Tens	Ones

Level 4: *cont.*

32. Ali is thinking of a number. What is the

a
b
c

largest possible number it could be?
When rounded to the nearest 1,000 it is 21,000.
When rounded to the nearest 100 it is 21,200.
When rounded to the nearest 10 it is 21,150.

- 21154 - 21,154

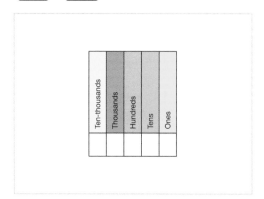

33. Using every number card once, make a number

a
b
c

that rounds to 2,000 when rounded to the nearest
1,000

- 1,942 - 1924 - 2,491 - 2,194 - 1942 - 2,149
- 2194 - 1,924 - 2,419 - 2491 - 2419 - 2149

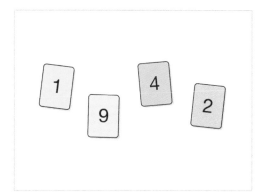

Read Roman numerals up to 1,000

Competency: Read Roman numerals to 1,000 (M) and recognise years written in Roman numerals.

Quick Search Ref: 10113

Correct: Correct.   Wrong: Incorrect, try again.   Open: Thank you.

Level 1: Understanding - How numbers are represented in Roman numerals.

🏵 Required: 7/10   🏵 Student Navigation: on   🏵 Randomised: off

1. In Roman numerals, which statements are correct?

5/7
- Repeated symbols are added. For example, XXX means 10 + 10 + 10 = 30.
- Symbols can only be repeated three times.
- Each digit in a number is represented by a symbol.
- V, L, D are never repeated.
- There is a symbol to represent 0.
- If the symbol of larger value comes first, the values are added. For example, VII means 5 + 1 + 1 = 7.
- If the symbol of smaller value comes first, it is subtracted from the next symbol. For example, IV means 5 - 1 = 4.

2. How is 3 represented in Roman numerals?

1/2
- III ▪ IIV

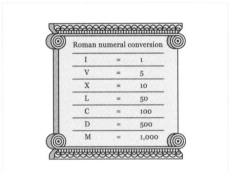

3. How is 6 represented in Roman numerals?

1/3
- VI ▪ IV ▪ IIIIII

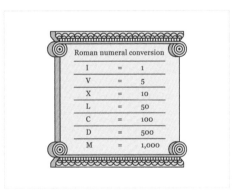

4. How is 4 represented in Roman numerals?

1/2
- IV ▪ IIII

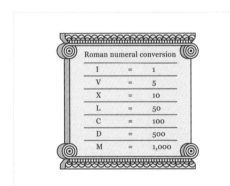

5. How is **70** represented in Roman numerals?

1/3
- LXX ▪ XXXC ▪ XXXXXXX

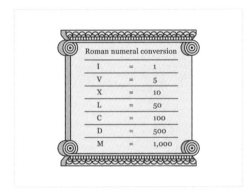

6. How is **300** represented in Roman numerals?

- CCC

7. How is 1,500 represented in Roman numerals?

 ▪ MD

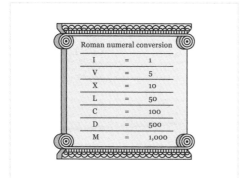

8. How is 7 represented in Roman numerals?

 ▪ VII ▪ IIIX

1/2

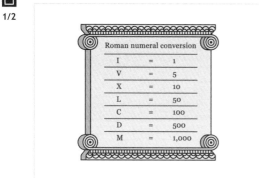

9. How is 40 represented in Roman numerals?

 ▪ XXXX ▪ XL

1/2

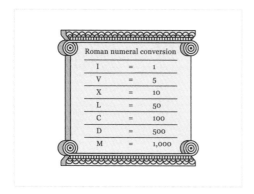

10. How is 800 represented in Roman numerals?

 ▪ DCCC

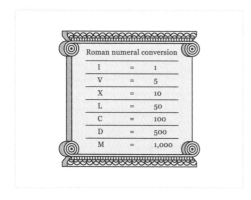

Level 2: Fluency - Representing numbers as Roman numerals (including simple calculations).

✹ **Required:** 7/10   ✹ **Student Navigation:** on
✹ **Randomised:** off

11. What number does **MDC** represent?

▪ 1600 ▪ 1,600

12. What is 32 in Roman numerals?

▪ XXXII

13. What is the answer to the following calculation?
XII + C = ___.
Give your answer in Roman numerals.

▪ CXII

14. What number does **MCC** represent?

▪ 1,200 ▪ 1200

15. What is the answer to the calculation L + XXX?
Give your answer in digits.

▪ 80

16. What is 274 in Roman numerals?

▪ CCLXXIV

17. What is the answer to the calculation D + XXIV?
Give your answer in digits.

▪ 524

18. What number does **XCVI** represent?

▪ 96

19. What is 99 in Roman numerals?

▪ XCIX

20. What is the answer to the calculation M + XL?

▪ 1,040 ▪ 1040

Level 3: Reasoning - Order and comparing Roman numerals.

✹ **Required:** 6/8   ✹ **Student Navigation:** on
✹ **Randomised:** off

21. The following sequence increases by 100 each time. What Roman numeral is missing?
C, CC, CCC, CD, D, ___, DCC, DCCC, CM, M.

▪ DC

Level 3: *cont.*

22. Arrange the following numerals in ascending order (smallest first).

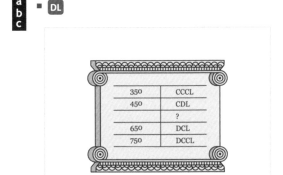

- VIII ∙ XXVI ∙ XLV ∙ C ∙ CDXL

23. What Roman numeral is missing from the table?

a
b
c

- DL

350	CCCL
450	CDL
	?
650	DCL
750	DCCL

24. Using each numeral card **once**, make the largest number possible.

Give your answer in Roman numerals.

1/4 ∙ DCXXL ∙ DCLXX ∙ DXCLX ∙ DXCXL

25. Beth says, "900 is written as CM". Is she correct? Explain your answer.

a
b
c

26. What numeral makes the following statement true?

a
b
c

CCCLV + _____ = D?

- CXLV

27. Calculate the difference between the money in the two purses.

1
2
3

Give your answer in digits.

- 238

28. Which numeral is of greater value **CCCLIV** or **CDXCII**? Explain how you know.

a
b
c

Level 4: Problem Solving - Using Roman numerals to solve problems.

✿ **Required:** 8/8 ✿ **Student Navigation:** on
✿ **Randomised:** off

29. The gravestone shows the dates of the Roman Emperor Nero's birth and death. How old was he when he **died**?

1
2
3

- 30

30. Move just **one** match stick to make the statement true.

Choose the matching statement from those provided.

1/5

- XI - II = XI ∙ X + II = IX ∙ XI + I = XI ∙ XI - II = IX
- X + II = XI

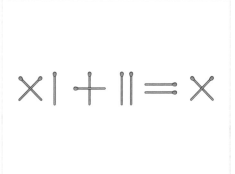

Level 4: cont.

31. In Ancient Rome, **Passus** and **Stadium** were units
a
b   of measure: I Stadium = CXXV Passus.
c   The perimeter of Julius's garden measured **XXV Passus**. If he walked V Stadium around its perimeter, how many times did he walk around the garden?
Give your answer in Roman numerals.

■ XXV

32. The year of release for each film is given in Roman
□   numerals.
☒   What film is indicated by the arrow on the
□   timeline?
1/5 Shrek - MMI
    Frozen - MMXIII
    Moana - MMXVI
    Finding Nemo - MMIII
    How to Train Your Dragon - MMX

■ **Shrek** ■ **Frozen** ■ **Moana** ■ **Finding Nemo**
■ **How to Train Your Dragon**

33. Complete the cross-number and make the largest
a   possible **Roman numeral** from the symbols in the
b   shaded squares.
c   Across:
    1) Write 134 in Roman numerals.
    3) Write 293 in Roman numerals.
    Down:
    2) Write 355 in Roman numerals.
    4) Write 68 in Roman numerals.
    5) Write 99 in Roman numerals.

■ CCXXVI

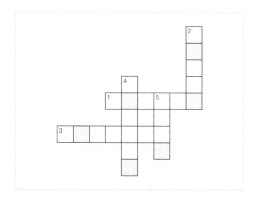

34. The scoreboard shows the result of a Roman
a   Gladiator contest. What is the difference between
b   Eques' and Thraex's scores?
c   *Give your answer in digits.*

■ 948

35. Write the date **13th November, 1993** in Roman
a   numerals in the form: Date.Month.Year.
b
c   ■ XIII.XI.MCMXCIII

36. Each coloured section is the **sum of the numbers**
a   **in the layer outside of it**. One quarter of the
b   wheel has been completed for you. Complete the
c   rest of the wheel and work out the value of the
    centre section.
    Give your answer in Roman numerals.

■ CLIV

Solve number problems: number and place value up to 1,000,000

Competency: Solve a range problems involving place value, powers of 10, negative numbers and rounding.

Quick Search Ref: 10126

Correct: Correct   Wrong: Incorrect, try again.   Open: Thank you.

Level 1:   Extracting and manipulating information.

✿ **Required:** 6/9   ✿ **Student Navigation:** on   ✿ **Randomised:** off

---

1. Sort the planets in **ascending** order (smallest diameter first).

- Mercury ▪ Mars ▪ Venus ▪ Neptune ▪ Uranus
- Saturn ▪ Jupiter

planet	diameter (km)
Mercury	4,879
Venus	12,104
Mars	6,779
Jupiter	142,984
Saturn	120,536
Uranus	50,724
Neptune	49,244

2. To the nearest **1,000**, the diameters of which **two** planets are rounded down?

2/7

- Mercury ▪ Venus ▪ Mars ▪ Jupiter ▪ Saturn
- Uranus ▪ Neptune

planet	diameter (km)
Mercury	4,879
Venus	12,104
Mars	6,779
Jupiter	142,984
Saturn	120,536
Uranus	50,724
Neptune	49,244

3. Which symbol makes the statement true?
Temperature in Oulu __ Temperature in Churchill.

1/3

▪ = ▪ > ▪ <

city (country)	average temp (°C)
Bangkok (Thailand)	27
Churchill (Canada)	-6
Dublin (Ireland)	10
Lisbon (Portugal)	17
Oulu (Finland)	3

4. Which planet has a diameter **closest** to 50,000 kilometres?

1/7

- Mercury ▪ Venus ▪ Mars ▪ Jupiter ▪ Saturn
- Uranus ▪ Neptune

planet	diameter (km)
Mercury	4,879
Venus	12,104
Mars	6,779
Jupiter	142,984
Saturn	120,536
Uranus	50,724
Neptune	49,244

5. Which city makes the statement true?
The temperature in Churchill + the temperature in _____ = 4°C.

1/4

▪ Lisbon ▪ Bangkok ▪ Dublin ▪ Oulu

city (country)	average temp (°C)
Bangkok (Thailand)	27
Churchill (Canada)	-6
Dublin (Ireland)	10
Lisbon (Portugal)	17
Oulu (Finland)	3

6. What is the temperature in Bangkok rounded to the nearest **10°C**?
Don't include the units in your answer.

▪ 30

city (country)	average temp (°C)
Bangkok (Thailand)	27
Churchill (Canada)	-6
Dublin (Ireland)	10
Lisbon (Portugal)	17
Oulu (Finland)	3

---

7. Which city has an average temperature closest to **freezing**?

- Bangkok ■ Churchill ■ Dublin ■ Lisbon ■ Oulu

1/5

city (country)	average temp (°C)
Bangkok (Thailand)	27
Churchill (Canada)	-6
Dublin (Ireland)	10
Lisbon (Portugal)	17
Oulu (Finland)	3

8. Starting with the diameter of Mercury, **count forwards** in steps of 100. How many steps must you count before you reach the diameter of Mars?

- 19

planet	diameter (km)
Mercury	4,879
Venus	12,104
Mars	6,779
Jupiter	142,984
Saturn	120,536
Uranus	50,724
Neptune	49,244

9. What is the **difference** in temperature between Churchill and Lisbon in degrees?
Don't include the units in your answer.

- 23

city (country)	average temp (°C)
Bangkok (Thailand)	27
Churchill (Canada)	-6
Dublin (Ireland)	10
Lisbon (Portugal)	17
Oulu (Finland)	3

10. Round the numbers 8,488 and 7,236 to the nearest 1,000 and add the values together. Then add 8,488 to 7,236 and round the answer to the nearest 10,000.

1/3   Which method is more **accurate**?

- Rounding both numbers and then adding them together.
- Adding the numbers together and then rounding them.
- Both methods are the same.

11. An aircraft needs to make an emergency landing 4,982 miles into a 10,000 mile journey. Is it quicker to return to its departure airport or carry on to its destination? Explain your answer.

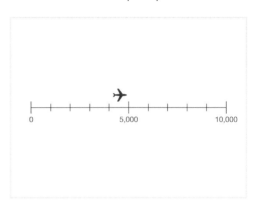

12. Corey is thinking of a number:
The number is smaller than 0.
It is a two digit number.
Both digits are odd.
The sum of the digits is 16.
The first digit is smaller than the second digit.
What is the number?

- -79

Level 2: *cont.*

13. Using every digit card once, make the
a b c **smallest** possible whole number.

▪ `1023456` ▪ `1,023,456`

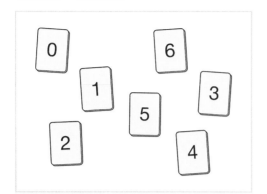

14. Letitia says, "When rounding to the nearest **100**,
a b c any number from 32,850 to 32,949 will round to 32,900". Is she correct? Explain your answer.

15. Tobias is thinking of a number:
a b c It is greater than 3,100 and smaller than 3,200.
All of the digits are different.
The number is divisible by 5.
Its digits add up to 18.
All of its digits are odd.
What is the number?

▪ `3,195` ▪ `3195`

16. Which **four** numbers when rounded to the nearest
10,000 equal 30,000?

▪ `30,095` ▪ 36,120 ▪ `25,037` ▪ `27,699` ▪ 14,876

4/7 ▪ `34,999` ▪ 22,374

17. Elliot is thinking of a 4-digit number which is 1,000
a b c when rounded to the **nearest hundred**. The digits in the number add up to 10. What could the number be?

▪ `1,018` ▪ `1,027` ▪ `1,045` ▪ `1027` ▪ `1045` ▪ `1,036`
▪ `1009` ▪ `1036` ▪ `1,009` ▪ `1018`

Level 3: Problem Solving - Using knowledge of number and place value to solve practical number problems.

✿ **Required:** 5/5 ✿ **Student Navigation:** on
✿ **Randomised:** off

18. Five paintings made it into the final of a national
↑ ↓ art competition. Using the clues, sort the paintings from 1st place to 5th place (first at the top).
The paintings in first and last place both have **odd digits** in the **ones** column.
The paintings in first and second place both have a place value column with **no value**.
The painting in fourth place has a value in the **tens column** which is a **multiple** of the values in its **ones** and **hundreds columns**.

▪ `605` ▪ `310` ▪ `478` ▪ `284` ▪ `537`

19. Mary is thinking of a **negative** number.
1 2 3 The number is greater than -162.
All of its digits are odd.
The number ends in a 5.
How many possible numbers can Mary be thinking of?

▪ `9`

20. Use the clues to identify Marietta's number on the grid:

1 2 3

Her number has 3 digits.

All of the digits are odd.

The digit in the tens column is greater than the digit in the ones column.

The digit in the hundreds column is not divisible by 3.

The sum of the digits is a multiple of 5.

▪ 591

347	317	8,942
42	973	531
795	591	897

21. Anna makes a number using base-ten blocks. She counts backwards from this number in **tens**. How **many numbers** will she say **before** she says a negative number?

1 2 3

▪ 17

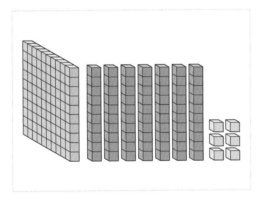

22. Freddie is writing a sequence of multiples of 10 starting at 190. What is the **23rd digit** that he writes down?

1 2 3

▪ 6

Mathematics

Y5

Addition and Subtraction

Mental Calculation

Written Methods Addition

Written Methods Subtraction

Rounding and Estimation

Add and subtract numbers mentally - Understanding

Competency: Add and subtract numbers mentally with increasingly large numbers.

Quick Search Ref: 10027

Correct: Correct   **Wrong:** Incorrect, try again.   **Open:** Thank you.

Level 1:   Understanding - Mental strategies for addition: count on, number bonds, partitioning, compensation and near doubles.

Required: 6/8   **Student Navigation:** on   **Randomised:** off

1.   What is 194 + 40?

1
2
3   ▪ **234**

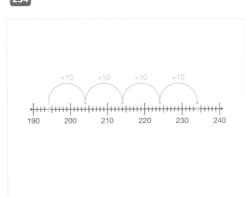

2.   What is 25 + 13 + 75?

1
2
3   ▪ **113**

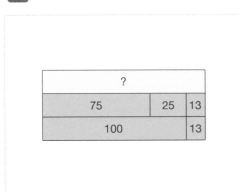

3.   What is the total of 382 and 130?

1
2
3   ▪ **512**

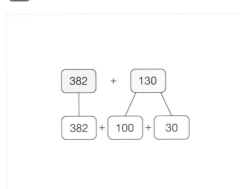

4.   Add together 436 and 55.

1
2
3   ▪ **491**

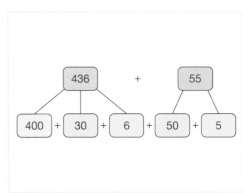

5.   Add together 199 and 105?

1
2
3   ▪ **304**

6.   Add together 3.6 and 3.5.

1
2
3   ▪ **7.1**

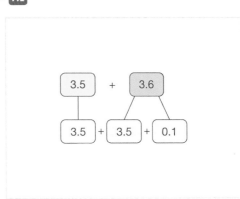

7.   What is 469 + 329?

1
2
3   ▪ **798**

Level 1: *cont.*

8. What is the sum of 301 and 298?

 ▪ **599**

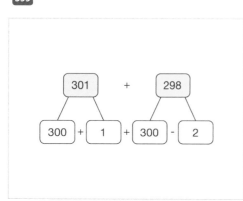

Level 2: Understanding - Mental strategies for subtraction: count back, count on, partitioning, compensation

✸ **Required:** 6/8   ✸ **Student Navigation:** on
✸ **Randomised:** off

9. What is 50 subtracted from 328.

 ▪ **278**

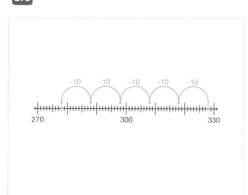

10. What is 27 less than 74?

▪ **47**

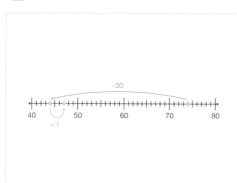

11. How many fewer is 214 than 534?

 ▪ **320**

12. How many more is 7,003 than 3,996?

▪ **3007**

13. What is 856 - 735?

 ▪ **121**

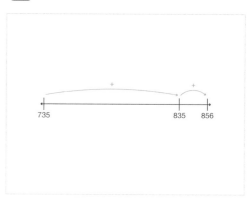

14. What is 160 less than 540?

▪ **380**

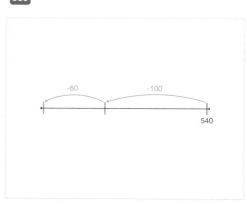

15. How many fewer is 14.6 than 15.3?

▪ **0.7**

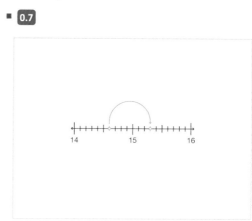

16. What is the difference between 109 and 1,008?

▪ **899**

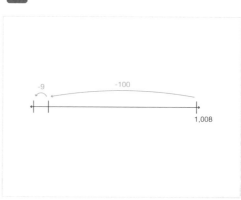

Add and subtract numbers with more than 4 digits using formal written methods

Competency: Add and subtract whole numbers with more than 4 digits, including using formal written methods (columnar addition and subtraction).

Quick Search Ref: 10229

Correct: Correct.   Wrong: Incorrect. Try again.   Open: Thank you.

Level 1: Understanding - Addition and subtraction with carrying or exchange.

✿ Required: 7/10   ✿ Student Navigation: on   ✿ Randomised: off

---

1. In the sum 17,325 + 21,544, which **digit** is missing from box *c*?

▪ **8**

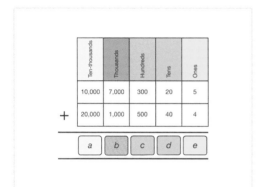

2. Calculate the answer to 12,935 + 11,427.
 ▪ **24,362** ▪ **24362**

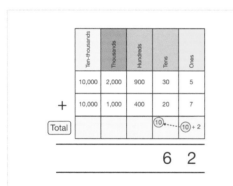

3. Calculate the answer to 49,270 + 10,628.
 ▪ **59,898** ▪ **59898**

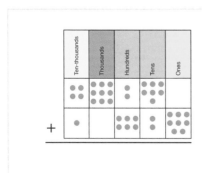

4. What is 26,903 + 12,488?
 ▪ **39,391** ▪ **39391**

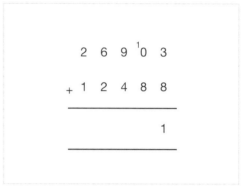

5. Write the **digit** which goes into box *b* as the answer to 25,734 - 14,432.
▪ **1**

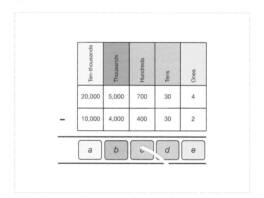

6. Calculate the answer to 36,271 - 22,433.
 ▪ **13,838** ▪ **13838**

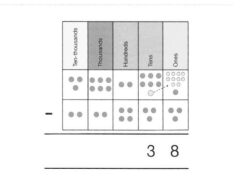

Level 1: *cont.*

7. What is 22,354 - 11,615?

  ▪ 10,739 ▪ 10739

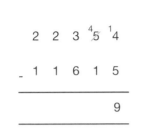

```
    2  2  3  ⁴5̷  ¹4
  _ 1  1  6  1  5
  _____
                   9
  _____
```

8. What is 30,004 + 42,005?

  ▪ 72,009 ▪ 72009

```
    3  0  0  0  4
  + 4  2  0  0  5
  _____
                   9
  _____
```

9. What is 58,201 - 45,102?

  ▪ 13,099 ▪ 13099

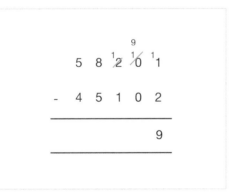

```
              9
    5  8  ¹2̷  ¹0̷  ¹1
  - 4  5  1  0  2
  _____
                   9
  _____
```

10. Calculate the answer to 20,043 + 40,056.

  ▪ 60099 ▪ 60,099

```
    2  0  0  4  3
  + 4  0  0  5  6
  _____
                   9
  _____
```

✿ Required: 7/10   **✿ Student Navigation:** on
✿ Randomised: off

11. A food processing company buys a new machine which costs £64,529. They also have to pay £12,906 in VAT. What is the total cost of the new machine?
Include the £ sign in your answer.

▪ £77435 ▪ £77,435

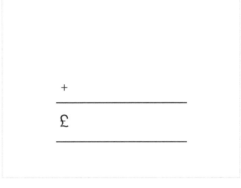

```
    +
  _____
  £
  _____
```

12. John bought a house for £63,084. He has made payments worth £20,275. How much does he still owe?
Include the £ sign in your answer.

▪ £42809 ▪ £42,809

```
    -
  _____
  £
  _____
```

13. Calculate the missing number in the equation _____ - 19,349 = 34,061 using the inverse operation.

▪ 53410 ▪ 53,410

```
    3  4  0  6  1
  + 1  9  3  4  9
  _____

  _____
```

Level 2: cont.

14. At a football match, 52,947 fans arrive to the game
a before kick off. 4,216 arrive late. How many fans
b attend the match in total?
c

■ 57163 ■ 57,163

15. Use the inverse operation to find the missing
a number in the equation **41,470 - ____ = 10,595**.
b
c ■ 30875 ■ 30,875

16. In 2017, there were 798,307 visitors at Green Park
a Zoo. In 2018, there was an **increase** of 16,858
b visitors. How many visitors were there in **2018?**
c

■ 815165 ■ 815,165

17. Blythe Sales buy two cars for the company to use
which cost a total of **£21,274**. They buy a
Tafi which costs **£9,436**. What model is the second
car?

1/4

■ Kasod ■ Dorf ■ Sinsan ■ Aki

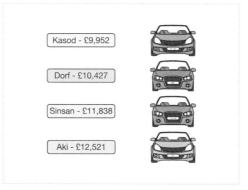

Kasod - £9,952

Dorf - £10,427

Sinsan - £11,838

Aki - £12,521

18. 30,575 people live in Jenkintown. It has 17,576
a visitors each year. How many people will have
b been to Jenkintown in one year?
c

■ 48151 ■ 48,151

19. A supermarket distribution centre has 92,745 tins
a of beans in stock. In one day, it sends 4,317 tins to
b its stores. How many tins of beans does it have
c remaining?

■ 88,428 ■ 88428

Level 2: cont.

20. For the last home match of the season, a football
a
b
c
team sold **17,536** adult tickets, **4,893** family tickets
and **3,206** concessionary tickets.
How many tickets in total were sold for the last
home game?

- 25635 - 25,635

Level 3: Reasoning - Reasoning about addition and
subtraction.

✹ **Required:** 5/5   ✹ **Student Navigation:** on
✹ **Randomised:** off

21. Four friends each own a house and have recorded
↑
↓
how much they have paid off their mortgage to
date. Sort the friends by how much they **still owe**
starting with the person who owes the **most.**

- Paul - Cath - Phil - Carol

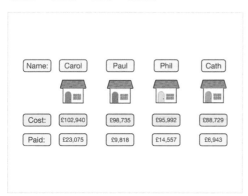

22. The number of men and women living in Ristown
a
b
c
is recorded each year. How many people were
living in Ristown in 2016?

- 36,115 - 36115

	2014	2015	2016	2017
men	12,259	15,589	17,907	14,542
women	14,587	15,875	18,208	13,894

23. Gina completes the calculation 587,324 + 351,997.
a
b
c
What has she done wrong? Explain your answer.

```
      5  8  7  3  2  4

  +   3  5  1  9  9  7
  _____

      8  3  8  2  1  1
  _____
```

24. Find the missing numbers in the calculation and
a
b
c
write the complete answer to the calculation.

- 38603 - 38,603

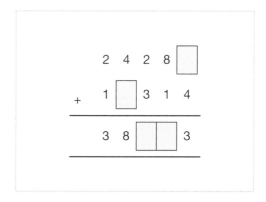

```
      2  4  2  8  □

  +   1  □  3  1  4
  _____

      3  8  □ □  3
  _____
```

25. Lorna says, "If you add a 4-digit number and 5-
a
b
c
digit number your answer will be a 9-digit
number."

Is Lorna correct? Explain your answer.

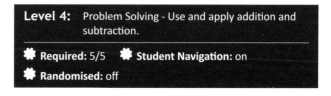

Level 4: Problem Solving - Use and apply addition and
subtraction.

✹ **Required:** 5/5   ✹ **Student Navigation:** on
✹ **Randomised:** off

26. The five number cards are used to complete the
1
2
3
column subtraction. What is the value of a?

- 9

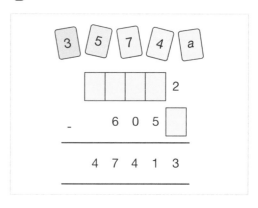

Level 4: *cont.*

27. Use column addition to find the value of *b*.

 ▪ 4

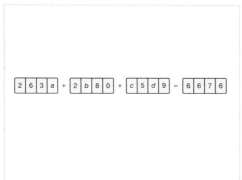

28. All numbers in a straight line have the same total.
What is the missing number?

a
b
c

▪ 16254   ▪ 16,254

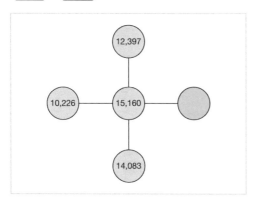

29. Tim wins £540,283 on the lottery. He buys a **house**
and a **car**. How much money does he have left
over?
Include the £ sign in your answer.

a
b
c

▪ £287,548   ▪ £287548

30. All numbers in a straight line in the pyramid have
the same total. Calculate the value of the missing
number.

a
b
c

▪ 22,750   ▪ 22750

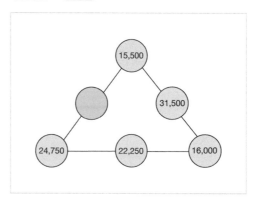

Solve addition and subtraction multi-step problems in context

Competency: Solve addition and subtraction multi-step problems in context deciding which operations and methods to use and why.

Quick Search Ref: 10088

Correct: Correct.   Wrong: Incorrect. Try again.   Open: Thank you.

Level 1: Problem Solving - To solve addition and subtraction multi-step problems in context.

🌼 Required: 7/10   🌼 Student Navigation: on   🌼 Randomised: off

---

1. Micky buys a football from a shop and gets £4.82
   a   change from £20. Charlie buys a rugby ball and
   b   gets £1.05 change from £10. What is the total cost
   c   of a rugby ball and a football?
       Include the £ sign in your answer.

   ▪ £24.13

2. Jerry goes to a restaurant and buys a lasagne, jam
   a   roly-poly and a glass of coke. He pays with a £20
   b   note and gets £6.58 change. How much is a glass
   c   of coke?
       Include the £ sign in your answer.

   ▪ £2.25

3. **246** adults, **117** children and **359** over 60s attend a
   a   cricket match at Anderton Cricket Club.
   b   In the next match, 84 fewer people attend. Find
   c   the **total** number of people who attended both
       matches.

   ▪ 1360 ▪ 1,360

4. A supermarket sells bottles of orange, pineapple
   a   and apple juice. In one week, there are **846 more**
   b   bottles of orange juice sold than apple juice and
   c   **118 more** bottles of apple juice sold than
       pineapple juice.
       The supermarket sells **656 bottles** of apple juice.
       How many bottles of juice are sold in total?

   ▪ 2696 ▪ 2,696

5. There are 348 children who attend Quiverton
   1   Primary School. Calculate the total number of **girls**
   2   who attend the school.
   3

   ▪ 203

	boys	girls	total
key stage 1	51		
key stage 2		135	229
total			348

6. Joel has **£7,061** in his bank account. He withdraws
   a   **£5,892** to buy a new car and **£427** for insurance.
   b   His salary of **£2,764** is then paid into his account.
   c   What is the balance of Joel's bank account?
       Include the £ sign in your answer.

   ▪ £3,506 ▪ £3506

7. Sally and Dan take all the money they have from
   a   their pockets and have a total of **£8.42**. Sally has
   b   **£1.96 more** than Dan. How much does **Sally** have?
   c   *Include the £ sign in your answer.*

   ▪ £5.19

8. Pat buys one kilogram each of mango, grapes and
   a   cherries. He gives the cashier £25 and gets £3.26
   b   change. How much does one kilogram of **cherries**
   c   cost?
       Include the £ sign in your answer.

   ▪ £12.56

fruit stall price list	
fruit	**cost per kilogram (kg)**
mango	£5.27
grapes	£3.91
melon	£1.16
oranges	£1.84
apples	£2.37

Level 1: cont.

9. There are 463 children who attend Red Rose
School. 257 of the pupils are boys. 128 girls have
school dinners. How many girls have a packed
lunch?

1
2
3

- 78

10. Chris buys one kilogram each of grapes, apples
and oranges. He pays with a £20 note. How much
change does Chris get back?
Include the £ sign in your answer.

a
b
c

- £11.88

fruit stall price list

fruit	cost per kilogram (kg)
mango	£5.27
grapes	£3.91
melon	£1.16
oranges	£1.84
apples	£2.37

Solve problems involving addition, subtraction, multiplication and division

Competency: Solve problems involving addition and subtraction, multiplication and division and a combination of these, including understanding the use of the equals sign.

Quick Search Ref: 10234

Correct: Correct.   **Wrong:** Incorrect, try again.   **Open:** Thank you.

Level 1: Problem Solving - Using the 4 operations to answer questions and solve problems.

✳ Required: 18/18   ✳ Student Navigation: on   ✳ Randomised: off

---

1. The symbols in the number square all have a value. Each line is added together with the total written at the end of the row or column. Calculate the value of a **star.**

▪ 52

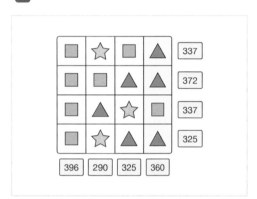

2. The total number of passengers on the Dublin ferry is **1,028** people. There are 451 women and 392 men. How many **children** are on board?

▪ 185

3. Four friends hire bikes for a **three day** adventure holiday. Alexandra and Leigh hire a **premium hybrid** bike. Rebecca hires a **triathlon** bike and Jordan hires a **mountain** bike. How much more does Rebecca pay than Jordan?
Include the £ sign in your answer.

▪ £56

4. **Three** consecutive (e.g. 22, 23, 24) numbers are added together to equal **75**. Write the number with the **largest** value.

▪ 26

5. George and Victor are packing bags at a supermarket for charity. George collects **£47.65** and Victor collects **£39.89**. What is the **average** amount each boy raises?
Include the £ sign in your answer.

▪ £43.77

6. There are **24 oranges** in a box and **15 apples** in a box. A greengrocer buys **42 boxes** of oranges and **76 boxes** of apples. How many pieces of fruit did the greengrocer buy?

▪ 2,148 ▪ 2148

7. Hannah has a piece of card which is **123** millimetres (mm) long and **61** millimetres wide. Kai has a piece of card which is **147** millimetres long and **65** millimetres wide. How much **larger** is the area of Kai's piece of card in square millimetres (mm²)?

Area of rectangle = length x width.

▪ 2,052 ▪ 2052

8. The two missing numbers in the statement have the **same value**. What number is missing?

▪ 17

9. A car park charges **£7** per car and collects **£1,869**. The capacity of the car park is **325** cars. How many **spare spaces** does the car park have?

▪ 58

Level 1: *cont.*

10. The numbers on each line have the **same** total. Calculate the missing number.

a
b
c ▪ 8,807 ▪ 8807

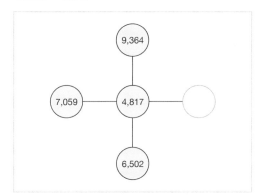

11. A supermarket creates a new basket of fruit to sell which consists of **10 apples** and **8 bananas**. How much will the new box cost in pounds?
Include the £ sign in your answer.

a
b
c

▪ £2.84

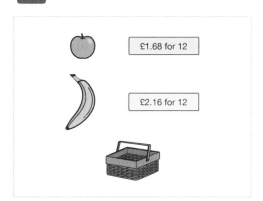

12. The rule for the number sequence below is: multiply the previous number by 6 and then subtract 187.

a
b
c

60, 173, 851, ___, 29, 327.

Find the **missing number** in the sequence.

▪ 4,919 ▪ 4919

13. A shop called Previous sells **1,215** red jackets and **936** blue jackets. The price of one jacket is **£9**. How much money has the shop taken on the sale of these jackets?
Remember to include the £ sign in your answer.

a
b
c

▪ £19,359 ▪ £19359

14. Select one number from each circle to balance the calculation. Which number goes in box *c*?

1
2
3 ▪ 44

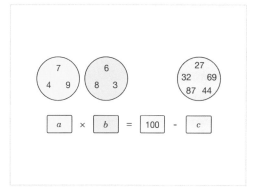

15. GB Bakers have **1,532** cakes at the beginning of the week. They sell **847** cakes in one week. If one cake costs **£3**, what is the **total** cost of the remaining cakes?
Include the £ sign in your answer.

a
b
c

▪ £2,055 ▪ £2055

16. The two missing numbers in the statement have the **same value**. What number is missing?

1
2
3 ▪ 21

17. **£1 = 10 Hong Kong Dollars**. 6 toy cars cost **4,698** Hong Kong Dollars. How much does **one car** cost in pounds?

a
b
c

▪ £78.30

18. **Three** consecutive numbers (e.g. 23,24,25) are added together to equal **150**. Write the number with the **smallest** value.

1
2
3

▪ 49

Use rounding to estimate sums and differences

Competency: Use rounding to check answers to calculate and determine, in the context of a problem, levels of accuracy.

Quick Search Ref: 10089

Correct: That's right. Wrong: No. Try again? Open: Thank you.

Level 1: Understanding - Rounding numbers to nearest 10/100/1000 to estimate calculations

Required: 7/10 **Student Navigation:** on **Randomised:** off

1. Select **all** the options which complete the following sentence correctly.

3/6

Rounding...

- **is when a number is altered to make it easier to calculate.**
- is when you put lots of 0s on the end.
- **is helpful with larger or complicated numbers.**
- is when you put a circle around the numbers.
- helps you get the exact answer to a calculation.
- **uses numbers close to the original values.**

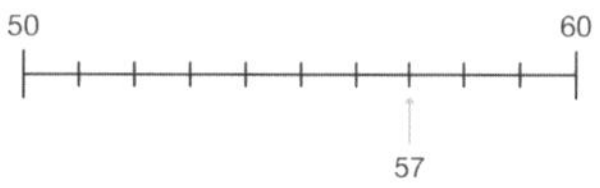

2. In the image there is a 2-digit number. Select **all** the possible digits for the ones column which would mean that you would round the number **up** to the **nearest 10**.

4/7

- 1
- 3
- 4
- **5**
- **6**
- **8**
- **9**

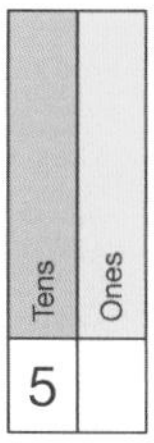

3. Round **2,864** to the nearest 10.

1/4

- **2,860**
- 2,870
- 2,900
- 3,000

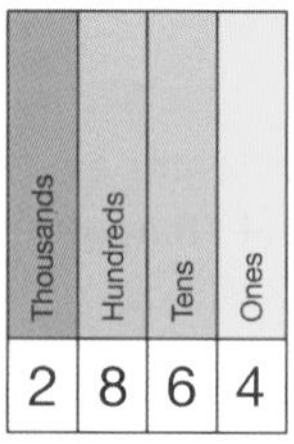

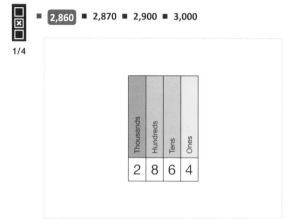

4. What is **8,751** rounded to the nearest 100?

1/4

- 8,700
- 8,750
- **8,800**
- 9,000

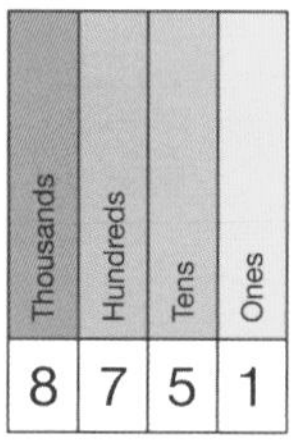

5. Which of these sums is **approximately** 24,000?

1/4

- 12,260 + 11,440
- **12,260 + 11,870**
- 12,260 + 12,610
- 12,260 + 12,990

sum	rounded to the nearest 1,000
12,260 + 11,440	12,000 + 11,000
12,260 + 11,870	12,000 + 12,000
12,260 + 12,610	12,000 + 13,000
12,260 + 12,990	12,000 + 13,000

Level 1: cont.

6. Estimate the answer to 3,152 + 4,321 by rounding
a
b   each number to the **nearest 10.**
c
 ▪ 7470 ▪ 7,470

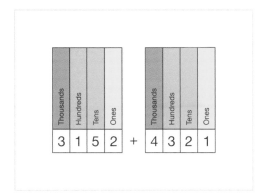

7. Round the numbers in the following calculation to
the **nearest 1,000**.
Select the symbol which makes the statement
true.
1/3

8,750 - 2,420 _____ 3,460 + 2,320.

▪ < ▪ > ▪ =

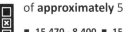

sum		
8,750 - 2,420	?	3,460 + 2,320

rounded to the nearest 1,000		
9,000 - ____	?	____ + 2,000

8. Which of these sums has a difference
of **approximately** 5,000?
1/4
 ▪ 15,470 - 8,400 ▪ 15,470 - 8,660 ▪ 15,470 - 9,420
 ▪ 15,470 - 9,690

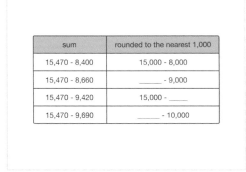

sum	rounded to the nearest 1,000
15,470 - 8,400	15,000 - 8,000
15,470 - 8,660	____ - 9,000
15,470 - 9,420	15,000 - ____
15,470 - 9,690	____ - 10,000

9. Estimate the answer to 48,684 - 15,563 by
a
b   rounding each number to the **nearest 1,000.**
c
 ▪ 33000 ▪ 33,000

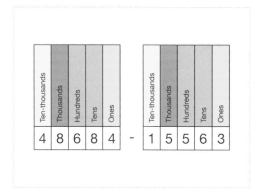

10. Select the sum which is **approximately** 32,500.
 ▪ 18,250 + 14,640 ▪ 18,250 + 14,190 ▪ 18,250 + 14,650
 ▪ 18,250 + 13,160
1/4

sum	rounded to the nearest 100
18,250 + 14,640	18,300 + ____
18,250 + 14,190	____ + 14,200
18,250 + 14,650	18,300 + ____
18,250 + 13,160	____ + 13,200

Level 2:   Fluency - Rounding 4 digit numbers and one
step word problems

✱ **Required:** 7/10   ✱ **Student Navigation:** on
✱ **Randomised:** off

11. 11,591 rounded to the nearest 1,000 is __.
a
b   ▪ 12000 ▪ 12,000
c

12. Round these numbers to the **nearest 100** and
a
b   estimate the answer to 3,827 + 4,142.
c
 ▪ 7,900 ▪ 7900

Level 2: cont.

13. Matt is a long distance lorry driver. He drives 1,782 miles in week 1 and 1,568 miles in week 2. **To the nearest 100 miles**, how many miles does he drive overall?

a
b
c

- **3,400** - **3400**

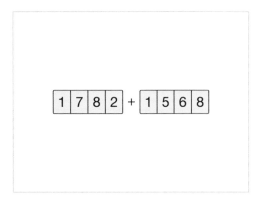

14. An annual village fair raises £1,152 on admissions. The cost of organising the fair is £347. **By rounding the values to the nearest £10**, how much profit does the fair make?
Include the £ in your answer.

a
b
c

- **£800**

15. Blue Water Caravans **reduce** the price of a caravan from £23,990 to £19,485 in the sale. **To the nearest £1,000**, estimate the **difference** in pounds.
Include the £ sign in your answer.

a
b
c

- **£5,000** - **£5000**

16. Noah buys a new laptop which costs £357.95 and a printer which costs £56.49. Round each price **to the nearest £10** and estimate the total cost in pounds.
Include the £ sign in your answer.

a
b
c

- **£420**

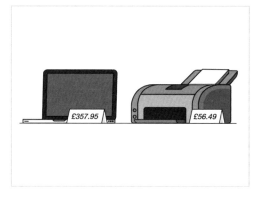

17. A farmer sells 10 boxes of eggs for a total of £11.53 and 10 packs of bacon for a total of £18.37 to the local butcher. **To the nearest pound**, what is the total of the eggs **and** bacon sold?
Include the £ sign in your answer.

a
b
c

- **£30**

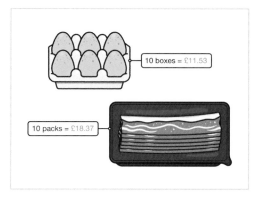

18. Alex buys two cars for his daughters. One costs £9,450 and the other costs £7,699. **To the nearest £1,000**, how much do the two cars cost?
Include the £ sign in your answer.

a
b
c

- **£17000** - **£17,000**

Level 2: *cont.*

19. The average temperature in New York in July is
1
2
3
26.8 degrees celsius and 14.2 degrees celsius in October. **To the nearest degree,** what is the difference between the two temperatures?

▪ 13

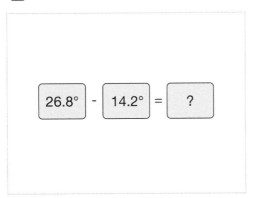

20. Becca's house is 1,564 metres from school and
a
b
c
Harriet's house is 2,364 metres from school. **To the nearest 100 metres,** how far is Becca's house from Harriet's?
Include the units in your answer.

▪ 800metres ▪ 800m

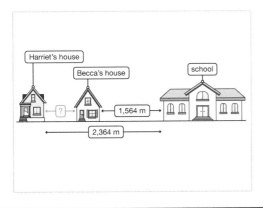

Level 3: Reasoning - Using estimation to find missing numbers

✿ **Required:** 5/5   ✿ **Student Navigation:** on
✿ **Randomised:** off

21. All numbers in a straight line total 10,000. The
a
b
c
number in the centre circle is a multiple of 100. Use rounding to find the value of the missing number.

▪ 3,800 ▪ 3800

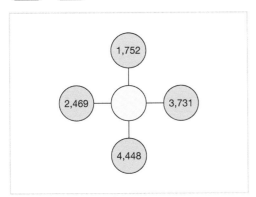

22. To calculate the area of a rectangle, you need to
a
b
c
multiply the length by the width.

Wendy needs some turf for her garden and says, *"My garden is 5.4 metres in length and 3.1 metres wide. Therefore, if I round these measurements, I need to buy exactly 15 square metres (m²) of turf to have enough to cover the whole garden."*

Is Wendy correct? Explain your answer.

23. Taylor makes a three digit number using the
1
2
3
number cards 3, 5, 6 and 9. When he subtracts his number from 1,000, the answer is 430 when rounded to the **nearest 10**. What is Taylor's number?

▪ 569

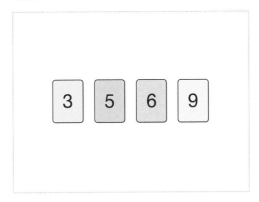

24. Round each number to the **nearest tenth** and
↑
↓
estimate the answer.
Sort the answers from the smallest value to the largest, with the smallest at the top.

▪ 0.21 + 0.27 ▪ 1.24 - 0.58 ▪ 3.76 - 3.09 ▪ 0.14 + 0.65

25. 6,053 + ____ = 10,024
a
b
c
Anderson says, *'"The estimate of the missing number is the same whether you round to the nearest 100 or the nearest 1,000."*

Is Anderson correct? Explain your answer.

Level 4: Problem Solving - Multi-step word problems

✿ **Required:** 5/5   ✿ **Student Navigation:** on
✿ **Randomised:** off

26. John takes part in an Ironman Challenge. To
a
b
c
complete the course, he must swim 3.86 kilometres (km), followed by a 180.25 km cycle ride and a 42.2 km run.
After completing 145.7 kilometres of the course, **to the nearest kilometre**, how far from the finish line is John?
Include the units km (kilometres) in your answer.

▪ 80kilometres ▪ 80km ▪ 81km

27. Andy has a meat stall on the local market and records his earnings for the week. How much more money does Andy make on Saturday and Sunday than he does on Thursday and Friday to the **nearest £10**?
Include the £ sign in your answer.

a
b
c

- £1490 - £1,490

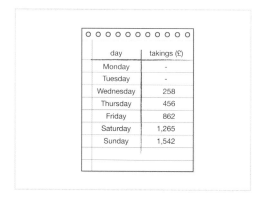

day	takings (£)
Monday	-
Tuesday	-
Wednesday	258
Thursday	456
Friday	862
Saturday	1,265
Sunday	1,542

28. Radio Poppins are hosting a summer concert. Attending the concert are: 4,532 children, 16,874 adults and 12,905 over 60s.
The arena holds 40,000 people.
To the nearest 100, how many **empty seats** will there be?

a
b
c

- 5700 - 5,700

29. 4,874 adults and 2,358 children attend a football match. 2,661 people are away supporters.
Approximately how many people are home fans to the **nearest 100?**

a
b
c

- 4,600 - 4600

30. Joanne makes 1,139 cupcakes to sell in her shop or donate to a local charity. At the end of the day there are 215 cup cakes left. The cakes were sold for £1.99 each and Joanne made approximately £1,600. Estimate how many cakes she **donated** to the nearest 10.

1
2
3

- 120

Mathematics

Multiplication and Division

Multiply and divide whole numbers and those involving decimals by 10, 100 and 1,000

Competency: Multiply and divide whole numbers and those involving decimals by 10, 100 and 1,000.

Quick Search Ref: 10186

Correct: Correct.   Wrong: Incorrect, try again.   Open: Thank you.

Level 1:   Understanding - Understanding the effect of multiplying and dividing by 10, 100 and 1,000.

✿ Required: 8/10   ✿ Student Navigation: on   ✿ Randomised: off

1. Multiplying a number by 10, 100 or 1,000 will:

- increase the value of the number.
- decrease the value of the number.
1/3 - have no effect on the value of the number.

2. Dividing a number by 10, 100 or 1,000 will:

- increase the value of the number.
- decrease the value of the number.
1/3 - have no effect on the value of the number.

3. 7.8 × 10 =

- 0.78 - 78 - 780

1/3
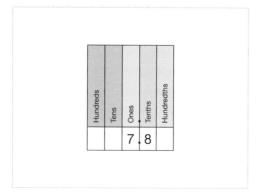

4. 457 ÷ 1,000 =

- 0.457 - 457,000 - 4.57 - 0.0457

1/4
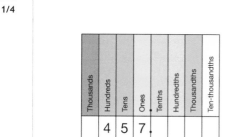

5. 8.37 × 100 =

- 837.00 - 837.0 - 837

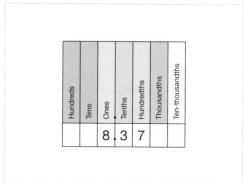

6. 0.98 ÷ 10 =

- 0.098

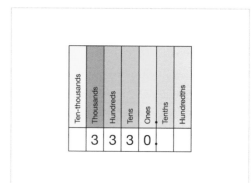

7. 3,330 ÷ 10 =

- 333.00 - 333 - 333.0

Level 1: *cont.*

8.   8.9 × 1,000 =

 a b c   ▪ 8,900 ▪ 8900

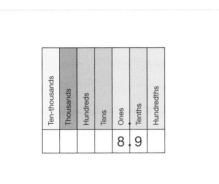

9.   987 ÷ 100 =

 a b c   ▪ 9.87

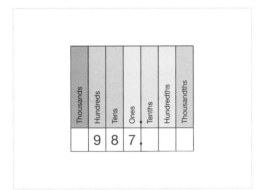

10. 12.2 ÷ 100 =

 a b c   ▪ 0.122

Level 2:   Fluency - Multiplying and dividing by 10, 100 and 1,000 in various contexts.

✹ Required: 8/10   ✹ Student Navigation: on
✹ Randomised: off

11. What number is one thousand times smaller than 308?

□⊠□   ▪ 3.08 ▪ 0.308 ▪ 308,000 ▪ 308

1/4

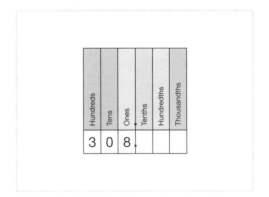

12. What is the missing number?

 a b c   ▪ 0.472

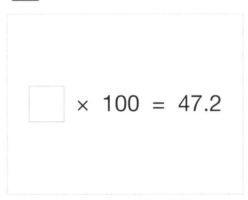

$$\boxed{} \times 100 = 47.2$$

13. Select the **two** options that make a calculation with the answer 5.8.

□⊠□   ▪ 0.058 ▪ 5.8 ▪ 5,800 ▪ 580 ▪ × 100 ▪ ÷ 10

2/7   ▪ × 1000

14. How many times larger is 3,700 than 3.7?

□⊠□   ▪ 10 times larger ▪ 100 times larger ▪ 1,000 times larger

1/3

15. What is the missing number?

 a b c   ▪ 0.00176

	÷10	÷100	÷1,000
847	84.7	8.47	0.847
1.76	0.176	0.0176	?

Level 2: *cont.*

16. Which calculation completes the following?
8.421 _ ___ = 842.1.

1/5 ■ ÷ 10 ■ ×100 ■ × 1,000 ■ ÷ 100 ■ × 10

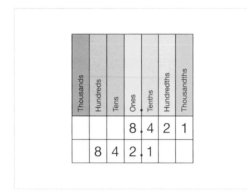

17. Which **three** calculations have the same value as 4 × 100?

3/6 ■ 0.04 × 1,000 ■ 400 ÷ 1,000 ■ 40 ÷ 10 ■ 4,000 ÷ 10
■ 0.4 × 1,000 ■ 40 × 10

18. What number is one hundred times larger than 2.39?

1 2 3 ■ 239

19. How many times smaller is 0.0076 than 7.6?

■ 1,000 times smaller ■ 100 times smaller
■ 10 times smaller

1/3

20. Which calculation completes the following?
4,832 _ ___ = 4.832.

■ ÷ 10 ■ × 100 ■ ÷ 1,000 ■ × 1,000 ■ ÷ 100

1/5

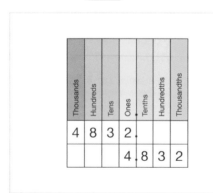

Level 3: Reasoning - Comparing calculations and using inverse. Showing understanding through written answers.

✹ **Required:** 5/7 ✹ **Student Navigation:** on
✹ **Randomised:** off

21. 2.4 × 10 × 100 × ___ ÷ 10 = 480.
What is the missing number?

1 2 3 ■ 2

22. Which two problems can you find the answer to by multiplying by 100?

2/3
■ 100 children have 3 pencils each. How many pencils do they have altogether?
■ A teacher has 340 grams of blueberries. She shares the blueberries equally between 100 children. How many grams of blueberries does each child get?
■ 100 counters are placed in a continuous line. If each counter is 2.3 centimetres in width, how long is the line of counters?

23. Kane says, "When multiplying whole or decimal numbers by 10, 100 or 1,000, you can just add zeros to the end of the number". Is Kane correct? Explain your answer.

a b c

24. Which symbol makes the following statement true?
4.7 × 100 ___ 3,800 ÷ 10

1/3 ■ < ■ = ■ >

25. 6 × 5 = 30, so explain how you know that 0.6 × 5 = 3.

a b c

26. Arrange the calculations in ascending order according to their value (smallest first).

■ 6,890 ÷ 1,000 ■ 0.0689 × 1,000 ■ 6,890 ÷ 10
■ 6.89 × 1,000 ■ 100 × 689

27. Which symbol makes the following statement true?
74.2 × 1,000 ___ 9,030,000 ÷ 100

1/3 ■ < ■ = ■ >

Level 4: Problem Solving - Using knowledge of multiplying and dividing by 10, 100 and 1,000 to solve problems.

✹ **Required:** 5/5 ✹ **Student Navigation:** on
✹ **Randomised:** off

28. The monkey can only cross the river when all of the stepping stones are in the correct order. Arrange the stones in ascending order according to their value (smallest first).

■ Stone 2 ■ Stone 4 ■ Stone 1 ■ Stone 3

Level 4: *cont.*

29. Barcelona to Andorra is 1.98 cm on the map.
Andorra to Madrid is 6.09 cm on the map.
If Panos drives from Barcelona to Andorra to
Madrid, how many **kilometres** does he travel?
Don't include the units in your answer.

- [807]

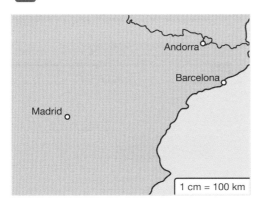

30. Using one card from each bag, how many different
ways can you find to make 16.2?

- [4]

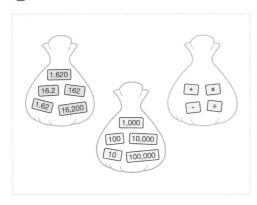

31. Move from 3 to 0.3 by taking a path through the
maze which makes **true** calculations. Select the
colours that represent the numbers you pass
through on your journey.

4/6

- [Green] ▪ Blue ▪ [Red] ▪ Purple ▪ [Orange] ▪ [Yellow]

3	x 10	300	x 1,000
÷ 100	0.3	÷ 10	300
0.03	÷ 10	3,000	÷ 1,000
x 1,000	30	x 100	0.3

32. Hannah is thinking of 3 numbers x, y and z. She
says, 'y is 10 times smaller than x, and z is 100
times larger than x'.
What is the value of $z \div y$?

- [1000] ▪ [1,000]

Multiply and divide numbers mentally

Competency: Multiply and divide numbers mentally drawing upon known facts.

Quick Search Ref: 10106

Correct: That's right.   Wrong: No. Try again?   Open: Thank you.

Level 1:   Understanding - Mental strategies, up to 3-digit numbers by 1-digit numbers.

✿ **Required:** 7/10   ✿ **Student Navigation:** on   ✿ **Randomised:** off

1. What is 3 x 40?

1 2 3 ▪ 120

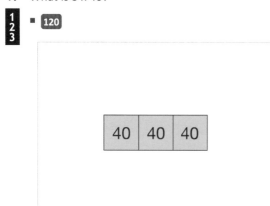

2. What is 32 ÷ 8?

1 2 3 ▪ 4

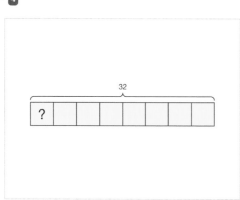

3. What is 16 multiplied by 5?

1 2 3 ▪ 80

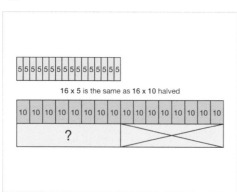
16 x 5 is the same as 16 x 10 halved

4. Find the product of 7 and 50.

1 2 3 ▪ 350

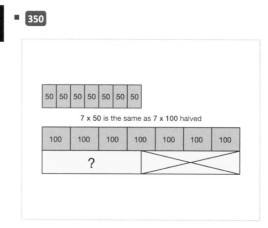
7 x 50 is the same as 7 x 100 halved

5. What is 100 doubled?

⊡ ▪ 200 ▪ 50 ▪ 10,000

1/3

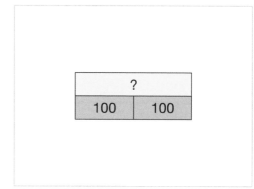

6. What is half of 38?

1 2 3 ▪ 19

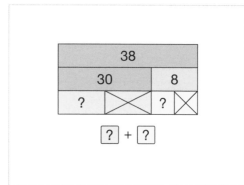

Level 1: *cont.*

7. Find the product of 16 and 3.

 ▪ **48**

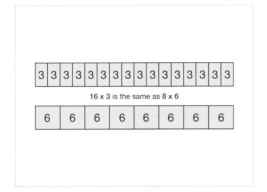

8. What is 320 divided by 5?

 ▪ **64**

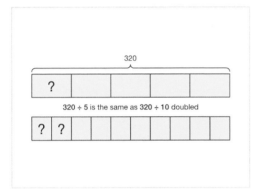

9. What is 248 shared into 4 equal parts.

 ▪ **62**

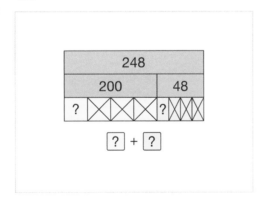

10. What is 610 divided into 5 equal parts?

 ▪ **122**

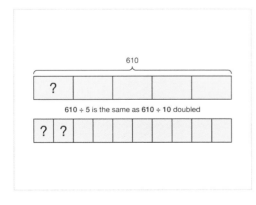

© Learning by Questions Ltd. 51 Ref:10106 Multiply and divide numbers mentally

Level 2: Fluency - Mental strategies, up to 4-digit numbers by 2-digit numbers.

✸ **Required:** 7/10 ✸ **Student Navigation:** on
✸ **Randomised:** off

11. What is 17 multiplied by 9?

 ▪ **153**

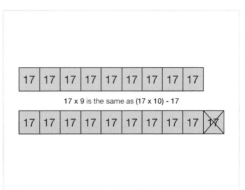

12. Find the product of 14 and 11.

 ▪ **154**

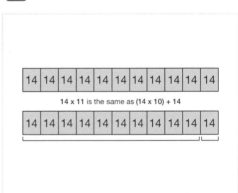

13. Find the product of 25 and 13.

 ▪ **325**

14. What is 143 x 21?

 ▪ **3003**

15. What is 800 divided between 50?

 ▪ **16**

16. What is £16 multiplied by 25?
a Give your answer in pounds.
b *Include the £ sign in your answer.*
c

▪ **£400** ▪ **£400.00** ▪ **400**

17. What is 115 kg x 18?
a *Give your answer in kg (kilograms).*
b
c ▪ **2070 kg** ▪ **2,070 kilograms** ▪ **2070 kilograms**
▪ **2,070 kg**

Level 2: *cont.*

18. What is 4,530 divided by 15?

1
2
3 ▪ 302

19. 1,500 blueberries are shared equally between 50 children.
How many blueberries does each child get?

1
2
3

▪ 30

20. 3,960 paperclips are divided equally into 30 boxes.
How many paperclips are in each box?

1
2
3 ▪ 132

Level 3:   Reasoning - To use and apply multiplication and division facts.

✿ **Required:** 6/8   ✿ **Student Navigation:** on
✿ **Randomised:** off

21. What is the missing number?

1
2
3   ____ ÷ 12 = 12

▪ 144

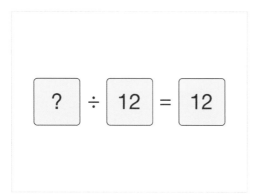

22. If 2 x 133 = 266, what is 4 times 133?

1
2
3 ▪ 532

23. Joel says, "Every number that ends in 4 is a multiple of 4".
Is he correct? Explain your answer.

a
b
c

Every number that ends in 4 is a multiple of 4.

24. Which **two missing numbers** balance the calculation?

☐
☒   4 x ____ = ____ ÷ 2
☐

2/7 ▪ 3 ▪ 9 ▪ 12 ▪ 36 ▪ 64 ▪ 72 ▪ 84

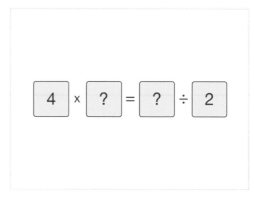

25. Three of the cards complete the calculation, but one of the cards has been turned over.
What digit must be on the turned over card?

1
2
3

▪ 3

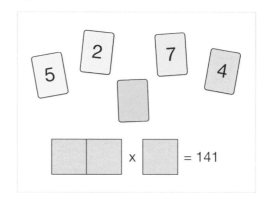

26. 10 times a number is 4,220, what is 9 times the same number?
Explain your answer.

a
b
c

27. Which **two missing numbers** balance the calculation?

☐
☒   180 ÷ ____ = 12 x ____
☐

2/7 ▪ 2 ▪ 3 ▪ 4 ▪ 5 ▪ 6 ▪ 7 ▪ 8

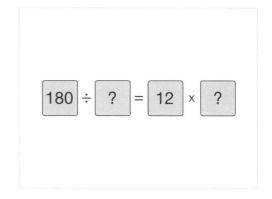

Level 3: *cont.*

28. Sarah says, 'At least one of the missing numbers must be an even number because the answer is an even number'.
Is Sarah correct? Explain your answer.

a
b
c

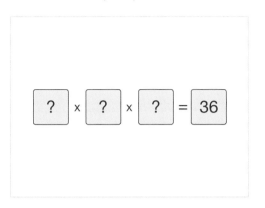

Level 4: Problem Solving - Using multiplication and division facts.

✹ **Required:** 8/8   ✹ **Student Navigation:** on
✹ **Randomised:** off

29. Bedding plants are sold in trays of 6.
Jacob needs 70 bedding plants to fill his containers.
How many trays must he buy?

1
2
3

▪ **12**

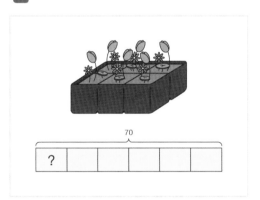

30. The numbers in the outer circles are all factors of the missing number, which is greater than 20 but less than 50.
What is the missing number?

1
2
3

▪ **36**

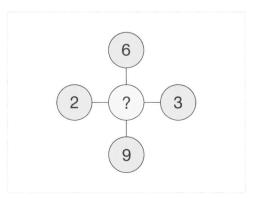

31. In the multiplication table what are the **two missing numbers**?

2/6

▪ 2 ▪ **3** ▪ 4 ▪ 6 ▪ **8** ▪ 9

x	2	?	5
4	8	12	20
6	12	18	30
?	16	24	40

32. The same number is missing from each of the boxes.
What is the missing number?

1
2
3

▪ **11**

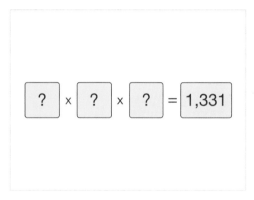

33. Kyle is doing a sponsored 164 mile walk for charity. If he walks 12 miles each day, how many days will it take him to complete the walk?

1
2
3

▪ **14**

34. One pack of football stickers costs 50 pence.
Xavier spends £7.50 on stickers and then stacks the packs on top of each other. Each pack is 1.8 millimetres thick.
In **centimetres**, how high is the stack of stickers?

1
2
3

▪ **2.7**

35. Grace's grandma is knitting her a new cardigan and
a she needs three balls of wool and six buttons.
b The buttons cost 75 pence each.
c The total cost of the cardigan is £15.00.
In **pounds**, what is the cost of **one ball of wool**?

▪ £3.50 ▪ 3.50

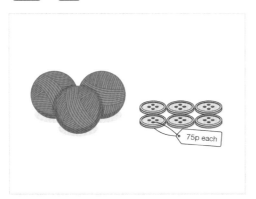

36. Adam is making a garden gate that needs to be 96
a centimetres wide.
b Lengths of wood are sold in packs of 6 for £36.00
c and each length of wood is 12 centimetres wide.
How much will the new garden gate cost in
pounds?

▪ £72.00 ▪ 72 ▪ £72

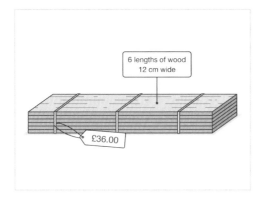

Multiply and divide whole numbers by 10, 100 and 1,000

Competency: Multiply and divide whole numbers by 10, 100 and 1,000.

Quick Search Ref: 10217

Correct: Correct.   **Wrong:** Incorrect, try again.   **Open:** Thank you.

Level 1:   Understanding - Understanding multiplication and division by 10, 100 and 1,000.

🌣 **Required:** 8/12   🌣 **Student Navigation:** on   🌣 **Randomised:** off

---

1. Which of the following statements is correct when multiplying by 10.

 1/4

- All the digits move one place to the right.
- **All the digits move one place to the left.**
- All the digits move two places to the left.
- All the digits move two places to the right.

2. What is 43 x 10?

- 430

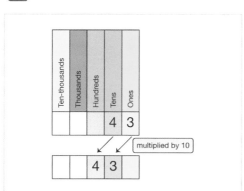

3. What is 358 multiplied by 100?

 1/6
- **35,800** ■ 358,000 ■ 3,580 ■ 35.8 ■ 3.58 ■ 358

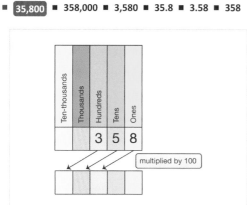

4. Find the product of 69 and 100.

- **6,900** ■ **6900**

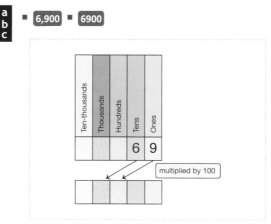

5. Which of the following statements is correct when dividing by 10?

 1/4

- All the digits move to the left two places.
- All the digits move to the right two places.
- **All the digits move one place to the right.**
- All the digits move one place to the left.

6. What is 720 ÷ 10?

- 72

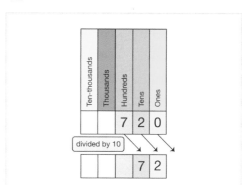

Level 1: cont.

7. What is 8,100 shared equally by 100?

 ▪ 81 ▪ 810 ▪ 8.1 ▪ 810,000

1/4

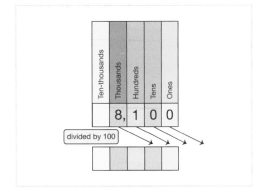

8. What is 36,000 divided by 100?

 ▪ 360

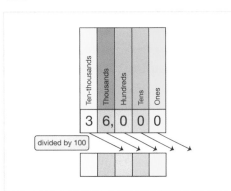

9. What is 271 x 1,000?

 ▪ 271,000 ▪ 27,100 ▪ 0.271 ▪ 2.71

1/4

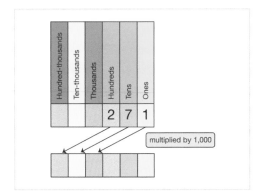

10. What is 25,000 ÷ 1,000?

 ▪ 25 ▪ 250 ▪ 25,000,000 ▪ 2,500,000

1/4

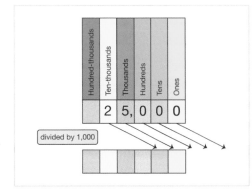

11. What is 96 multiplied by 1,000?

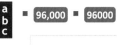 ▪ 96,000 ▪ 96000

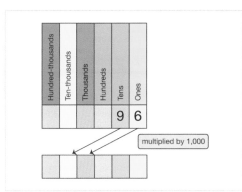

12. What is 410,000 shared equally by 1,000?

a b c ▪ 410

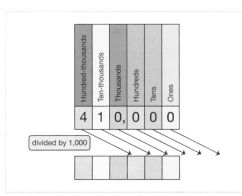

Level 2: Fluency - Using knowledge of multiplication and division by 10, 100 and 1,000.

✱ **Required:** 7/10   ✱ **Student Navigation:** on
✱ **Randomised:** off

13. What is 56,000 x 10?

a b c ▪ 560,000 ▪ 560000

14. What is 73,000 ÷ 10?

a b c ▪ 7,300 ▪ 7300

15. What is the missing number from the calculation?
420 x _____ = 42,000

a b c ▪ 100

16. What is the missing number from the calculation?
8,100 ÷ _____ = 810

a b c ▪ 10

17. What is the missing number from the calculation?
_____ x 1,000 = 930,000

a b c ▪ 930

Level 2: cont.

18. What is the missing number from the calculation?

a
b
c

_____ ÷ 100 = 2,510

▪ **251,000** ▪ **251000**

19. What is the missing number from the calculation?

a
b
c

_____ x 100 = 63,100

▪ **631**

20. What is the missing number from the calculation?

a
b
c

_____ ÷ 1,000 = 79.4

▪ **79400** ▪ **79,400**

21. Complete the calculation.

528 ___ 10 = 5,280

▪ **x** ▪ ÷

1/2

22. Complete the calculation.

6,396 ___ 1,000 = 6.396

▪ **÷** ▪ x

1/2

Level 3: Reasoning - To apply knowledge of multiplication and division by 10, 100 and 1,000.

✿ **Required:** 6/8   ✿ **Student Navigation:** on
✿ **Randomised:** off

23. What is the missing number to balance the

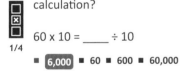

calculation?

60 x 10 = _____ ÷ 10

1/4

▪ **6,000** ▪ **60** ▪ **600** ▪ **60,000**

24. How many ten pounds notes make one million

a
b
c

pounds?

▪ **100,000** ▪ **100000**

25. 8 x 9 = 72. How can this multiplication fact be used

a
b
c

to solve the following calculation?

800 x 900 = _____

Explain your method.

26. What is 10 kilometres in centimetres?

a
b
c

▪ **1,000,000** ▪ **1000000**

27. The same number is missing from each box.
What is the missing number?

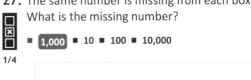

1/4

▪ **1,000** ▪ 10 ▪ 100 ▪ 10,000

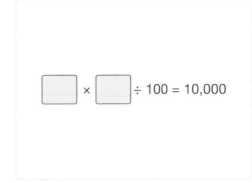

28. Florence has saved £25. She wants to buy a new

a
b
c

bicycle for ten times this amount.
How much more does Florence need to save? Give your answer in pounds.

▪ **£225**

29. The number in the centre circle completes the

a
b
c

calculation for the answers in the outer circles.
What number is missing from the centre circle?

▪ **13400** ▪ **13,400**

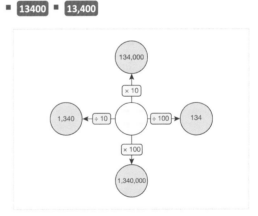

30. Use seven of the digit cards to complete the

a
b
c

calculation.
Basil says, 'The blank digit card must be a zero'.
Is he correct? Explain your answer.

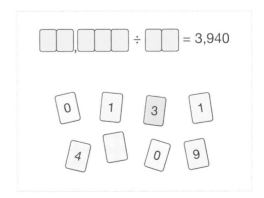

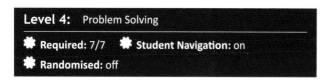

Level 4: Problem Solving

✱ **Required:** 7/7   ✱ **Student Navigation:** on
✱ **Randomised:** off

31. How many pounds is two thousand five pence coins?
Don't include the £ sign in your answer.

▪ 100

32. Select <, > or = to make the following calculation correct.

4,517 x 100 _____ 451,700 ÷ 100

1/3

▪ < ▪ > ▪ =

33. Paper clips are sold in packets of 50.
There are 20 packets in a box.
How many paper clips in 250 boxes?

▪ 250000 ▪ 250,000

34. Three numbers multiplied together equal 100.
All three numbers are less than 15.
All the numbers are different.
The sum of the three numbers is less than 20.
3/6 What are the three numbers?

▪ 0 ▪ 1 ▪ 2 ▪ 5 ▪ 10 ▪ 15

35. What is the missing number in the calculation?
_____ x 10 ÷ 100 x 1,000 = 89,200

▪ 892

36. On holiday, Jimmy collects 500 shells.
Nelson collects ten times more than Jimmy.
Teddy collects a hundred times less than Nelson.
How many shells do the boys collect altogether?

▪ 5,550 ▪ 5550

37. Molly has 475 stickers.
She buys 25 stickers every week.
In ten weeks, how many stickers will Molly have altogether?

▪ 725

Practise Multiplying by 10, 100 and 1,000

Competency: Children quickly multiply numbers by 10, 100 and 1,000, progressing to decimals.

Quick Search Ref: 10531

Correct: Correct.   **Wrong:** Incorrect. Try again.   **Open:** Thank you.

Level 1: Understanding - I can multiply whole numbers by 10, 100 and 1,000.

⚙ **Required:** 15/30   ⚙ **Student Navigation:** off   ⚙ **Randomised:** on

1. 1×10
[123] ▪ 10

2. 24×10
[123] ▪ 240

3. 3×10
[123] ▪ 30

4. 41×10
[123] ▪ 410

5. 15×10
[123] ▪ 150

6. 765×10
[abc] ▪ 7650 ▪ 7,650

7. 127×10
[abc] ▪ 1,270 ▪ 1270

8. 952×10
[abc] ▪ 9520 ▪ 9,520

9. $1,192 \times 10$
[abc] ▪ 11920 ▪ 11,920

10. $7,021 \times 10$
[abc] ▪ 70,210 ▪ 70210

11. 7×100
[123] ▪ 700

12. 9×100
[123] ▪ 900

13. 4×100
[123] ▪ 400

14. 21×100
[abc] ▪ 2,100 ▪ 2100

15. 48×100
[abc] ▪ 4,800 ▪ 4800

16. 79×100
[abc] ▪ 7900 ▪ 7,900

17. 345×100
[abc] ▪ 34,500 ▪ 34500

18. 947×100
[abc] ▪ 94,700 ▪ 94700

19. 801×100
[abc] ▪ 80,100 ▪ 80100

20. $2,692 \times 100$
[abc] ▪ 269200 ▪ 269,200

21. $9 \times 1,000$
[abc] ▪ 9000 ▪ 9,000

22. $4 \times 1,000$
[abc] ▪ 4,000 ▪ 4000

Level 1: *cont.*

23. $7 \times 1{,}000$

a
b
c

▪ **7,000** ▪ **7000**

24. $73 \times 1{,}000$

a
b
c

▪ **73000** ▪ **73,000**

25. $94 \times 1{,}000$

a
b
c

▪ **94,000** ▪ **94000**

26. $51 \times 1{,}000$

a
b
c

▪ **51000** ▪ **51,000**

27. $754 \times 1{,}000$

a
b
c

▪ **754,000** ▪ **754000**

28. $436 \times 1{,}000$

a
b
c

▪ **436000** ▪ **436,000**

29. $871 \times 1{,}000$

a
b
c

▪ **871000** ▪ **871,000**

30. $3{,}472 \times 1{,}000$

a
b
c

▪ **3,472,000** ▪ **3472000**

Level 2: Understanding - I can multiply decimal numbers by 10, 100 and 1,000.

✱ **Required:** 15/30   ✱ **Student Navigation:** off
✱ **Randomised:** on

31. 2.3×10

1
2
3

▪ **23**

32. 5.6×10

1
2
3

▪ **56**

33. 12.3×10

1
2
3

▪ **123**

34. 0.19×10

1
2
3

▪ **1.9**

35. 1.78×10

1
2
3

▪ **17.8**

36. 45.07×10

1
2
3

▪ **450.7**

37. 56.102×10

1
2
3

▪ **561.02**

38. 0.031×10

1
2
3

▪ **0.31**

39. 5.214×10

1
2
3

▪ **52.14**

40. $2{,}315.59 \times 10$

a
b
c

▪ **23,155.9** ▪ **23155.9**

41. 3.4×100

a
b
c

▪ **340**

42. 0.9×100

a
b
c

▪ **90**

43. 9.7×100

a
b
c

▪ **970**

44. 1.27×100

a
b
c

▪ **127**

45. 67.82×100

a
b
c

▪ **6,782** ▪ **6782**

46. 94.58×100

a
b
c

▪ **9,458** ▪ **9458**

47. 5.023×100

a
b
c

▪ **502.3**

Level 2: *cont.*

48. 0.181×100

a
b
c
■ 18.1

49. 53.139×100

a
b
c
■ 5313.9 ■ 5,313.9

50. $3,872.159 \times 100$

a
b
c
■ 387215.9 ■ 387,21.9

51. $0.5 \times 1,000$

a
b
c
■ 500

52. $7.1 \times 1,000$

a
b
c
■ 7,100 ■ 7100

53. $52.1 \times 1,000$

a
b
c
■ 52100 ■ 52,100

54. $0.72 \times 1,000$

a
b
c
■ 720

55. $6.29 \times 1,000$

a
b
c
■ 6290 ■ 6,290

56. $34.92 \times 1,000$

a
b
c
■ 34,920 ■ 34920

57. $0.275 \times 1,000$

a
b
c
■ 275

58. $5.712 \times 1,000$

a
b
c
■ 5712 ■ 5,712

59. $64.117 \times 1,000$

a
b
c
■ 64,117 ■ 64117

60. $6,189.456 \times 1,000$

a
b
c
■ 6,189,456 ■ 6189456

Multiply numbers up to 4 digits by a one-digit number

Competency: Multiply numbers up to 4 digits by a one-digit number using a formal written method

Quick Search Ref: 10220

Correct: That's right.   Wrong: No. Try again.   Open: Thank you.

Level 1: Understanding - Concept of multiplication; multiplying numbers up to four digits by one-digit numbers.

✸ **Required:** 7/10   ✸ **Student Navigation:** on   ✸ **Randomised:** off

---

1. Select all options which complete the sentence below correctly.

3/5

Multiplication is...

- the opposite of division.   ■ the same as division.
- a way of adding the same number repeatedly.
- a way of subtracting the same number repeatedly.
- shown by a x sign.

2. Which statements represent the counters in the image? Select **all** which are correct.

3/5

- 3 x 5 = 15   ■ 3 x 6 = 18   ■ 6 lots of 3 = 18
- 3 groups of 3 is equal to 18.
- The product of 6 and 3 is 18.

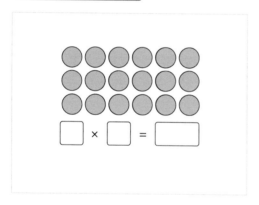

3. Which image shows 124 x 2?

- a)   ■ b)

1/2

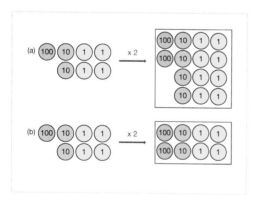

4. Which image represents 4 x 5 = 20?

■ a) ■ b) ■ c) ■ d)

1/4

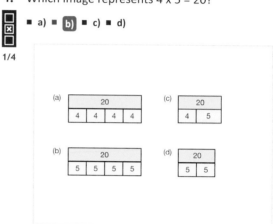

5. Calculate the answer to 122 x 4.

■ 488

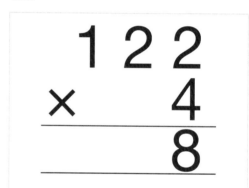

6. Use the written method to calculate 1,202 x 4.

■ 4808 ■ 4,808

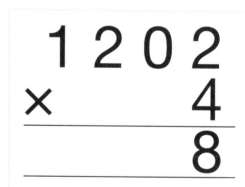

Level 1: *cont*.

7. 6,055 multiplied by 5 equals ___.

Use the formal written method to calculate.

▪ 30,275 ▪ 30275

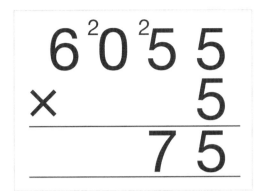

8. 645 multiplied by 2 equals ___.

Use the formal written method to calculate.

▪ 1290 ▪ 1,290

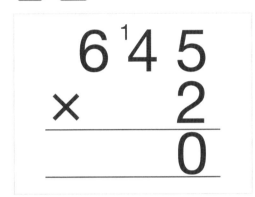

9. 4,134 multiplied by 2 equals ___.

▪ 8268 ▪ 8,268

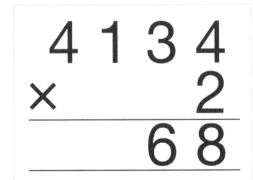

10. 4,215 multiplied by 3 equals ___.

▪ 12,645 ▪ 12645

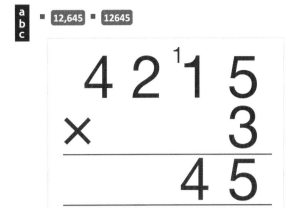

Level 2: Fluency - Multiply four digit numbers by one digit numbers including 1-step word problems.

✾ **Required:** 7/10   ✾ **Student Navigation:** on
✾ **Randomised:** off

11. 1,204 multiplied by 3 equals __.

▪ 3,612 ▪ 3612

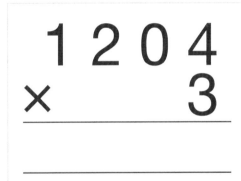

12. Find the product of 3,424 and 6.

▪ 20544 ▪ 20,544

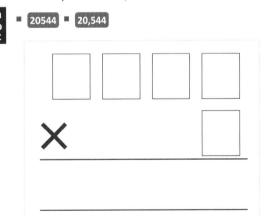

Level 2: *cont.*

13. Calculate the answer to 3,642 x 4.

a b c ▪ 14,568 ▪ 14568

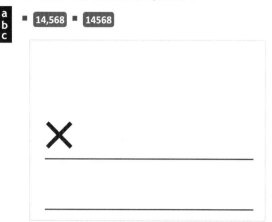

14. What is the product of 2,941 and 9?

a b c ▪ 26469 ▪ 26,469

15. Choose the correct symbol.

 5,621 x 2 ____ 1,634 x 9

1/3 ▪ = ▪ > ▪ <

$$5,621 \times 2 \; \boxed{} \; 1,634 \times 9$$

16. There are 6 eggs in a box. How many eggs will there be in 2,071 boxes?

a b c ▪ 12,426 ▪ 12426

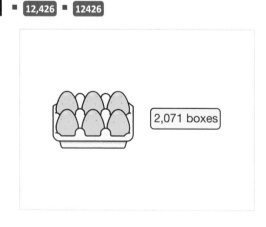

2,071 boxes

17. Alana is collecting football stickers. There are 8 stickers on every page. Her sticker book has 2,532 pages and all the pages are full. How many **stickers** does she have in total?

a b c ▪ 20,256 ▪ 20256

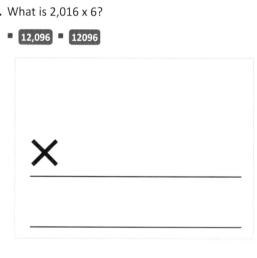

2,532 pages

8 stickers on each page

18. Find the product of 3,120 and 3.

a b c ▪ 9360 ▪ 9,360

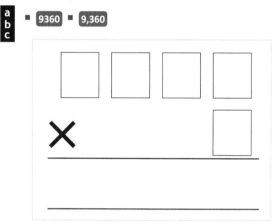

19. What is 2,016 x 6?

a b c ▪ 12,096 ▪ 12096

Level 2: cont.

20. There are 6 peas in a pod. How many peas will there be in 3,201 pods?

■ 19,206 ■ 19206

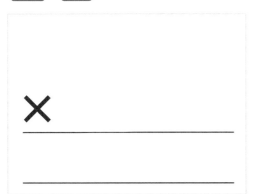

Level 3: Reasoning - Reasoning about multiplication.

✸ **Required:** 5/5   ✸ **Student Navigation:** on
✸ **Randomised:** off

21. Reasoning Raymond is trying to solve a maths problem.

abc

_____ ÷ 7 = 4,239.

He says, *"I can use multiplication to solve this problem."*
Is he correct? Explain why.

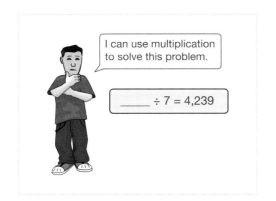

I can use multiplication to solve this problem.

_____ ÷ 7 = 4,239

22. Find the value of the missing digit labelled *a* in the calculation.

■ 9

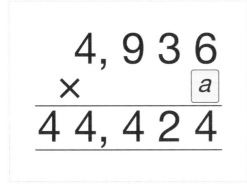

$$4{,}936 \times a$$
$$\overline{44{,}424}$$

23. Find the missing digit to make the equation correct.

1
2
3

■ 4

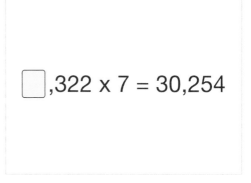

$$\square,322 \times 7 = 30{,}254$$

24. Sajid is trying to solve a maths problem. He says, *"I think my answer is too small."*

abc

Is he correct? Explain why.

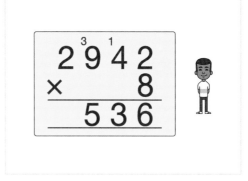

$$2\,9\,4\,2 \times 8$$
$$\overline{5\,3\,6}$$

25. Sammy has completed a maths question. Has he got it correct? If he has made a mistake, explain what he has done wrong.

abc

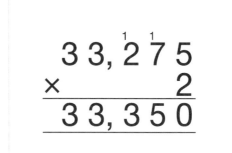

$$3\,3{,}2\,7\,5 \times 2$$
$$\overline{3\,3{,}3\,5\,0}$$

Level 4: Problem Solving - Using and applying
multiplication to solve multi-step problems.

★ **Required:** 5/5   ★ **Student Navigation:** on
★ **Randomised:** off

26. Find the value of the missing digit labelled *a*.

 ▪ **3**

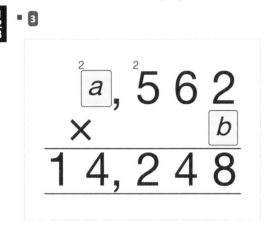

27. In the multiplication pyramid, a number is made
by multiplying the two boxes below it.
Find the value of *d*.

▪ **9,984** ▪ **9984**

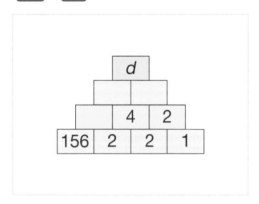

28. A builder has a budget (the money he has
available to spend) of **£100,000** to build a
house. The table shows some of the materials and
the cost per item.
Calculate how much money he has **remaining**.
Include the £ sign in your answer.

▪ **£43661** ▪ **£43,661**

material	cost per item	quantity
bags of cement	£5	2,321
pallet of bricks	£7	5,302
box of tiles	£4	1,905

29. In the image of a plot of land at an airport, the
area of **both of the runways** is ___ square meters
(m²).

area = length x width.

▪ **6,951** ▪ **6951**

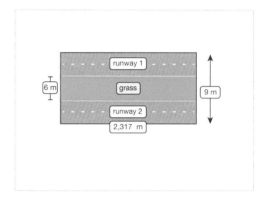

30. You have 5 digit cards. Arrange them on the
multiplication grid.
What is the largest number you can make without
using the same card twice?

▪ **34560** ▪ **34,560**

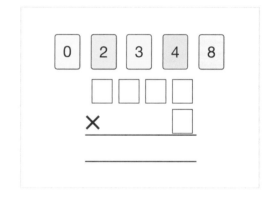

Multiply up to 4 digits by a 2-digit number (long multiplication)

Competency: Multiply multi-digit numbers up to 4 digits by a 2-digit number using long multiplication.

Quick Search Ref: 10015

Correct: Correct. **Wrong:** Incorrect, try again. **Open:** Thank you.

Level 1: Understanding - Calculating sections of 4-digit by 2-digit multiplication questions.

✿ **Required:** 7/10 ✿ **Student Navigation:** on ✿ **Randomised:** off

1. What number goes in the highlighted box?

a b c ▪ 21576 ▪ 21,576

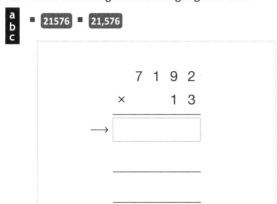

2. For the second part of the calculation, what number goes in the highlighted box?

a b c ▪ 71920 ▪ 71,920

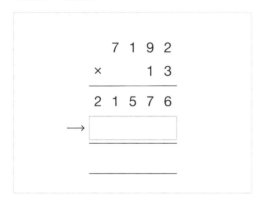

3. What is the answer to 7,192 × 13?

a b c ▪ 93,496 ▪ 93496

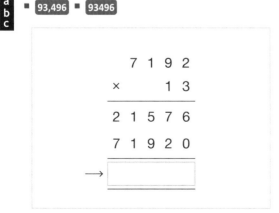

4. What are the two numbers missing from line A and line B?

▪ 3,271 ▪ 9,813 ▪ 32,710 ▪ 42,523

2/4

5. Use the following calculations to find the answer to 4,245 × 16:
4,245 × 6 = 25,470.
4,245 × 10 = 42,450.

▪ 67,920 ▪ 67920

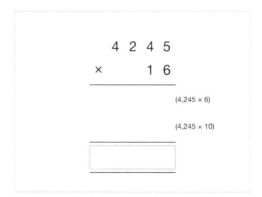

6. Find the answer to 2,101 × 15.

a b c ▪ 31515 ▪ 31,515

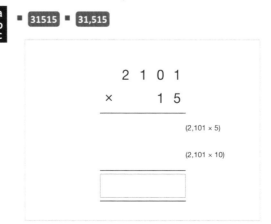

Level 1: *cont.*

7. What is 3,241 × 29?

   ▪ 93989   ▪ 93,989

```
        3 2 4 1
    ×       2 9
    ─────────────
                    (3,241 × 9)

                    (3,241 × 20)

        ┌─────────┐
        └─────────┘
    ─────────────
```

8. What are the two numbers missing from line A and line B?

   ▪ 4,191   ▪ 41,910   ▪ 25,146   ▪ 67,056

2/4

```
        4 1 9 1
    ×       1 6
    ┌─────────────┐
    │   line A    │
    ├─────────────┤
    │   line B    │
    └─────────────┘
    ─────────────
```

9. Find the answer to 8,523 × 14.

   ▪ 119322   ▪ 119,322

```
        8 5 2 3
    ×       1 4
    ─────────────
                    (8,523 × 4)

                    (8,523 × 10)

        ┌─────────┐
        └─────────┘
    ─────────────
```

10. Find the answer to 432 × 12.

   ▪ 5,184   ▪ 5184

```
          4 3 2
      ×   1 2
      ─────────
                    (432 × 2)

                    (432 × 10)

      ┌─────────┐
      └─────────┘
```

Level 2:   Fluency - Multiplying 4-digit numbers by 2-digit numbers.
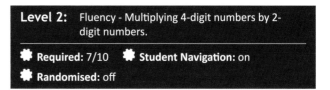
✿ **Required:** 7/10   ✿ **Student Navigation:** on
✿ **Randomised:** off

11. Calculate the answer to 8,452 × 14.

   ▪ 118328   ▪ 118,328

```
        8 4 5 2
    ×       1 4
    ┌─────────────┐
    └─────────────┘
    ┌─────────────┐
    └─────────────┘
    ┌─────────────┐
    └─────────────┘
```

12. What is 2,735 × 13?

▪ 35,555   ▪ 35555

```
        2 7 3 5
    ×       1 3
    ┌─────────────┐
    └─────────────┘
    ┌─────────────┐
    └─────────────┘
    ┌─────────────┐
    └─────────────┘
```

Level 2: *cont.*

13. 5,812 people attend a concert. If one ticket costs
£17, what is the **total amount** raised by ticket
sales?
Include the £ sign in your answer.

a
b
c

- £98804 - £98,804.00 - £98,804 - £98804.00

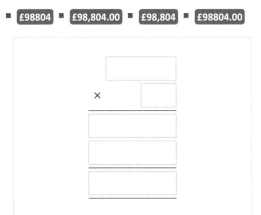

14. What is the answer to 9,201 × 18?

a
b
c

- 165,618 - 165618

15. The jackpot of a local lottery is shared by 16
people. If each person wins £2,191, what was the
total jackpot?
Include the £ sign in your answer.

a
b
c

- £35056.00 - £35056 - £35,056.00 - £35,056

16. Calculate the answer to 4,008 × 14.

a
b
c

- 56112 - 56,112

17. Aisha's baby sister is two months old and weighs
15 pounds. If 1 pound (lb) = 454 grams (g), what
does Aisha's sister weigh in **grams**?
Include the unit g (grams) in your answer.

a
b
c

- 6,810 grams - 6,810 g - 6810 g - 6810 grams

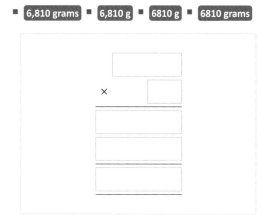

18. What is 4,321 × 12?

a
b
c

- 51852 - 51,852

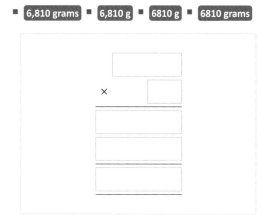

Level 2: *cont.*

19. Calculate the answer to 2,527 × 12.

a
b
c
  ▪ 30324 ▪ 30,324

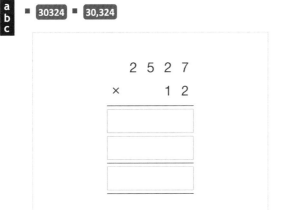

```
      2 5 2 7
  ×       1 2
  _____
```

20. Katie is paid £1,764 per month. How much does she earn in one year?
Include the £ sign in your answer.

a
b
c

  ▪ £21,168.00 ▪ £21168 ▪ £21168.00 ▪ £21,168

```
  ×
```

Level 3: Reasoning - Using long multiplication to find missing numbers.

✱ **Required:** 5/5   ✱ **Student Navigation:** on
✱ **Randomised:** off

21. Use the calculation 4,293 × 12 = 51,516 to find the answer to 4,293 × 36.

a
b
c ▪ 154,548 ▪ 154548

22. Qasim says, "I have calculated the answer to 1,542 × 13 but my answer looks too small." Explain the mistake he has made.

a
b
c

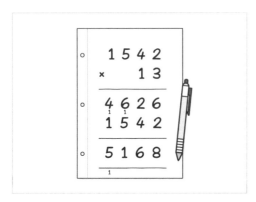

```
      1 5 4 2
  ×       1 3
  _____
      4 6 2 6
    1 5 4 2
  _____
      5 1 6 8
            1
```

23. What digit is missing from the calculation?

1
2
3 ▪ [4]

```
          3 9 1 8
      ×         2 □
  _____
      1 5 6 7 2
      7 8 3 6 0
  _____
      9 4 0 3 2
```

24. Use the calculation 1,391 × 30 = 41,730 to find the answer to 1,391 × 32.

a
b
c ▪ 44,512 ▪ 44512

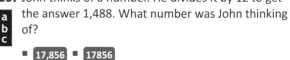

25. John thinks of a number. He divides it by 12 to get the answer 1,488. What number was John thinking of?

a
b
c ▪ 17,856 ▪ 17856

...divide by 12   ...equals 1,488

Level 4: Problem Solving - Multi step problems.

✱ **Required:** 5/5   ✱ **Student Navigation:** on
✱ **Randomised:** off

26. The same digit is missing from the calculation in three places. What is the missing digit?

1
2
3 ▪ [3]

```
      □ 4 7 □
  ×       2 □
  _____
      7 9 8 7 9
```

27. Use the number cards to create a 3-digit number to complete the equation.

1
2
3

$\_\_\_ \times 32 = 7,392.$

- 231

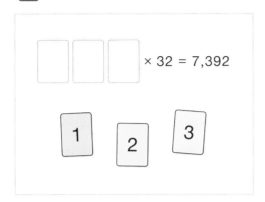

28. A section of land at an airport measures 29,127 square metres (m²). A new runway measuring 37 metres (m) wide and 772 metres (m) long is built on the land. In square metres (m²), how much **spare** land will there be after the runway has been built?

a
b
c

- 563

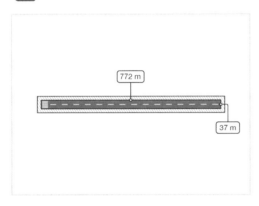

29. A post office has 4,592 stamps left in a book. The book has 24 pages and each page has 17 rows and 23 columns. How many stamps has the post office sold?

a
b
c

- 4,792 - 4792

30. Multiply two side-by-side numbers to find the value of the box above. What number goes in the highlighted box?

a
b
c

- 646866 - 646,866

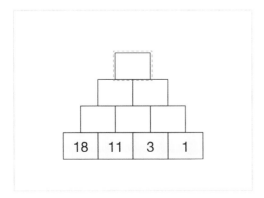

Divide numbers up to 4 digits by a one-digit number (short division)

Competency: Divide numbers up to 4 digits by a one-digit number using the formal written method of short division and interpret remainders appropriately for the context.

Quick Search Ref: 10161

Correct: Correct.   **Wrong:** Incorrect, try again.   **Open:** Thank you.

Level 1: Understanding - Divide numbers up to four digits.

✱ **Required:** 7/10   ✱ **Student Navigation:** on   ✱ **Randomised:** off

---

1. Select **all** options which correctly complete the sentence.

3/4

Division....

- ☐ is the opposite of multiplication.
- ☐ involves sharing or grouping.
- ■ is when a number is added to another number.
- ☐ is the same as repeatedly subtracting the same number.

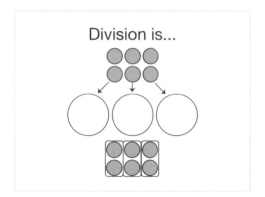

2. In division, a **remainder** is:

1/4

- ■ the number of times one number divides into another.
- ■ the number which is being divided.
- ☐ the amount left over when a number has been divided.
- ■ the number which a value is being divided by.

3. If a digit in each place value does not divide exactly, what do you do with the **remaining value?**

1/4

- ■ Add it to the digit in your answer.
- ■ Add it on at the end as a remainder.
- ☐ Carry it to the place value column on the right.
- ■ Do not include it in your calculations.

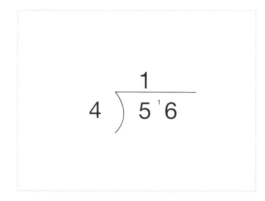

4. What is 248 **divided** by 2?

- ■ 124

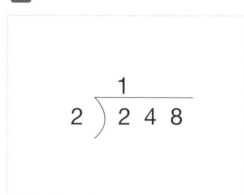

5. 56 **divided** by 4 equals __.

- ■ 14

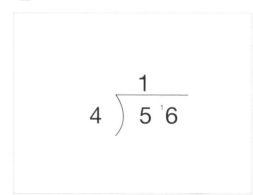

Level 1: *cont.*

6. Six friends have a total of 438 football cards. How many cards does each friend receive if the cards are shared equally?

▪ **73**

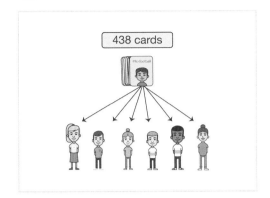

7. 4,804 **divided** by 4 equals __.

▪ **1201** ▪ **1,201**

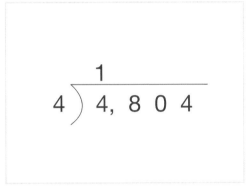

8. Calculate the answer to 93 ÷ 3.

▪ **31**

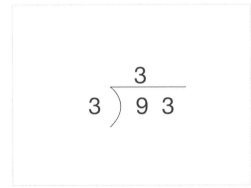

9. Harry has 393 sweets and he puts an equal amount into 3 jars. How many sweets are in each jar?

▪ **131**

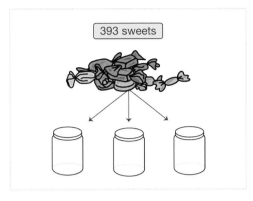

10. Calculate the answer to 735 ÷ 5.

▪ **147**

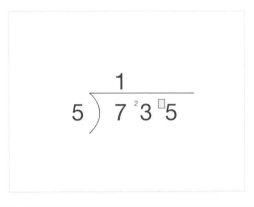

Level 2: Fluency - Divide numbers up to four digits with remainders.

✿ **Required:** 7/10   ✿ **Student Navigation:** on
✿ **Randomised:** off

11. A remainder can be written separately as a 'left over'. Select **two** other ways a remainder can be expressed.

2/5   ▪ **Decimal** ▪ Equation ▪ **Fraction** ▪ Ratio
▪ **Square number**

12. 523 ÷ 4 = **130r3**.
Select **two** other ways you can write the answer including the remainder.

2/4   ▪ 130.3 ▪ **130.75** ▪ 130 and 1/3 ▪ **130 and ¾**

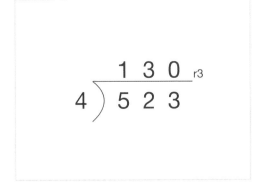

Level 2: *cont.*

13. 47 **divided** by 4 equals __.

Use an **r** to show any remainders. For example, 7 ÷ 2 = 3r1.

- 11r3

14. What is the answer to 964 **divided** by 6?

- 16r4 ■ 160 ■ 160r4 ■ 164

1/4

15. Two DVD players cost £191. Use short division to calculate the price of **each** DVD player.
Include the £ sign in your answer.

- £95.50

16. Calculate the answer to 5,437 ÷ 5.

Use an **r** to show any remainders. For example, 7 ÷ 2 = 3r1.

- 1,087r2 ■ 1087r2

17. 249 divided by 2 equals **124r1.** Select **two** other ways you can write this answer.

2/4

- 124.1 ■ 124.5 ■ 124 and ¼ ■ 124 and ½

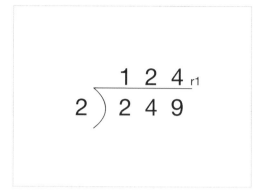

18. Calculate 885 **divided** by 8.

- 11r5 ■ 110 ■ 110r5 ■ 115

1/4

19. Asifa has 294 t-shirts and splits them into packs of 4. How many spare t-shirts will she have left over after they have been packed?

- 2

20. What is 194 **divided** by 6?

Use an **r** to show any remainders. For example, 7 ÷ 2 = 3r1.

- 32r2

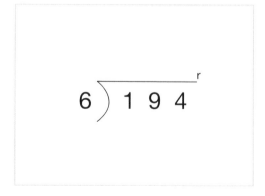

Level 3: Reasoning - Using short division to find missing numbers and compare values.

✹ **Required:** 5/5   ✹ **Student Navigation:** on

✹ **Randomised:** off

21. Find the missing number that will balance the following calculation.

$3,448 \div 8 =$ _____ $\times 2$

▪ 215.5

22. Henry has divided 586 by 7 and got the answer 83.5. What has Henry done wrong? Explain your answer.

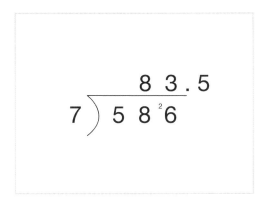

$$7 \overline{)\,5\,8\,{}^26} = 8\,3.5$$

23. B.T.V Electronics offer their customers a choice of bundles when buying multiple televisions.

Which bundle offers the **best value** for money (where the TVs are cheapest)?

▪ Bundle A ▪ Bundle B ▪ Bundle C ▪ Bundle D

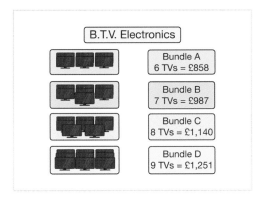

B.T.V. Electronics

Bundle A
6 TVs = £858

Bundle B
7 TVs = £987

Bundle C
8 TVs = £1,140

Bundle D
9 TVs = £1,251

24. Franky says, 'There will be no remainders in the question 1,876 ÷ 5.'

Is Franky correct? Explain your answer.

25. Using the statement in the box, select the correct **short division** calculation.

▪ A ▪ B ▪ C ▪ D

1/4

$$9 \times 341 = 3,069$$
$$+\underline{\quad 8}$$
$$3,077$$

A
$$8 \overline{)\,3,0\,6\,9} = 3\,4\,1\ r9$$

C
$$8 \overline{)\,3,0\,7\,7} = 3\,4\,1\ r9$$

B
$$9 \overline{)\,3,0\,6\,9} = 3\,4\,1\ r8$$

D
$$9 \overline{)\,3,0\,7\,7} = 3\,4\,1\ r8$$

Level 4: Problem Solving - Using short division to solve problems.

✹ **Required:** 5/5   ✹ **Student Navigation:** on

✹ **Randomised:** off

26. Some digits have been removed from the numbers in this calculation. Find the the missing number marked with an **a**.

▪ 5

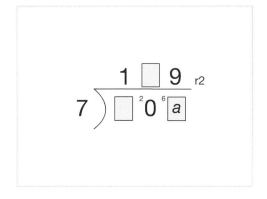

$$7 \overline{)\,\square\,{}^2 0\,{}^6 \boxed{a}} = 1\,\square\,9\ r2$$

Level 4: *cont.*

27. Jerry buys two rectangular happy birthday signs
for his son's birthday party.

Remember: *Area = Length x Width*

Sign A is **9 centimetres** wide and has an area of
4,401 square centimetres (cm²).
Sign B is **7 centimetres** wide and has an area of
4,305 square centimetres.

How much **longer,** in centimetres, is sign B than
sign A?
Don't include the units in your answer.

▪ 126

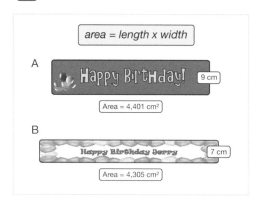

28. In a multiplication pyramid, two numbers next to
each other are multiplied together to equal the
number in the box above. Find the value of the
number marked with an **a.**

▪ 136

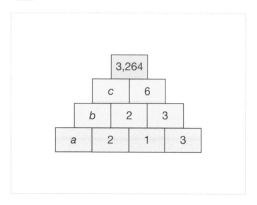

29. Ellen reads a book with **315 pages** for **three hours**
per night. She finishes the book in **one week**. How
many pages does she read **per hour?**

▪ 15

30. Sunnygreen Avenue is **9 metres** wide with an area
of **1,242 square metres (m²).** Bluetop Lane is **6**
metres wide and has an area of **756 square**
metres. Both roads are **rectangular**. How many
metres longer is Sunnygreen Avenue than Bluetop
Lane?
Include the units m (metres) in your answer.

▪ 12 m ▪ 12 metres

Number problems: multiplication and division including factors and multiples, squares and cubes

Competency: Solve problems involving multiplication and division including their knowledge of factors and multiples, squares and cubes.

Quick Search Ref: 10031

Correct: Correct.   **Wrong:** Incorrect, try again.   **Open:** Thank you.

Level 1: Problem solving - Use and apply knowledge of multiplication and division

❋ **Required:** 10/10   ❋ **Student Navigation:** on   ❋ **Randomised:** off

1. Barry pays £46 for some tickets to a football
   match. An adult ticket costs £9 and a child ticket
   costs £4. How many tickets did Barry buy?
   `1 2 3`
   ▪ 9

2. How many **factors** of 128 are **cube numbers?**
   `1 2 3`   ▪ 3

3. Use the numbers 3, 4 and 8 to make a 3-digit
   number which is a **multiple** of both 4 and 8.
   `1 2 3`   ▪ 384

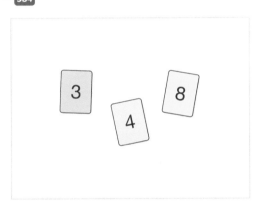

4. Identify the four numbers on the chart that are a
   multiple of 3 but **not** a multiple of 2 or 5. **Multiply**
   the smallest number by the largest.
   `a b c`
   ▪ 819

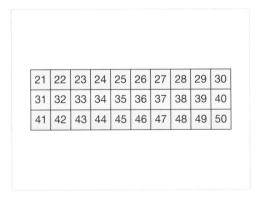

21	22	23	24	25	26	27	28	29	30
31	32	33	34	35	36	37	38	39	40
41	42	43	44	45	46	47	48	49	50

5. Look at the multiplication pyramid. What is the
   missing number labelled y?
   `1 2 3`   ▪ 8

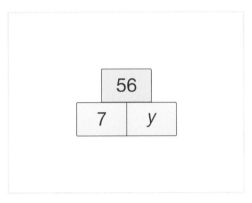

6. How many **factors** of 100 are **square numbers?**
   `1 2 3`   ▪ 4

7. Look at the multiplication pyramid. What is the
   missing number labelled x?
   `1 2 3`   ▪ 2

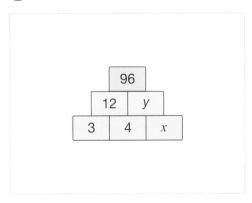

8. Phillipe is thinking of two numbers between 1 and 20. They are **not** any of the following:

 - Factor of 24.
 - Multiple of 5.
 - A square number.
 - An odd number.

What is the **product** of Phillipe's numbers?

- 252

1	2	3	4	5
6	7	8	9	10
11	12	13	14	15
16	17	18	19	20

9. Mrs Salvy buys some calculators for her class at a cost of **£5 each**. She buys **at least** 8 calculators for £5, but the shop she goes to doesn't have enough in stock so she has to pay **£6 each** for the remaining calculators at a different shop.
She pays **£72** in total. How many calculators does she buy?

- 14

10. Fill in the missing numbers of the multiplication grid and find the value of *y*.

- 165

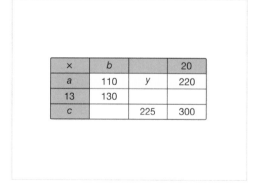

×	b		20
a	110	y	220
13	130		
c		225	300

Ref:10031   Number problems: multiplication and di...

Mathematics

Y5

Fractions

Addition

Subtraction

Multiplication

Division

Equivalent Fractions

Improper Fractions and Mixed Numbers

Decimals and Percentages

Add and Subtract Fractions with the Same and Common Denominators

Competency: Add and subtract fractions with the same denominator and denominators that are multiples of the same number.

Quick Search Ref: 10181

Correct: Correct.   Wrong: Incorrect, try again.   Open: Thank you.

Level 1: Understanding terminology and adding with like denominators.

✿ **Required:** 7/10   ✿ **Student Navigation:** on   ✿ **Randomised:** off

1. What is a **denominator**?

1/4

■ The top number in a fraction, which shows how many parts of a whole there are.
■ The bottom number in a fraction, which shows how many equal parts the whole is divided into.
■ A fraction which has the same value as another. For example, 1/2 = 2/4.
■ The smallest positive number that is a multiple of two or more numbers.

2. What is a **numerator**?

1/4

■ The smallest positive number that is a multiple of two or more numbers.
■ The bottom number in a fraction, which shows how many equal parts the whole is divided into.
■ A fraction which has the same value as another. For example, 1/2 = 2/4.
■ The top number in a fraction, which shows how many parts of a whole there are.

3. What is an **equivalent** fraction?

1/3

■ The bottom number in a fraction, which shows how many equal parts the whole is divided into.
■ The top number in a fraction, which shows how many parts of the whole there are.
■ Fractions that have the same value but are shown with different numbers.

$$\frac{1}{2} = \frac{2}{4}$$

4. What is a **lowest common multiple**?

1/4

■ The bottom number in a fraction, which shows how many equal parts the whole is divided into.
■ The smallest positive number that is a multiple of two or more numbers.
■ The top number in a fraction, which shows how many parts of a whole there are.
■ A fraction which has the same value as another. For example, 1/2 = 2/4.

multiples of	
2	6
①	①
②	②
	3
	6

5. If you add 3/8 and 4/8, what is the denominator?

1/5

■ 3 ■ 4 ■ **8** ■ 16 ■ 7

$$\frac{3}{8} + \frac{4}{8} = \frac{?}{?}$$

6. What is 9/14 - 2/14?

■ **7/14** ■ **1/2**

$$\frac{9}{14} - \frac{2}{14} = \frac{?}{14}$$

Level 1: *cont.*

7. What is 3/12 + 1/12?

 ▪ 1/3 ▪ 2/6 ▪ 4/24 ▪ 4/12 ▪ 1/6

1/5

$$\frac{3}{12} + \frac{1}{12} = \frac{?}{?}$$

8. 13/16 - 2/16 - 3/16 =

 ▪ 8/16 ▪ 4/8 ▪ 1/2 ▪ 2/4

$$\frac{13}{16} - \frac{2}{16} - \frac{3}{16} = \frac{?}{16}$$

9. 4/15 + 1/15 = ___.

 ▪ 5/15 ▪ 1/3

$$\frac{4}{15} + \frac{1}{15} = \frac{?}{?}$$

10. What is 3/12 - 1/12?

 ▪ 2/0 ▪ 4/12 ▪ 1/3 ▪ 2/12 ▪ 1/6

1/5

$$\frac{3}{12} - \frac{1}{12} = \frac{?}{?}$$

Level 2: Adding with mixed number fractions and denominators with common multiples.

✿ Required: 7/10   ✿ Student Navigation: on
✿ Randomised: off

11. 2/8 + 8/16 = ___.

a b c ▪ 3/4 ▪ 6/8 ▪ 12/16

$$\frac{2}{8} + \frac{8}{16} = \frac{?}{?}$$

12. 8/16 - 1/4 =

a b c ▪ 4/16 ▪ 2/8 ▪ 1/4

$$\frac{8}{16} - \frac{1}{4}$$

13. What is 4 3/10 + 3 4/10?
Give your answer as a mixed number fraction.

a b c ▪ 7 7/10

$$4\frac{3}{10} + 3\frac{4}{10} = ?\frac{?}{?}$$

Level 2: *cont.*

14. What is 5 8/10 - 3 1/10?

 ▪ 2 7/10

$$5\frac{8}{10} \; - \; 3\frac{1}{10} \; = \; ?\frac{?}{?}$$

15. 56/100 - 1/10 - 3/10 =

 ▪ 8/50 ▪ 4/25 ▪ 16/100

$$\frac{56}{100} \; - \; \frac{1}{10} \; - \; \frac{3}{10} \; = \; \frac{?}{?}$$

16. Kelsey and Freya have a cereal bar to share between them. Kelsey eats 2/8 and Freya eats 6/24. How much do they eat altogether?

▪ 2/4 ▪ 1/2 ▪ 12/24

17. Gemma and Steph have a bag of marbles. Gemma takes 3/8 of the marbles and Steph takes 6/24. As a **fraction**, what is the difference between the amount of marbles that they each have?

▪ 3/24 ▪ 1/8

18. What is the missing fraction?

 ▪ 5/7

$$\frac{13}{7} \; + \; \frac{?}{?} \; = \; \frac{18}{7}$$

19. 4/9 - 4/27 =

▪ 8/27

$$\frac{4}{9} \; - \; \frac{4}{27} \; = \; \frac{?}{?}$$

20. What is 5 1/10 + 1 6/10?

▪ 6 7/10

$$5\frac{1}{10} \; + \; 1\frac{6}{10} \; = \; ?\frac{?}{?}$$

Level 3: Adding fractions in word problems and comparing values.

✳ **Required:** 5/5   ✳ **Student Navigation:** on
✳ **Randomised:** off

21. The square has one **1/4** that is shaded and
a one **1/8** that is shaded.
b
c Explain how you would work out the fraction of
the square that **is not shaded**.

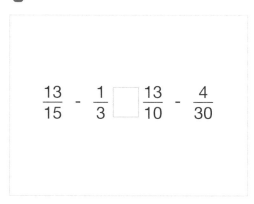

22. Which sign makes the statement true?
a 13/15 - 1/3 ___ 13/10 - 4/30
b
c ▪ **<**

$$\frac{13}{15} - \frac{1}{3} \;\square\; \frac{13}{10} - \frac{4}{30}$$

23. Miss Kay conducted a survey of weekend bed
a times. She says, "More than half of the children in
b my class go to bed before 9.00 p.m.".
c Is she correct? Explain how you know.

time	fraction of people
before 8:00 p.m.	$\frac{3}{12}$
8:00 p.m. - 8:29 p.m.	$\frac{3}{24}$
8:30 p.m. - 8:59 p.m.	$\frac{1}{4}$
9:00 p.m. - 9:29 p.m.	$\frac{1}{6}$
9:30 p.m. - 10:00 p.m.	$\frac{1}{8}$
after 10:00 p.m.	$\frac{1}{12}$

24. Harry says that 30/48 - 5/12 = 25/36.
a Explain his mistake.
b
c

25. The diagram shows three fields.
Which has the largest perimeter?

1/3
▪ **field (a)**   ▪ field (b)   ▪ field (c)

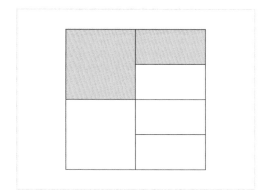

Level 4: Adding fractions to solve problems.

✳ **Required:** 5/5   ✳ **Student Navigation:** on
✳ **Randomised:** off

26. Sienna baked a cake and cut it into eight
a pieces. **How many pieces of cake** did she eat?
b
c
Her dad ate one-quarter of the cake.
Her mum ate one-eighth of the cake.
Her brother ate two pieces of cake.
Sienna ate the rest of the cake.

▪ **3**

27. Which fractions equal **1** when added together?
Select more than two fractions.

4/6
▪ **1/6** ▪ 1/20 ▪ 3/5 ▪ **4/15** ▪ **3/20** ▪ **5/12**

28. Use the clues below and the table to convert each
a fraction to a letter and then work out the 5-letter
b word.
c

1. 12/4 + 7/4
2. 11/20 + 6/2
3. 3 + 7/8
4. 3/2 + 43/20
5. 7/14 + 23/28

▪ **angle** ▪ **angle.**

A	$4\frac{3}{4}$	H	$1\frac{7}{15}$	O	$2\frac{1}{4}$	U	$1\frac{1}{2}$
B	$1\frac{1}{3}$	I	$7\frac{11}{56}$	P	$2\frac{5}{12}$	V	$3\frac{3}{10}$
C	$\frac{7}{12}$	J	$2\frac{7}{12}$	Q	$1\frac{2}{3}$	W	$\frac{13}{15}$
D	$\frac{11}{12}$	K	$3\frac{1}{5}$	R	$6\frac{3}{56}$	X	$4\frac{2}{15}$
E	$1\frac{9}{28}$	L	$3\frac{13}{20}$	S	$1\frac{11}{30}$	Y	$6\frac{1}{4}$
F	$5\frac{2}{5}$	M	$1\frac{5}{6}$	T	$2\frac{5}{8}$	Z	$1\frac{9}{20}$
G	$3\frac{7}{8}$	N	$3\frac{11}{20}$				

29.
a
b
c
The rectangle has a perimeter of 26/5 cm.
Work out the value of x.
Give your answer as a whole number and include the units cm (centimetres) in the answer.

- 1 centimetre ▪ 1 cm ▪ 1 centimetres

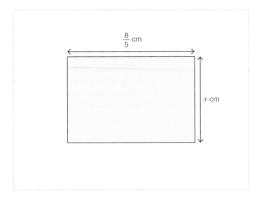

$\frac{8}{5}$ cm

x cm

30. To cross the river, calculate the answer to each of the problems and arrange the stepping stones (smallest answer first).

- 7/8 - 5/6 ▪ 8/9 - 3/4 ▪ 1/3 - 1/8 ▪ 5/6 - 1/2
- 1 1/2 - 7/8

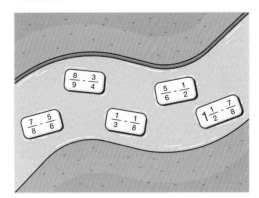

Add fractions with the same and common denominators

Competency: Add fractions with the same denominator and denominators that are multiples of the same number.

Quick Search Ref: 10103

Correct: Correct.   **Wrong:** Incorrect, try again.   **Open:** Thank you.

Level 1: Understanding terminology and adding with like denominators.

✹ **Required:** 8/10   ✹ **Student Navigation:** on   ✹ **Randomised:** off

1. What is a **denominator**?

1/4

- The top number in a fraction, which shows how many parts of a whole there are.
- **The bottom number in a fraction, which shows how many equal parts the whole is divided into.**
- A fraction which has the same value as another. For example, 1/2 = 2/4.
- The smallest positive number that is a multiple of two or more numbers.

2. What is a **numerator**?

1/4

- The smallest positive number that is a multiple of two or more numbers.
- The bottom number in a fraction, which shows how many equal parts the whole is divided into.
- A fraction which has the same value as another. For example, 1/2 = 2/4.
- **The top number in a fraction, which shows how many parts of a whole there are.**

3. What is an **equivalent** fraction?

1/3

- The bottom number in a fraction, which shows how many equal parts the whole is divided into.
- The top number in a fraction, which shows how many parts of the whole there are.
- **Fractions that have the same value but are shown with different numbers.**

$$\frac{1}{2} = \frac{2}{4}$$

4. What is a **lowest common multiple**?

1/4

- The bottom number in a fraction, which shows how many equal parts the whole is divided into.
- **The smallest positive number that is a multiple of two or more numbers.**
- The top number in a fraction, which shows how many parts of a whole there are.
- A fraction which has the same value as another. For example, 1/2 = 2/4.

multiples of	
2	6
①	①
②	②
	3
	6

5. What is 13/30 + 10/30?

- **23/30**

$$\frac{13}{30} + \frac{10}{30} = \frac{?}{?}$$

6. If you add 3/8 and 4/8, what is the denominator?

1/5

- 3 ■ 4 ■ **8** ■ 16 ■ 7

$$\frac{3}{8} + \frac{4}{8} = \frac{?}{?}$$

Level 1: *cont.*

7. 4/16 + 2/16 + 3/16 =

 ▪ 9/16

$$\frac{4}{16} + \frac{2}{16} + \frac{3}{16} = \frac{?}{?}$$

8. What is 3/12 + 1/12?

1/5

▪ 1/3 ▪ 2/6 ▪ 4/24 ▪ 4/12 ▪ 1/6

$$\frac{3}{12} + \frac{1}{12} = \frac{?}{?}$$

9. 4/15 + 1/15 = ___.

 ▪ 5/15 ▪ 1/3

$$\frac{4}{15} + \frac{1}{15} = \frac{?}{?}$$

10. What is 2/14 + 5/14?

abc ▪ 7/14 ▪ 1/2

$$\frac{2}{14} + \frac{5}{14} = \frac{?}{?}$$

Level 2: Adding with mixed number fractions and denominators with common multiples.

✸ **Required:** 8/10   ✸ **Student Navigation:** on
✸ **Randomised:** off

11. 2/8 + 8/16 = ___.

abc ▪ 12/16 ▪ 3/4 ▪ 6/8

$$\frac{2}{8} + \frac{8}{16} = \frac{?}{?}$$

12. What is 4 3/10 + 3 4/10?
Give your answer as a mixed number fraction.

abc ▪ 7 7/10

$$4\frac{3}{10} + 3\frac{4}{10} = ?\frac{?}{?}$$

13. 1/12 + 20/48 =

abc ▪ 2/4 ▪ 8/16 ▪ 6/12 ▪ 4/8 ▪ 24/48 ▪ 12/24 ▪ 1/2 ▪ 3/6

$$\frac{1}{12} + \frac{20}{48} = \frac{?}{?}$$

Level 2: *cont.*

14. 37/100 + 1/10 + 3/10 =

 ▪ 77/100

$$\frac{37}{100} + \frac{1}{10} + \frac{3}{10} = \frac{?}{?}$$

15. 1/9 + 4/27 =

 ▪ 7/27

$$\frac{1}{9} + \frac{4}{27} = \frac{?}{?}$$

16. 2/6 + 10/18 =

▪ 16/18 ▪ 8/9

$$\frac{2}{6} + \frac{10}{18} = \frac{?}{?}$$

17. What is the missing fraction?

 ▪ 5/7

$$\frac{13}{7} + \frac{?}{?} = \frac{18}{7}$$

18. Kelsey and Freya have a cereal bar to share between them. Kelsey eats 2/8 and Freya eats 6/24. How much do they eat altogether?

▪ 12/24 ▪ 1/2

19. What is 5 1/10 + 1 6/10?

 ▪ 6 7/10

$$5\frac{1}{10} + 1\frac{6}{10} = ?\frac{?}{?}$$

20. 8/10 + 3/20 =

▪ 19/20

$$\frac{8}{10} + \frac{3}{20} = \frac{?}{?}$$

Level 3: Adding fractions in word problems and comparing values.

❋ **Required:** 5/7   ❋ **Student Navigation:** on
❋ **Randomised:** off

21. Choose **two** fractions that make the statement true.

 ▪ 1/6 ▪ 13/18 ▪ 7/9 ▪ 2/3 ▪ 2/9

2/5

$$\frac{?}{?} + \frac{?}{?} = \frac{15}{18}$$

22. Which sign makes the following statement true?

 4/6 + 1/2 __ 3/4 + 5/12

■ < ■ = ■ >

1/3

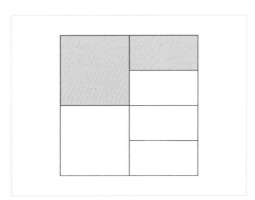

$$\frac{4}{6} + \frac{1}{2} \boxed{} \frac{3}{4} + \frac{5}{12}$$

23. The square has one **1/4** that is shaded and
 one **1/8** that is shaded.
Explain how you would work out the fraction of
the square that **is not shaded**.

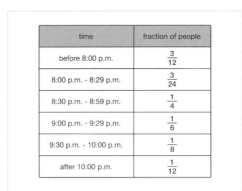

24. Which two fractions make the **smallest**
number when added?

■ 5/4 ■ 6/3 ■ 3/5 ■ 6/4 ■ 3/6 ■ 5/3 ■ 4/5

?/7

25. Miss Kay conducted a survey of weekend bed
times. She says, "More than half of the children in
my class go to bed before 9.00 p.m.".
Is she correct? Explain how you know.

time	fraction of people
before 8:00 p.m.	$\frac{3}{12}$
8:00 p.m. - 8:29 p.m.	$\frac{3}{24}$
8:30 p.m. - 8:59 p.m.	$\frac{1}{4}$
9:00 p.m. - 9:29 p.m.	$\frac{1}{6}$
9:30 p.m. - 10:00 p.m.	$\frac{1}{8}$
after 10:00 p.m.	$\frac{1}{12}$

26. Which sign makes the statement true?

4/15 + 1/3 __ 3/8 + 14/20

■ <

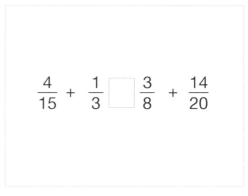

$$\frac{4}{15} + \frac{1}{3} \boxed{} \frac{3}{8} + \frac{14}{20}$$

27. The diagram shows three fields.
Which has the largest perimeter?

■ field (a) ■ field (b) ■ field (c)

1/3

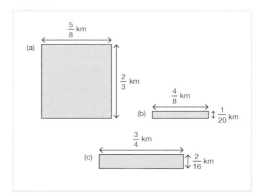

28. Add two side-by-side fractions to find the answer
to the box above.
What fraction goes in the highlighted box?
Give your answer as a mixed number fraction.

■ 1 1/3 ■ 1 8/24 ■ 1 4/12

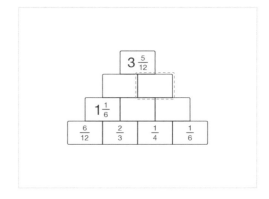

Level 4: *cont.*

29. Dom and his family were completing with a 100-piece jigsaw. What fraction of the jigsaw did Dom complete?
His uncle completed 1/5 of the jigsaw.
His grandma completed 3/8 of the jigsaw.
His cousin completed 25 pieces.
Dom finished the rest of the jigsaw.

a
b
c

▪ 7/40

30. In metres, what is the perimeter of the swimming pool?
Give your answer as an improper fraction.
Hint: Start by finding the values of x and y.

a
b
c

▪ 180/12 ▪ 90/6

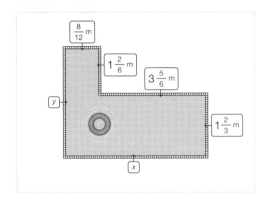

31. Which fractions equal **1** when added together?
Select more than two fractions.

▪ 1/6 ▪ 1/20 ▪ 3/5 ▪ 4/15 ▪ 3/20 ▪ 5/12

4/6

32. Use the clues below and the table to convert each fraction to a letter and then work out the 5-letter word.

a
b
c

1. 12/4 + 7/4
2. 11/20 + 6/2
3. 3 + 7/8
4. 3/2 + 43/20
5. 7/14 + 23/28

▪ angle ▪ angle.

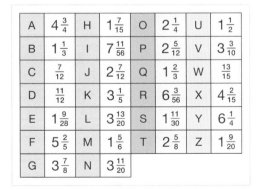

A	$4\frac{3}{4}$	H	$1\frac{7}{15}$	O	$2\frac{1}{4}$	U	$1\frac{1}{2}$
B	$1\frac{1}{3}$	I	$7\frac{11}{56}$	P	$2\frac{5}{12}$	V	$3\frac{3}{10}$
C	$\frac{7}{12}$	J	$2\frac{7}{12}$	Q	$1\frac{2}{3}$	W	$\frac{13}{15}$
D	$\frac{11}{12}$	K	$3\frac{1}{5}$	R	$6\frac{3}{56}$	X	$4\frac{2}{15}$
E	$1\frac{9}{28}$	L	$3\frac{13}{20}$	S	$1\frac{11}{30}$	Y	$6\frac{1}{4}$
F	$5\frac{2}{5}$	M	$1\frac{5}{6}$	T	$2\frac{5}{8}$	Z	$1\frac{9}{20}$
G	$3\frac{7}{8}$	N	$3\frac{11}{20}$						

33. To collect the treasure, turn the keys in the correct order. Use the clues to work out the correct order and then sort the colours (first at the top).

↑
↓

1st: 3 1/4 + 1 5/8
2nd: 2 7/15 + 2/5
3rd: 3 1/4 + 1 11/12
4rd: 3 3/10 + 1 2/3
5th: 1 3/4 + 2/3

▪ pink ▪ blue ▪ rurple ▪ green ▪ red

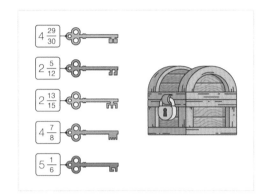

Practise Adding Fractions with Related Denominators

Competency: Children practise 20 randomised questions adding proper fractions with related denominators (one conversion required).

Quick Search Ref: 10428

Correct: Correct.   Wrong: Incorrect. Try again.   Open: Thank you.

Level 1: I can add proper fractions with related denominators (one conversion required).

✿ Required: 17/17   ✿ Student Navigation: off   ✿ Randomised: on

1. 1/2 + 1/4
a b c ▪ 3/4 ▪ 6/8

2. 1/4 + 2/8
a b c ▪ 1/2 ▪ 8/16 ▪ 2/4 ▪ 16/32 ▪ 4/8

3. 3/16 + 1/8
a b c ▪ 40/128 ▪ 5/16 ▪ 20/64 ▪ 10/32

4. 1/8 + 3/4
a b c ▪ 7/8 ▪ 28/32 ▪ 14/16

5. 1/5 + 3/15
a b c ▪ 2/5 ▪ 6/15 ▪ 30/75

6. 3/10 + 2/5
a b c ▪ 7/10 ▪ 35/50

7. 1/9 + 2/3
a b c ▪ 7/9 ▪ 21/27

8. 6/9 + 1/36
a b c ▪ 25/36 ▪ 75/108 ▪ 225/324

9. 2/5 + 2/10
a b c ▪ 30/50 ▪ 15/25 ▪ 3/5 ▪ 6/10

10. 1/70 + 4/7
a b c ▪ 41/70 ▪ 287/490

11. 13/45 + 2/9
a b c ▪ 23/45 ▪ 207/405

12. 12/15 + 1/15 + 4/30
a b c ▪ 45/45 ▪ 15/15 ▪ 9/9 ▪ 225/225 ▪ 450/450 ▪ 90/90 ▪ 1 whole ▪ 1

13. 5/6 + 1/18
a b c ▪ 32/36 ▪ 8/9 ▪ 16/18 ▪ 96/108

14. 5/11 + 27/99
a b c ▪ 72/99 ▪ 264/363 ▪ 8/11 ▪ 792/1089 ▪ 792/1,089 ▪ 88/121

15. 5/14 + 1/7
a b c ▪ 49/98 ▪ 1/2 ▪ 7/14

16. 45/100 + 2/10
a b c ▪ 13/20 ▪ 650/1,000 ▪ 65/100 ▪ 325/500 ▪ 650/100

17. 2/13 + 20/26
a b c ▪ 24/26 ▪ 12/13 ▪ 156/169 ▪ 312/338

Level 2: I can add fractions with related denominators (answers greater than 1).

✿ Required: 3/3   ✿ Student Navigation: off
✿ Randomised: on

18. 37/50 + 47/100
a b c ▪ 1 1,050/5,000 ▪ 1 21/100 ▪ 1210/1000 ▪ 121/100 ▪ 6,050/5,000 ▪ 1 1050/5000 ▪ 1 210/1,000 ▪ 1 210/1000 ▪ 605/500 ▪ 1,210/1,000 ▪ 6050/5000

19. 62/100 + 417/1,000
a b c ▪ 1 3,700/100,000 ▪ 1 925/25000 ▪ 103,700/100,000 ▪ 1 185/5000 ▪ 1 185/5,000 ▪ 1 1,850/50,000 ▪ 25,925/25,000 ▪ 51,850/50,000 ▪ 1 3700/100000 ▪ 1 37/1000 ▪ 1 1850/50000 ▪ 1 37/1,000 ▪ 51850/50000 ▪ 25925/25000 ▪ 5,185/5,000 ▪ 1037/1000 ▪ 103700/100000 ▪ 5185/5000 ▪ 1 925/25,000

20. 17/75 + 24/25
a b c ▪ 2,225/1,875 ▪ 445/375 ▪ 1 14/75 ▪ 1 350/1875 ▪ 2225/1875 ▪ 89/75 ▪ 1 70/375 ▪ 1 350/1,875

Practise Subtracting Fractions with Related Denominators

Competency: Children practise 20 randomised questions subtracting proper fractions with related denominators (one conversion required).

Quick Search Ref: 10431

Correct: Correct.   Wrong: Incorrect. Try again.   Open: Thank you.

Level 1: I can subtract proper fractions with related denominators (one conversion required).

✿ **Required:** 20/20   ✿ **Student Navigation:** off   ✿ **Randomised:** off

1. $1/2 - 1/4$
   a b c ▪ 2/8 ▪ 1/4

2. $1/4 - 2/8$
   a b c ▪ 0/32 ▪ 0/8 ▪ 0

3. $15/16 - 1/8$
   a b c ▪ 13/16 ▪ 104/128 ▪ 52/64 ▪ 26/32

4. $7/8 - 3/4$
   a b c ▪ 4/32 ▪ 1/8 ▪ 2/16

5. $8/15 - 1/5$
   a b c ▪ 1/3 ▪ 25/75 ▪ 5/15

6. $9/10 - 2/5$
   a b c ▪ 1/2 ▪ 5/10 ▪ 25/50

7. $8/9 - 2/3$
   a b c ▪ 2/9 ▪ 6/27

8. $2/3 - 1/36$
   a b c ▪ 23/36 ▪ 69/108

9. $4/5 - 2/10$
   a b c ▪ 3/5 ▪ 6/10 ▪ 15/25 ▪ 30/50

10. $4/7 - 3/70$
    a b c ▪ 259/490 ▪ 37/70

11. $23/45 - 2/9$
    a b c ▪ 39/135 ▪ 117/405 ▪ 13/45

12. $12/15 - 1/15 - 8/30$
    a b c ▪ 105/225 ▪ 14/30 ▪ 21/45 ▪ 7/15 ▪ 210/450

13. $5/6 - 1/18$
    a b c ▪ 42/54 ▪ 84/108 ▪ 21/27 ▪ 7/9 ▪ 14/18

14. $10/11 - 34/99$
    a b c ▪ 616/1,089 ▪ 616/1089 ▪ 56/99

15. $5/14 - 1/7$
    a b c ▪ 21/98 ▪ 3/14

16. $45/100 - 3/10$
    a b c ▪ 150/1,000 ▪ 15/100 ▪ 75/500 ▪ 150/1000 ▪ 3/20

17. $20/26 - 4/13$
    a b c ▪ 6/13 ▪ 12/26 ▪ 78/169 ▪ 156/338

18. $71/100 - 12/50$
    a b c ▪ 1,175/2,500 ▪ 2,350/5,000 ▪ 1175/2500 ▪ 47/100 ▪ 235/500 ▪ 2350/5000

19. $59/100 - 47/1,000$
    a b c ▪ 13575/25000 ▪ 543/1,000 ▪ 54300/100000 ▪ 13,575/25,000 ▪ 54,300/100,000 ▪ 543/1000 ▪ 2,71/5,000 ▪ 27,150/50,000 ▪ 2715/5000 ▪ 27150/50000

20. $56/75 - 13/25$
    a b c ▪ 425/1875 ▪ 85/375 ▪ 425/1,875 ▪ 17/75

Subtract fractions with the same and common denominators

Competency: Subtract fractions with the same denominator and denominators that are multiples of the same number.

Quick Search Ref: 10077

Correct: Correct.   **Wrong:** Incorrect, try again.   **Open:** Thank you.

Level 1: Understanding terminology and subtracting with like denominators.

✱ **Required:** 8/10   ✱ **Student Navigation:** on   ✱ **Randomised:** off

1. What is a **denominator**?

1/4

- The top number in a fraction, which shows how many parts of a whole there are.
- **The bottom number in a fraction, which shows how many equal parts the whole is divided into.**
- A fraction which has the same value as another. For example 1/2 = 2/4.
- The smallest positive number that is a multiple of two or more numbers.

2. What is a **numerator**?

1/4

- The smallest positive number that is a multiple of two or more numbers.
- The bottom number in a fraction, which shows how many equal parts the whole is divided into.
- A fraction which has the same value as another. For example, 1/2 = 2/4.
- **The top number in a fraction, which shows how many parts of a whole there are.**

3. What is an equivalent fraction?

1/3

- **Fractions that have the same value but are shown with different numbers.**
- The bottom number in a fraction, which shows how many equal parts the whole is divided into.
- The top number in a fraction, which shows how many parts of the whole there are.

$$\frac{1}{2} = \frac{2}{4}$$

4. What is a **lowest common multiple**?

1/4

- The bottom number in a fraction, which shows how many equal parts the whole is divided into.
- **The smallest positive number that is a multiple of two or more numbers.**
- The top number in a fraction, which shows how many parts of a whole there are.
- A fraction which has the same value as another. For example, 1/2 = 2/4.

5. If you **subtract** 3/8 from 4/8, what denominator do you get?

1/4

- 3 ▪ 4 ▪ **8** ▪ 0

$$\frac{4}{8} - \frac{3}{8} = \frac{?}{?}$$

6. What is 3/12 - 1/12?

1/5

- 2/0 ▪ **2/12** ▪ 4/12 ▪ 1/3 ▪ **1/6**

$$\frac{3}{12} - \frac{1}{12} = \frac{?}{?}$$

7. 4/15 - 1/15 =

- **3/15** ▪ **1/5**

$$\frac{4}{15} - \frac{1}{15} = \frac{?}{?}$$

Level 1: *cont.*

8. 13/16 - 2/16 - 3/16 =

 ▪ 2/4 ▪ 4/8 ▪ 1/2 ▪ 8/16

$$\frac{13}{16} - \frac{2}{16} - \frac{3}{16} = \frac{?}{16}$$

9. What is 13/30 - 10/30?

▪ 3/30 ▪ 1/10

$$\frac{13}{30} - \frac{10}{30} = \frac{?}{30}$$

10. What is 9/14 - 2/14?

 ▪ 7/14 ▪ 1/2

$$\frac{9}{14} - \frac{2}{14} = \frac{?}{14}$$

Level 2: Subtracting with mixed number fractions and denominators with shared multiples.

✹ **Required:** 8/10   ✹ **Student Navigation:** on
✹ **Randomised:** off

11. 8/16 - 1/4 =

▪ 1/4 ▪ 4/16 ▪ 2/8

$$\frac{8}{16} - \frac{1}{4}$$

12. 20/48 - 1/12 =

▪ 1/3 ▪ 8/24 ▪ 4/12 ▪ 16/48

$$\frac{20}{48} - \frac{1}{12} = \frac{?}{?}$$

13. What is 5 8/10 - 3 1/10?

▪ 2 7/10

$$5\frac{8}{10} - 3\frac{1}{10} = ?\frac{?}{?}$$

Level 2: cont.

14. 56/100 - 1/10 - 3/10 =

■ 8/50   ■ 4/25   ■ 16/100

$$\frac{56}{100} - \frac{1}{10} - \frac{3}{10} = \frac{?}{?}$$

15. 4/9 - 4/27 =

■ 8/27

$$\frac{4}{9} - \frac{4}{27} = \frac{?}{?}$$

16. 4/6 - 10/18 =

■ 1/9   ■ 2/18

$$\frac{4}{6} - \frac{10}{18} = \frac{?}{?}$$

17. What is the missing fraction?

■ 1/8   ■ 2/16

$$\frac{11}{16} - \frac{?}{?} = \frac{9}{16}$$

18. Gemma and Steph have a bag of marbles. Gemma takes 3/8 of the marbles and Steph takes 6/24. As a **fraction**, what is the difference between the amount of marbles that they each have?

■ 1/8   ■ 3/24

19. What is 5 9/10 - 1 6/10?
Give your answer as a mixed number fraction.

■ 4 3/10

$$5\frac{9}{10} - 1\frac{6}{10} = ?\frac{?}{?}$$

Level 2: *cont.*

20. 8/10 - 3/20 =

· **13/20**

$$\frac{8}{10} - \frac{3}{20} = \frac{?}{?}$$

Level 3: Subtracting fractions in word problems and comparing values.

✲ **Required:** 5/6   ✲ **Student Navigation:** on
✲ **Randomised:** off

21. Choose the **two** fractions that make the statement true.

· **1/6** · 1/3 · **15/18** · 7/9 · 3/9

2/5

$$\frac{?}{?} - \frac{?}{?} = \frac{2}{3}$$

22. Which sign makes the following statement true?
4/6 - 1/2 ___ 2/3 - 5/12

· **<** · = · >

1/3

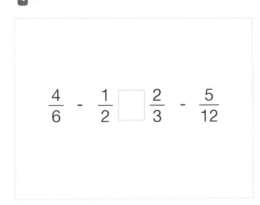

$$\frac{4}{6} - \frac{1}{2} \boxed{\phantom{<}} \frac{2}{3} - \frac{5}{12}$$

23. Harry says that 30/48 - 5/12 = 25/36.
Explain his mistake.

24. Every day, Lexi has football practice for 5/6 of an hour. If she has been practising for 2/5 of an hour, what fraction of an hour does she have left?

· **13/30**

25. Explain how to find the difference between 2/3 and 3/7.

26. Which sign makes the statement true?
13/15 - 1/3 ___ 13/10 - 4/30

· **<**

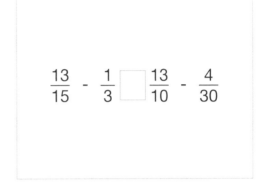

$$\frac{13}{15} - \frac{1}{3} \boxed{\phantom{<}} \frac{13}{10} - \frac{4}{30}$$

Level 4: Subtracting fractions to solve problems.

✲ **Required:** 5/5   ✲ **Student Navigation:** on
✲ **Randomised:** off

27. Sienna baked a cake and cut it into eight pieces. How many **pieces of cake** did she eat?

Her dad ate one-quarter of the cake.
Her mum ate one-eighth of the cake.
Her brother ate two pieces of cake.
Sienna ate the rest of the cake.

· **3**

28. The rectangle has a perimeter of 26/5 cm. Work out the value of *x*.
Give your answer as a whole number and include the units cm (centimetres) in the answer.

· **1 cm** · **1 centimetres**

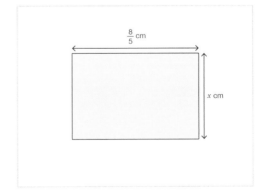

29. To open the safe, press the buttons in the correct order. Use the clues below to work out the correct order and then sort the colours (first at the top).

1st: 3 1/4 - 1 5/8
2nd: 2 7/15 - 2/5
3rd: 3 1/4 - 1 11/12
4th: 3 3/10 - 1 2/5
5th: 1 3/4 -2/3
6th: 4 1/5 - 1 7/10

■ purple ■ black ■ green ■ blue ■ pink ■ red

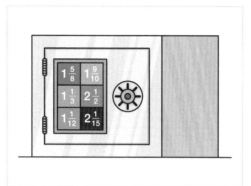

30. Use the clues below and the table to convert each fraction to a letter and then work out the 5-letter word.

1. 2 14/30 - 1 1/10
2. 4 2/3 - 3 1/5
3. 4 5/6 - 1/12
4. 2 5/6 - 1 5/12
5. 2 - 19/28

■ shape

A	$4\frac{3}{4}$	H	$1\frac{7}{15}$	O	$2\frac{1}{4}$	U	$1\frac{1}{2}$
B	$2\frac{1}{3}$	I	$7\frac{11}{56}$	P	$1\frac{5}{12}$	V	$3\frac{3}{10}$
C	$\frac{7}{12}$	J	$2\frac{7}{12}$	Q	$1\frac{2}{3}$	W	$\frac{13}{15}$
D	$\frac{11}{12}$	K	$3\frac{1}{5}$	R	$6\frac{3}{56}$	X	$4\frac{2}{15}$
E	$1\frac{9}{28}$	L	$3\frac{13}{20}$	S	$1\frac{11}{30}$	Y	$6\frac{1}{4}$
F	$5\frac{2}{5}$	M	$1\frac{5}{6}$	T	$2\frac{5}{8}$	Z	$1\frac{7}{20}$
G	$3\frac{7}{8}$	N	$3\frac{11}{20}$				

31. To cross the river, calculate the answer to each of the problems and arrange the stepping stones (smallest answer first).

■ 7/8 - 5/6   ■ 8/9 - 3/4   ■ 1/3 - 1/8   ■ 5/6 - 1/2
■ 1 1/2 - 7/8

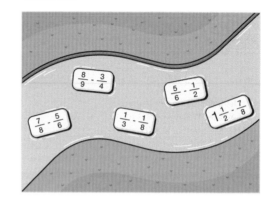

Multiply Mixed Number Fractions by Whole Numbers

Competency: Use diagrams to multiply proper fractions and mixed numbers by whole numbers.

Quick Search Ref: 10198

Correct: Correct.   **Wrong:** Incorrect, try again.   **Open:** Thank you.

Level 1:   Understanding - Converting improper fractions and multiplying simple mixed numbers.

✹ **Required:** 7/10   ✹ **Student Navigation:** on   ✹ **Randomised:** off

---

1. What is the definition of a mixed number fraction?

- The bottom number in a fraction, which shows how many equal parts the whole is divided into.
1/4
- The top number in a fraction, which shows how many parts of the whole there are.
- **A number which contains a whole number (integer) and a fraction.**
- A fraction where the numerator is equal to or larger than the denominator.

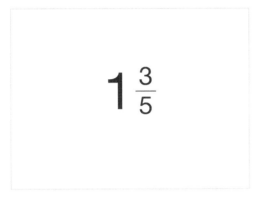

2. What is an equivalent fraction?

- **Fractions that have the same value but are shown with different numbers.**
1/3
- The bottom number in a fraction, which shows how many equal parts the whole is divided into.
- The top number in a fraction, which shows how many parts of the whole there are.

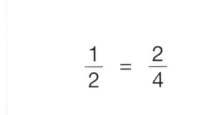

3. Select the values that are equivalent to 8/4.

- **2** ▪ 2/4 ▪ **16/8** ▪ 4/8

1/4

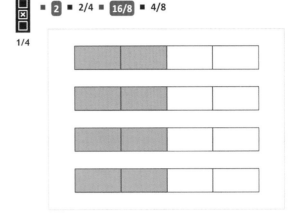

4. What is 45/11 as a mixed number fraction?

a
b
c
- **4 1/11**

$$5 \times \frac{9}{11} = \frac{45}{11}$$

5. What is 10/8 as a mixed number fraction?

a
b
c
- **1 2/8** ▪ **1 1/4**

6. What is 3 × 1 1/7?
Give your answer as a mixed number fraction.

a
b
c
- **3 3/7**

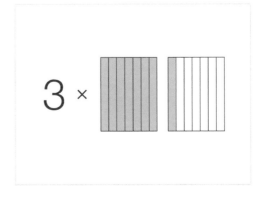

Level 1: *cont.*

7. What whole number is 18/6 equivalent to?

 ▪ **3**

8. 5 × 1 1/9 = ___.
Give your answer as a mixed number fraction.

 ▪ **5 5/9**

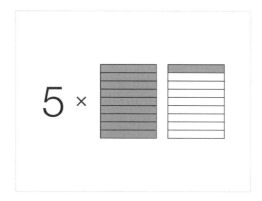

9. 2 × 2 1/3 = ___.
Give your answer as a mixed number fraction.

a b c ▪ **4 2/3**

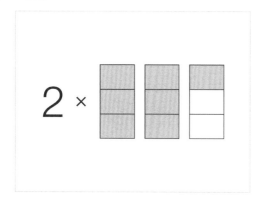

10. What is 28/10 as a mixed number fraction?

a b c ▪ **2 4/5** ▪ **2 8/10**

Level 2: Fluency - Multiplying mixed number fractions by whole numbers.

❋ **Required:** 7/10   ❋ **Student Navigation:** on
❋ **Randomised:** off

11. 4 × 2 1/3 = ___.
Give your answer as a mixed number fraction.

▪ **8 1/3** ▪ **9 1/3** ▪ **28/3** ▪ **1 1/3**

1/4

$$4 \times 2\frac{1}{3} = ?\frac{?}{?}$$

12. 3 × 1 4/9 = ___.
Give your answer as a mixed number fraction.

a b c ▪ **4 1/3** ▪ **4 3/9**

$$3 \times 1\frac{4}{9} = ?\frac{?}{?}$$

13. What is the missing mixed number fraction?

a b c ▪ **1 1/2** ▪ **1 4/8** ▪ **1 2/4**

multiplication	improper fraction	mixed number
$2 \times \frac{6}{8}$	$\frac{12}{8}$	
$10 \times \frac{2}{7}$	$\frac{20}{7}$	$2\frac{6}{7}$

Level 2: *cont.*

14. 5 × 1 5/6 = ___.

a
b
c
Give your answer as a mixed number fraction.

▪ 9 1/6

$$5 \times 1\frac{5}{6} = ?\frac{?}{?}$$

15. Ian buys four pieces of wood which each measure
a　1 3/7 metres (m). What is the total length of the
b　four pieces of wood?
c　*Give your answer as a mixed number fraction.*
Don't include units in your answer.

▪ 5 5/7　▪ 5 5/7 m　▪ 5 5/7 metres

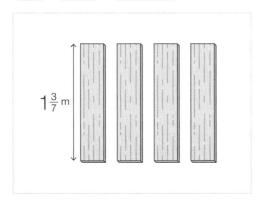

$1\frac{3}{7}$ m

16. Maggie walks 10 km (kilometres) in 1 3/4 hours. If
a　she walks 10 km three times in one week, how
b　many hours does she walk for in total?
c　*Give your answer as a mixed number fraction.*
Don't include units in your answer.

▪ 5 1/4　▪ 5 1/4 hours

17. 2 × 4 4/5 = ___.

a
b
c
Give your answer as a mixed number fraction.

▪ 9 3/5

$$2 \times 4\frac{4}{5} = ?\frac{?}{?}$$

18. What is the missing mixed number fraction?

a
b　▪ 6 4/7
c

multiplication	improper fraction	mixed number
$2 \times 3\frac{2}{7}$	$\frac{46}{7}$	
$3 \times 2\frac{2}{5}$	$\frac{36}{5}$	$7\frac{1}{5}$

19. Calculate 4 × 1 3/5.
a
b　*Give your answer as a mixed number fraction.*
c　▪ 6 2/5

$$4 \times 1\frac{3}{5} = ?\frac{?}{?}$$

20. Each oil drum contains 2 2/3 litres (l) of oil. How
a　much oil is there in 4 drums?
b　*Give your answer as a mixed number fraction.*
c　*Don't include units in your answer.*

▪ 10 2/3　▪ 10 2/3 l　▪ 10 2/3 litres

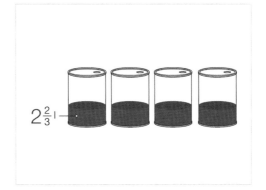

$2\frac{2}{3}$ l

Level 3: Reasoning - Comparing and reasoning with fraction multiplications.

❋ **Required:** 5/5 ❋ **Student Navigation:** on
❋ **Randomised:** off

21. Sally says that 6 × 1 3/4 = 4 1/2.

Explain the mistake she has made.

$$6 \times 1\frac{3}{4} = 4\frac{1}{2}$$

22. 2 × 1 5/9 ___ 2 × 1 1/4.
Which sign makes the statement true?

▪ < ▪ = ▪ >

1/3

$$2 \times 1\frac{5}{9} \ \square \ 2 \times 1\frac{1}{4}$$

23. Find the missing mixed number fraction in the equation:
a
b
c
___ ÷ 5 = 1 2/9.

▪ 6 1/9

$$?\frac{?}{?} \div 5 = 1\frac{2}{9}$$

24. Which two calculations have the same answer?

▪ 16 × 4 1/16 ▪ 4 × 16 1/16 ▪ 16 × 4 1/4 ▪ 4 × 16 1/4

2/4

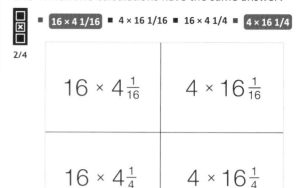

$16 \times 4\frac{1}{16}$	$4 \times 16\frac{1}{16}$
$16 \times 4\frac{1}{4}$	$4 \times 16\frac{1}{4}$

25. Amy says, "5 × 4 1/5 is greater than 4 × 5 1/4
a
b
c
because the number the fraction is multiplied by is greater".
Is Amy correct? Explain your answer.

$$5 \times 4\frac{1}{5} > 4 \times 5\frac{1}{4}$$

Level 4: Problem Solving - Problem solving with fraction multiplications.

❋ **Required:** 5/5 ❋ **Student Navigation:** on
❋ **Randomised:** off

26. Julie wants to make 12 portions of coconut
a
b
c
macaroons. In ounces, what is the total weight of her ingredients?
Don't include the units in your answer.

▪ 25 7/8

recipe
○ makes 4 macarons
$2\frac{1}{2}$ oz. coconut
$4\frac{1}{2}$ oz. sugar
○ $1\frac{5}{8}$ oz. butter

27. Arrange the calculations in ascending order (smallest first).

▪ 1 2/8 × 4 ▪ 2 5/7 × 3 ▪ 3 4/6 × 4 ▪ 4 2/4 × 4
▪ 6 1/9 × 3

Level 4: *cont.*

28. To sink the pirate ship, you need to fire the cannons in the correct order. Arrange the colours from first at the top to fifth at the bottom.
1st: 20/21
2nd: 5
3rd: 1 7/9
4th: 3/5
5th: 5 1/2

▪ Green ▪ Pink ▪ Purple ▪ Blue ▪ Black

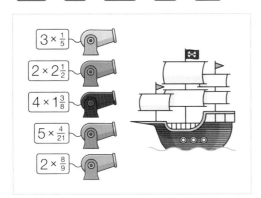

29. A children's toy is packed 8 per box. The weight of one toy is 2 3/5 kilograms (kg). A customer orders 7 boxes. What is the total weight of the order?
Give your answer as a mixed number fraction.
Don't include units in your answer.

▪ 145 3/5 ▪ 145 3/5 kilograms ▪ 145 3/5 kg

30. A primary school orders 30 boxes of pencils and gives 2 3/7 boxes to each of its six classes. How many boxes are left?
Give your answer as a mixed number fraction.

▪ 15 3/7 boxes ▪ 15 3/7

Multiply proper fractions and mixed number fractions by whole numbers

Competency: Use diagrams to multiply proper fractions and mixed numbers by whole number.

Quick Search Ref: 10005

Correct: Correct.   **Wrong:** Incorrect, try again.   **Open:** Thank you.

Level 1:   Understanding - Terminology, multiplying a fraction by an integer and converting answers to a mixed number fraction.

✿ **Required:** 7/10   ✿ **Student Navigation:** on   ✿ **Randomised:** off

---

1. What is the definition of a mixed number fraction?

1/4

- The bottom number in a fraction, which shows how many equal parts the whole is divided into.
- The top number in a fraction, which shows how many parts of the whole there are.
- **A number which contains a whole number and a fraction.**
- A fraction where the numerator is equal to or larger than the denominator.

$$1\frac{3}{5}$$

2. What is the definition of an improper fraction?

1/4

- The bottom number in a fraction, which shows how many equal parts the whole is divided into.
- The top number in a fraction, which shows how many parts of the whole there are.
- A number which consists of a whole number and a fraction.
- **A fraction where the numerator is equal to or larger than the denominator.**

$$\frac{6}{4}$$

3. What is an equivalent fraction?

1/3

- The top number in a fraction, which shows how many parts of the whole there are.
- The bottom number in a fraction, which shows how many equal parts the whole is divided into.
- **Fractions that have the same value but are shown with different numbers.**

$$\frac{1}{2} = \frac{2}{4}$$

4. If you multiply 4/7 by 3, what will the denominator be?

- **7**

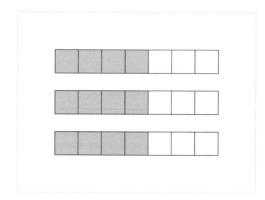

5. 2 × 5/8 = 10/8.

 Give the answer as a mixed number fraction.

▪ 1 2/8 ▪ 1 1/4

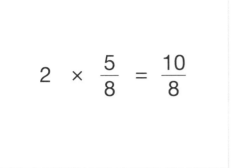

$$2 \ \times \ \frac{5}{8} \ = \ \frac{10}{8}$$

6. If you multiply 5/9 by 5, what will the numerator be?

 ▪ 25

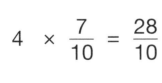

7. 4 × 7/10 = 28/10.

What is the answer as a mixed number fraction?

▪ 2 8/10 ▪ 2 4/5

$$4 \ \times \ \frac{7}{10} \ = \ \frac{28}{10}$$

8. 4 × 2/4 = 8/4.

 What is the answer as a whole number?

▪ 2

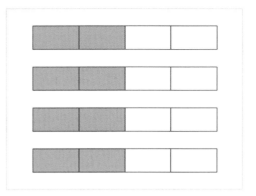

9. 5 × 9/11 = 45/11.

What is the answer as a mixed number fraction?

▪ 4 1/11

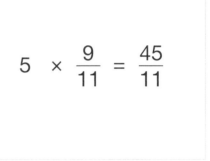

$$5 \ \times \ \frac{9}{11} \ = \ \frac{45}{11}$$

10. 6 × 3/6 = 18/6.

What is the answer as a whole number?

▪ 3

$$6 \ \times \ \frac{3}{6} \ = \ \frac{18}{6}$$

Level 2: Fluency - Multiplying proper and mixed number fractions by whole numbers.

✱ **Required:** 7/10 ✱ **Student Navigation:** on
✱ **Randomised:** off

11. $3/10 × 6 =$ ___.

Give your answer as a mixed number fraction.
■ 1 4/5 ■ 18/10 ■ 1 8/10 ■ 18/60 ■ 3/10

1/5

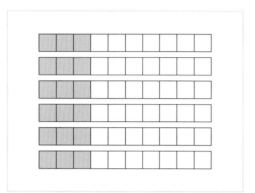

12. $4 × 1/3 =$ ___.

Give your answer as a mixed number fraction.
■ 1 1/3

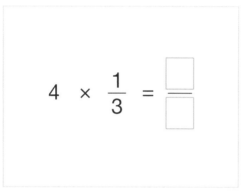

13. $2 × 8/13 =$ ___.
Give your answer as a mixed number fraction.
■ 1 3/13

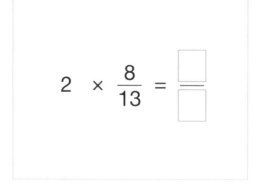

14. $4 × 2 1/3 =$ ___.

Give your answer as a mixed number fraction.
■ 8 1/3 ■ 9 1/3 ■ 7/3 ■ 28/3 ■ 8 4/12

1/5

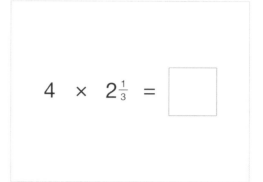

15. What is the missing improper fraction?
■ 7/5 ■ 14/10

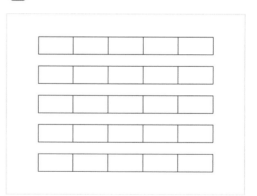

multiplication	improper fraction	mixed number
$3 × \frac{5}{8}$	$\frac{15}{8}$	$1\frac{7}{8}$
$2 × \frac{7}{10}$		$1\frac{4}{10} = 1\frac{2}{5}$
$5 × \frac{3}{4}$	$\frac{15}{4}$	$3\frac{3}{4}$

16. How many blocks do you need to shade to represent 5 × 3/5?
■ 15

Level 2: *cont.*

17. $3 \times 1\ 4/9 =$ ___.

 Give your answer as a mixed number fraction.

■ 4 3/9 ■ 4 1/3

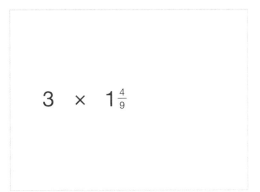

$$3 \times 1\frac{4}{9}$$

18. What is the missing mixed number fraction?

 ■ 1 1/2 ■ 1 4/8

multiplication	improper fraction	mixed number
$2 \times \frac{6}{8}$	$\frac{12}{8}$	
$10 \times \frac{2}{7}$	$\frac{20}{7}$	$3\frac{6}{7}$

19. $2 \times 4\ 4/5 =$ ___.

 Give your answer as a mixed number fraction.

■ 9 3/5

$$2 \times 4\frac{4}{5}$$

20. $3 \times 2/3 =$ ___.

 ■ 6/3 ■ 2

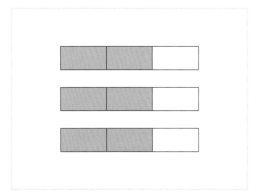

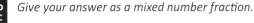
Level 3: Reasoning - Comparing, ordering and reasoning with fraction multiplications.

❋ **Required:** 6/8   ❋ **Student Navigation:** on
❋ **Randomised:** off

21. What is the answer to the next calculation in the sequence?

 Give your answer as a mixed number fraction.

■ 1 1/2 ■ 1 2/4

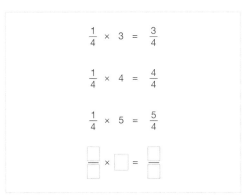

$$\frac{1}{4} \times 3 = \frac{3}{4}$$
$$\frac{1}{4} \times 4 = \frac{4}{4}$$
$$\frac{1}{4} \times 5 = \frac{5}{4}$$

22. $2 \times$ ___ $= 1\ 1/9$.

What is the missing fraction?

■ 5/9

23. Hamza says, "When I multiply 2 by 5/8 and 2/1 by 5/8, I get the same answer". Explain why Hamza is correct.

$$2 \times \frac{5}{8} \qquad \frac{2}{1} \times \frac{5}{8}$$

Level 3: *cont.*

24. Mick and Finn ate 3/4 of a pizza each. Which two numbers do they need to multiply to work out how much they ate altogether?

2/7 ▪ 3/4 ▪ 3 ▪ 1/2 ▪ 2 ▪ 2/3 ▪ 1/4 ▪ 4

25. 3 × 4/7 __ 4 × 2/3.
Which sign makes the statement true?

▪ < ▪ = ▪ >

1/3

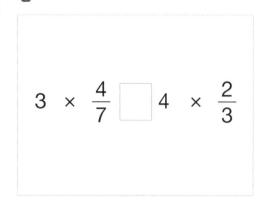

$$3 \times \frac{4}{7} \quad \square \quad 4 \times \frac{2}{3}$$

26. Arrange the calculations in descending order (largest first).

▪ 5 × 2/3 ▪ 7 × 1/3 ▪ 3 × 2/3 ▪ 4 × 1/3 ▪ 2 × 1/3

27. Sally says that 6 × 1 3/4 = 4 1/2.
Explain the mistake she has made.

$$6 \times 1\frac{3}{4} = 4\frac{1}{2}$$

28. 2 × 1 5/9 __ 2 × 1 1/4.
Which sign makes the statement true?

▪ < ▪ = ▪ >

1/3

$$2 \times 1\frac{5}{9} \quad \square \quad 2 \times 1\frac{1}{4}$$

Level 4: Problem Solving - Problem solving with fraction multiplications.

✿ **Required:** 6/6   ✿ **Student Navigation:** on
✿ **Randomised:** off

29. Luigi hosts pizza parties at his restaurant. The table shows how many guests he is expecting for the week. If each guest gets 3/4 of a pizza, on which days will Luigi have pizza left over?

2/5

▪ Monday ▪ Tuesday ▪ Wednesday ▪ Thursday
▪ Friday

day	guests	amount of pizza
Monday	8	
Tuesday	6	
Wednesday	12	
Thursday	4	
Friday	10	

30. Julie wants to make 12 portions of coconut macaroons. In ounces, what is the total weight of her ingredients?
Give your answer as a mixed number fraction and don't include the units.

▪ 25 7/8

recipe

○ makes 4 macarons

$2\frac{1}{2}$ oz. coconut

$4\frac{1}{2}$ oz. sugar

$1\frac{5}{8}$ oz. butter

31. Arrange the calculations in ascending order (smallest first).

▪ 1 2/8 × 4 ▪ 2 5/7 × 3 ▪ 3 4/6 × 4 ▪ 4 2/4 × 4
▪ 6 1/9 × 3

Level 4: *cont*.

32. The diagram shows the number of trays of
vegetables eaten by year 1 at lunch time.
a
b The same amount of vegetables is also eaten
c by years 2, 3, 4, 5 and 6. As a **mixed number**
fraction, how many trays of vegetables are eaten
in total?

▪ **2 2/5**

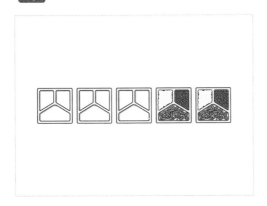

33. A bakery uses 4/5 of a bag of flour in their cake
recipe and each cake is cut into 8 slices. If a
a
b customer orders enough cake to feed 56 people
c (one slice each), how much flour is needed?
Give your answer as a mixed number fraction.

▪ **5 3/5**

34. To sink the pirate ship, you need to fire the
cannons in the correct order. Arrange the colours
↑
↓ from first at the top to fifth at the bottom.
1st: 20/21
2nd: 5
3rd: 1 7/9
4th: 3/5
5th: 5 1/2

▪ green ▪ pink ▪ purple ▪ blue ▪ black

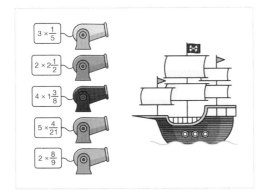

Multiply Proper Fractions by Whole Numbers

Competency: Use diagrams to multiply proper fractions and mixed numbers by whole numbers.

Quick Search Ref: 10045

Correct: Correct.   Wrong: Incorrect, try again.   Open: Thank you.

Level 1: Understanding - Multiplying unit fractions by whole numbers.

⚙ **Required:** 7/10   ⚙ **Student Navigation:** on   ⚙ **Randomised:** off

---

1. What is the definition of an improper fraction?

1/4

- The bottom number in a fraction, which shows how many equal parts the whole is divided into.
- The top number in a fraction, which shows how many parts of the whole there are.
- A number which consists of a whole number and a fraction.
- **A fraction where the numerator is equal to or larger than the denominator.**

$$\frac{6}{4}$$

2. What is an equivalent fraction?

1/3

- The bottom number in a fraction, which shows how many equal parts the whole is divided into.
- The top number in a fraction, which shows how many parts of the whole there are.
- **Fractions that have the same value but are shown with different numbers.**

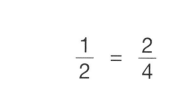

$$\frac{1}{2} = \frac{2}{4}$$

3. If you multiply 1/7 by 3, what will the denominator be?
1 2 3
- **7**

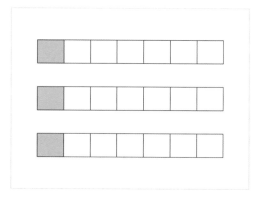

4. If you multiply 1/5 by 4, what will the numerator be?
1 2 3
- **4**

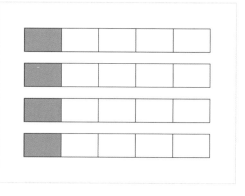

5. What is 7 × 1/10?
1/3
- 1/70 ■ **7/10** ■ 7/70

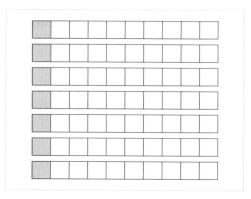

6. Calculate 5 × 1/8.

 ▪ 5/8

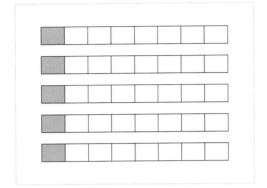

7. What is 1/6 × 7?
Give your answer as an improper fraction.

▪ 7/6

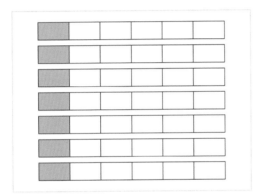

8. If you multiply 1/7 by 5, what will the numerator be?

 ▪ 5

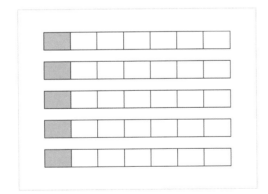

9. Calculate 9 × 1/11.

▪ 9/11

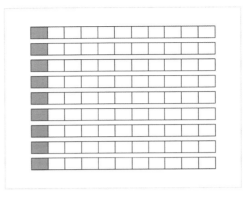

10. What is 1/5 × 12?
Give your answer as an improper fraction.

▪ 12/5

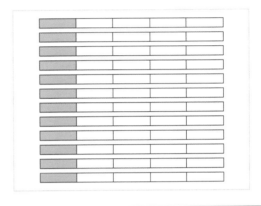

Level 2: Fluency - Multiplying proper fractions by whole numbers.

❋ **Required:** 7/10   ❋ **Student Navigation:** on
❋ **Randomised:** off

11. 2/7 × 6 = ___.
Give your answer as an improper fraction.

▪ 1 5/7 ▪ 12/7 ▪ 2/42 ▪ 12/42

1/4

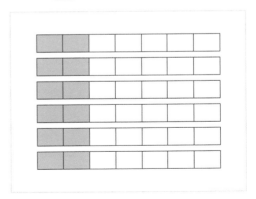

Level 2: cont.

12. $4 \times 2/3 =$ ___.

`a`
`b` *Give your answer as an improper fraction.*
`c` ▪ `8/3`

$$4 \times \frac{2}{3} = \frac{?}{?}$$

13. What is the missing improper fraction?

`a`
`b` ▪ `7/5` ▪ `14/10`
`c`

multiplication	improper fraction
$3 \times \frac{5}{8}$	$\frac{15}{8}$
$2 \times \frac{7}{10}$	
$5 \times \frac{3}{4}$	$\frac{15}{4}$

14. $2 \times 8/13 =$ ___.

`a`
`b` *Give your answer as an improper fraction.*
`c` ▪ `16/13`

$$2 \times \frac{8}{13} = \frac{?}{?}$$

15. How many blocks do you need to shade to represent $5 \times 3/5$?

`1`
`2` ▪ `15`
`3`

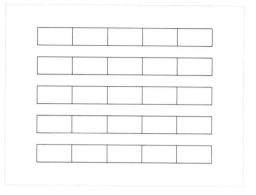

16. $3 \times 2/3 =$ ___.

`a` ▪ `2` ▪ `6/3`
`b`
`c`

$$3 \times \frac{2}{3} = \frac{?}{?}$$

17. Dan, Luke and Ellie eat 2/7 of a cake each. How much of the cake do they eat in total?

`a`
`b` ▪ `6/7`
`c`

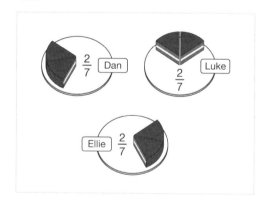

Level 2: *cont.*

18. What is the missing improper fraction?

 ▪ 7/2 ▪ 35/10

multiplication	improper fraction
$5 \times \frac{3}{5}$	$\frac{15}{5}$
$5 \times \frac{7}{10}$	
$3 \times \frac{12}{20}$	$\frac{36}{20}$

19. 4 × 4/5 = ___.
Give your answer as an improper fraction.

 ▪ 16/5

$$4 \times \frac{4}{5} = \frac{?}{?}$$

20. How many blocks do you need to shade to represent 7 × 2/3?

1 2 3 ▪ 14

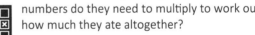

Level 3: Reasoning - Comparing, ordering and reasoning with fraction multiplications.

✹ **Required:** 5/5   ✹ **Student Navigation:** on
✹ **Randomised:** off

21. What is the missing fraction?
Give your answer as an improper fraction.

abc ▪ 10/9

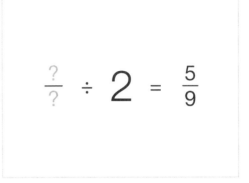

$$\frac{?}{?} \div 2 = \frac{5}{9}$$

22. Hamza says, "When I multiply 2 by 5/8 and 2/1 by 5/8, I get the same answer". Explain why Hamza is correct.

abc

$$2 \times \frac{5}{8}$$

$$\frac{2}{1} \times \frac{5}{8}$$

23. Mick and Finn ate 3/4 of a pizza each. Which two numbers do they need to multiply to work out how much they ate altogether?

2/7 ▪ 3/4 ▪ 3 ▪ 1/2 ▪ 2 ▪ 2/3 ▪ 1/4 ▪ 4

24. 3 × 4/7 __ 4 × 2/3.
Which sign makes the statement true?

1/3 ▪ < ▪ = ▪ >

$$3 \times \frac{4}{7} \square 4 \times \frac{2}{3}$$

Level 3: *cont.*

25. Arrange the calculations in descending order (largest first).

↑↓ ▪ 5 × 2/3 ▪ 7 × 1/3 ▪ 3 × 2/3 ▪ 4 × 1/3 ▪ 2 × 1/3

Level 4: Problem Solving - Problem solving with fraction multiplications.

✱ **Required:** 5/5   ✱ **Student Navigation:** on
✱ **Randomised:** off

26. Luigi hosts pizza parties at his restaurant. The table shows how many guests he is expecting for the week. If each guest gets 3/4 of a pizza, on which days will Luigi have pizza left over?

2/5

▪ Monday ▪ Tuesday ▪ Wednesday ▪ Thursday
▪ Friday

day	guests	amount of pizza
Monday	8	
Tuesday	6	
Wednesday	12	
Thursday	4	
Friday	10	

27. The diagram shows the number of trays of vegetables eaten by year 1 at lunch time. The same amount of vegetables is also eaten by years 2, 3, 4, 5 and 6.
As an **improper fraction**, how many trays of vegetables are eaten in total?

a b c

▪ 12/5

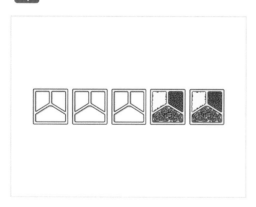

28. A bakery uses 4/5 of a bag of flour in their cake recipe and each cake is cut into 8 slices. If a customer orders enough cake to feed 56 people (one slice each), how much flour is needed?
Give your answer as an improper fraction.

a b c

▪ 28/5

29. To sink the pirate ship, you need to fire the cannons in the correct order. Arrange the colours from first at the top to fifth at the bottom.

↑↓ **1st:** 18/21
2nd: 5
3rd: 15/9
4th: 3/5
5th: 11/2

▪ Green ▪ Pink ▪ Purple ▪ Blue ▪ Black

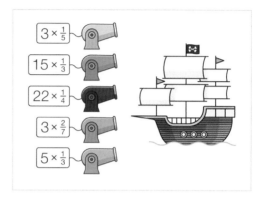

30. The ingredients for one portion of a meal is:
1/12 kg onions.
4/12 kg chicken.
2/12 kg mushrooms.
Alan makes dinner for five people. What is the total weight of the ingredients Alan needs?
Give your answer as an improper fraction. Include the units kg (kilograms) in your answer.

a b c

▪ 35/12 kg ▪ 35/12 kilograms

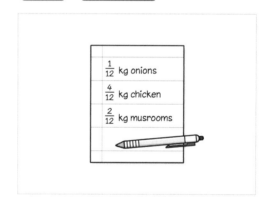

Solve problems involving multiplication and division with fractions

Competency: Solve problems involving multiplication and division with fractions.

Quick Search Ref: 10165

Correct: Correct.   Wrong: Incorrect, try again.   Open: Thank you.

Level 1: Problem solving involving fractions.

✿ Required: 10/10   ✿ Student Navigation: on   ✿ Randomised: off

---

1. In a class of 36, **4/6** children have school dinners. How many children have school dinners?

1
2
3

▪ 24

2. There are 164 lemurs in an area of Madagascan grassland. 3/4 of the lemurs are ring-tailed. How many lemurs are **not** ring-tailed?

1
2
3

▪ 41

3. There are 45 children in a play and **3/5** are girls. How many boys are in the play?
Give your answer as a whole number.

1
2
3

▪ 18

4. In a box of 120 crayons, 25 are blue. What fraction of crayons are **not blue**?

a
b
c

▪ 19/24   ▪ 95/120

5. How many stars are painted on Jen's ceiling if the image shows 1/8 of the stars?

a
b
c

▪ 56

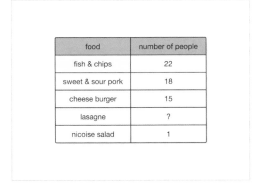

6. 80 people were asked to choose their favourite food. What fraction of the people said lasagne?

a
b
c

▪ 6/20   ▪ 3/10   ▪ 24/80   ▪ 12/40

food	number of people
fish & chips	22
sweet & sour pork	18
cheese burger	15
lasagne	?
nicoise salad	1

7. 5 children each have **3/4** of a bag of popcorn. If they pour all of their popcorn into a large bucket and then fully refill each bag, what fraction of a bag of popcorn will be left over?

a
b
c

▪ 3/4

8. Julie wants to make **9** portions of pizza dough. In kilograms, what is the **total weight** of the ingredients she needs?
Give your answer as a mixed number fraction.

a
b
c

▪ 1 44/100   ▪ 1 22/50   ▪ 1 22/50 kilograms   ▪ 1 11/25
▪ 1 44/100 kilgrams   ▪ 1 11/25 kilgrams   ▪ 1 11/25 kg
▪ 1 44/100 kg   ▪ 1 22/50 kg

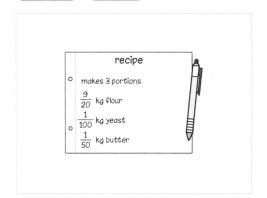

recipe
○ makes 3 portions
9/20 kg flour
○ 1/100 kg yeast
1/50 kg butter

9. Calculate the answers to the following problems. Use the table to convert your answers to letters and reveal the secret word.

a
b
c

1. 4/5 of 35
2. 1/3 of 96
3. 3/7 of 49
4. 7/10 of 120
5. 11/12 of 60

▪ equal

A	84	H	81	O	54	U	21
B	50	I	7	P	72	V	31
C	11	J	90	Q	32	W	25
D	24	K	51	R	61	X	13
E	28	L	55	S	19	Y	8
F	39	M	30	T	83	Z	18
G	47	N	46				

10. During the Easter holidays, Frank completed **3/7** of his favourite computer game. In the Summer holidays, he completed the other **96** levels. How many levels are there in Frank's computer game altogether?

▪ 168

Compare and order fractions: denominators with common multiples

Competency: Compare and order fractions where the denominators are multiples of the same number.

Quick Search Ref: 10070

Correct: Correct.   **Wrong:** Incorrect, try again.   **Open:** Thank you.

Level 1:   Understanding - Terminology and comparing fractions of shapes.

❋ **Required:** 7/10   ❋ **Student Navigation:** on   ❋ **Randomised:** off

---

1. What is a **denominator**?

1/4

- A number that is a multiple of two or more numbers.
- The bottom number in a fraction, which shows how many equal parts the whole is divided into.
- The top number in a fraction, which shows how many parts of a whole there are.
- A fraction that is equal to or larger than one whole.

2. What is a **common multiple**?

1/4

- A fraction that is equal to or larger than one whole.
- A number which is a factor of two or more numbers.
- A number that is a multiple of two or more numbers.
- A fraction with the same value as another.

3. What is a **numerator**?

1/4

- A fraction that is equal to or larger than one whole.
- The bottom number in a fraction, which shows how many equal parts the whole is divided into.
- A number consisting of a whole number and a proper fraction.
- The top number in a fraction, which shows how many parts of a whole there are.

4. Which is the **largest** fraction?

1/2

- 7/10 ■ 3/5

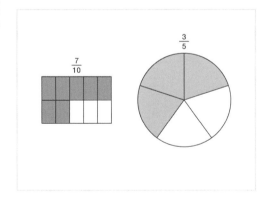

5. Which is the **smallest** fraction?

1/2

- 4/12 ■ 3/6

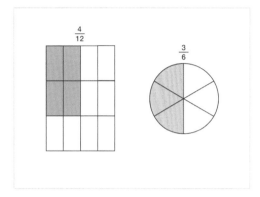

6. How many parts of shape (b) do you need to shade to make a fraction **equal** to shape (a)?

- 9

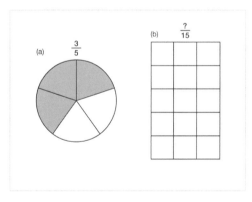

7. Which **three** fractions have **denominators** which have a common multiple less than 20?

3/6

- 2/3 ■ 5/14 ■ 1/7 ■ 1/6 ■ 2/12 ■ 3/5

8. Is this statement true or false?
8/12 is smaller than 8/24 because the denominator is smaller.

1/2

- True ■ False

Level 1: *cont.*

9. Which is the **largest** fraction?

 ▪ 3/4 ▪ 5/8

1/2

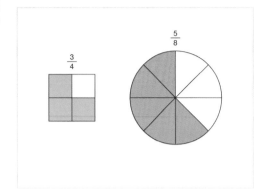

10. Which is the **smallest** fraction?

 ▪ 3/8 ▪ 1/2

1/2

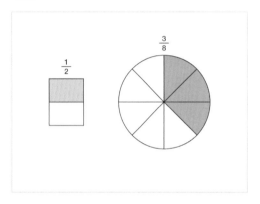

Level 2: Fluency - Converting fractions to order and compare.

❋ **Required:** 7/10   ❋ **Student Navigation:** on
❋ **Randomised:** off

11. Select the symbol that makes the following statement true:
3/4 __ 11/16

1/3   ▪ < ▪ = ▪ >

$$\frac{3}{4} \ \square \ \frac{11}{16}$$

12. Arrange the fractions in **ascending** order (smallest first).

 ▪ 1/10 ▪ 3/15 ▪ 2/5 ▪ 5/10

13. What is the missing denominator?

 ▪ 8

$$\frac{2}{4} \ = \ \frac{4}{?} \ = \ \frac{8}{16}$$

14. Which **three** are equivalent fractions?

▪ 1/2 ▪ 3/4 ▪ 6/8 ▪ 16/24 ▪ 12/16

3/5

15. Which **four** fractions have a value greater than 6/14?

▪ 1/7 ▪ 4/7 ▪ 2/7 ▪ 6/7 ▪ 3/7 ▪ 5/7 ▪ 7/7

4/7

16. What is the missing numerator?

 ▪ 2

$$\frac{1}{4} \ = \ \frac{?}{8}$$

17. Which fraction is **smaller**: 8/15 or 11/20?

▪ 8/15 ▪ 11/20

1/2

18. Is this statement true or false?
6/18 = 4/12

▪ True ▪ False

1/2

Level 2: *cont.*

19. Select the symbol that makes the following statement true:
5/10 __ 10/20

1/3 ■ < ■ = ■ >

$$\frac{5}{10} \square \frac{10}{20}$$

20. Arrange the fractions in **descending** order (largest first).

■ 3/3 ■ 10/12 ■ 3/6 ■ 1/3 ■ 3/12 ■ 1/6

Level 3: Reasoning - Convert, order and compare fractions.

🌼 **Required:** 5/5   🌼 **Student Navigation:** on
🌼 **Randomised:** off

21. Two of the calculations give the same answer; which is the **odd one out**?

■ 2/4 of 48 ■ 5/8 of 48 ■ 1/2 of 48

1/3

22. How many parts of the grid do you need to shade to make a fraction **equal to** 2/3?

■ 14

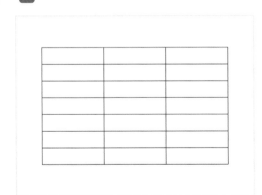

23. Bailey says, "To compare 3/4 and 6/12 I can just simplify 6/12 to 2/4 instead of finding the lowest common multiple of both denominators".
Is this possible for **all** fractions? Explain your answer.

24. Which **three** fractions are equal to the fraction shown by the arrow?

3/7   ■ 4/16 ■ 7/10 ■ 3/4 ■ 1/4 ■ 8/16 ■ 2/8 ■ 3/6

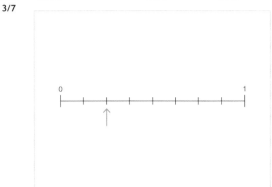

25. Is the following statement correct? Explain your answer.
The larger the denominator, the larger the fraction.

Level 4: Problem Solving - Fractions with denominators of shared multiples.

🌼 **Required:** 6/6   🌼 **Student Navigation:** on
🌼 **Randomised:** off

26. What fraction of the 100 square is **not shaded**? Express the fraction in its simplest form.

■ 1/4

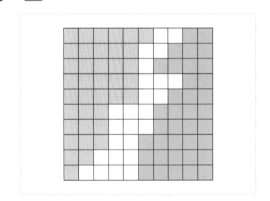

27. What is the **smallest** fraction you can make using the digit cards?

■ 1/378 ■ 17/38 ■ 1/873 ■ 873/1 ■ 3/178

1/5

Level 4: *cont.*

28. Macy's grandma's sewing box contains coloured buttons. What colour button does she have the most of?

1/5 ▪ green ▪ red ▪ yellow ▪ orange ▪ purple

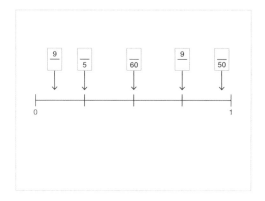

green buttons	$\frac{1}{12}$
red buttons	$\frac{8}{24}$
yellow buttons	$\frac{1}{6}$
orange buttons	$\frac{9}{36}$
purple buttons	$\frac{2}{12}$

29. Arrange the numbers in the correct order to complete the fractions on the number line.

▪ 100 ▪ 2 ▪ 30 ▪ 12 ▪ 47

| $\frac{9}{\quad}$ | $\frac{\quad}{5}$ | $\frac{\quad}{60}$ | $\frac{9}{\quad}$ | $\frac{\quad}{50}$ |

0 ———————————————— 1

30. An 8 by 8 grid is filled with counters, which are 5 different colours. What fraction of the counters are **black**? Give your answer in its **simplest form**.

a
b
c

4/32 of the counters are **yellow.**
1/4 of the counters are **blue.**
3/8 of the counters are **orange.**
1 full row is filled with **green.**
The rest of the counters are black.

▪ 1/8

31. Which two fractions make **one whole** when added together?

2/7

▪ 11/72 ▪ 10/12 ▪ 1/4 ▪ 2/36 ▪ 3/9 ▪ 4/24 ▪ 8/36

$\frac{11}{72}$	$\frac{3}{6}$	$\frac{10}{12}$
$\frac{1}{4}$	$\frac{2}{36}$	$\frac{3}{9}$
$\frac{4}{24}$	$\frac{1}{3}$	$\frac{8}{36}$

Identify, write and name equivalent fractions

Competency: Identify, name and write equivalent fractions of a given fraction, including tenths and hundredths.

Quick Search Ref: 10153

Correct: Correct. **Wrong:** Incorrect, try again. **Open:** Thank you.

Level 1: Understanding terminology and equivalence

⚙ **Required: 7/10** ⚙ **Student Navigation:** on ⚙ **Randomised:** off

1. What is an equivalent fraction?

1/3
- The bottom number in a fraction, which shows how many equal parts the whole is divided into.
- **Fractions that have the same value but are shown with different numbers.**
- The top number in a fraction, which shows how many parts of the whole there are.

2. What is the definition of denominator?

1/3
- **The bottom number in a fraction, which shows how many equal parts the whole is divided into.**
- Fractions that have the same value but are shown with different numbers.
- The top number in a fraction, which shows how many parts of the whole there are.

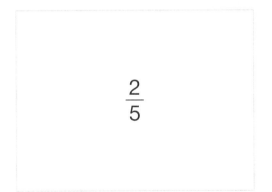

3. Choose one fraction that is equivalent to 1/2.

1/6
- **3/6** ▪ 15/28 ▪ 10/22 ▪ **5/10** ▪ 7/15 ▪ **12/24**

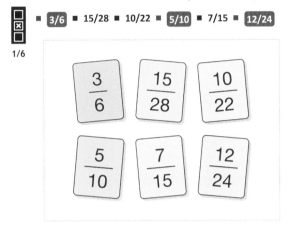

4. 2/3 is **equivalent** to 10/15. True or false?

1/2
- **True** ▪ False

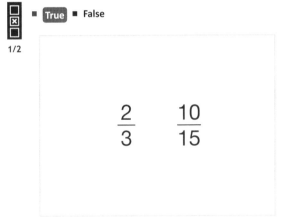

5. Select the fraction that is equivalent to 8/16.

1/3
- **1/2** ▪ 4/12 ▪ 2/8

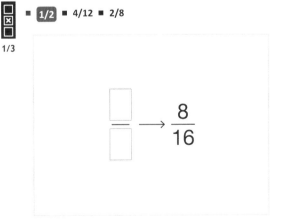

Level 1: *cont.*

6. How many parts of shape (b) must be shaded to make it equivalent to shape (a)?

 ▪ 1 ▪ **2** ▪ 3 ▪ 4 ▪ 5

1/5

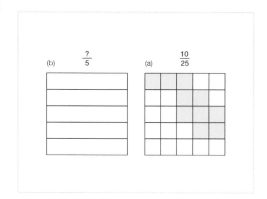

7. Select one fraction that is equivalent to 1/4.

 ▪ **25/100** ▪ **10/40** ▪ 4/9 ▪ 5/25 ▪ 4/12 ▪ **5/20**
▪ 8/40

1/7

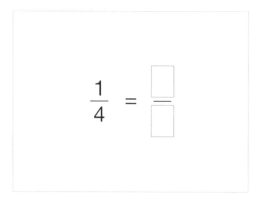

8. How many parts of shape (b) do you need to shade to make it equivalent to shape (a)?

▪ 1 ▪ **2** ▪ 3 ▪ 4 ▪ 5 ▪ 6

1/6

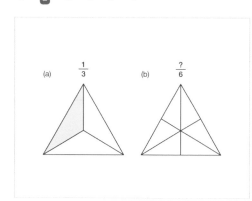

9. Select the fraction that is equivalent to 3/9.

a
b
c   ▪ **1/3**

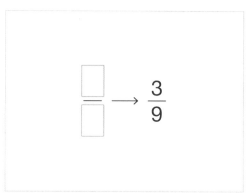

10. 1/5 is **equivalent** to 2/10. True or false?

▪ **True** ▪ False

1/2

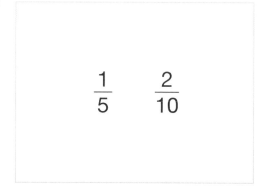

Level 2: Recognising equivalent fractions in numbers and shapes, including simplifying and comparing.

✹ **Required:** 7/10   ✹ **Student Navigation:** on
✹ **Randomised:** off

11. How many parts of the grid do you need to shade to make the shaded fraction equivalent to 8/12?

1
2
3   ▪ **24**

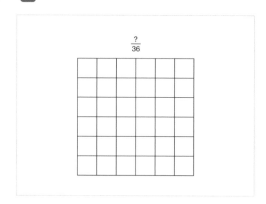

12. Which of the following fractions are equal to 3/4?
Select three answers.

▪ **9/12** ▪ 5/50 ▪ **300/400** ▪ 9/27 ▪ 6/30 ▪ 2/4
3/7 ▪ **60/80**

Level 2: cont.

13. What is the missing denominator?
1/? = 5/25.
- **5**

14. What is the missing numerator?
6/8 = **?**/28
- **21**

15. What sign makes the following statement true?
4/5 _ 12/15
- < ▪ **=** ▪ >

1/3

$$\frac{4}{5} \quad \square \quad \frac{12}{15}$$

16. Which fractions are equivalent to 1/10?
Select three answers.
- **9/90** ▪ 5/10 ▪ **35/350** ▪ 9/27 ▪ 6/63 ▪ 2/40
3/7 ▪ **2/20**

17. How many parts of the circle do you need to shade so that the shaded fraction is equivalent to 12/48?
- **4**

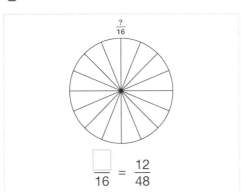

$$\frac{\square}{16} = \frac{12}{48}$$

18. Three-quarters is equal to ____-eighths. What is the missing value?
Give your answer in words.
- **six**

19. What is the missing denominator?
1/**?** = 9/54
- **6**

$$\frac{1}{\square} = \frac{9}{54}$$

20. ?/12 = 6/72.
- **1**

Level 3: Reasoning with equivalent fractions using fractional number lines, shapes and digit cards.

✿ **Required:** 6/8   ✿ **Student Navigation:** on
✿ **Randomised:** off

21. Use every digit card once to make a fraction equivalent to 75/100.
- **36/48**

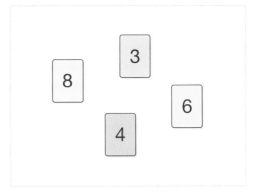

22. Jack says, "You can only find equivalent fractions for fractions that have an even numerator and denominator".
Is Jack correct? Explain how you know.

23. Which fractions are equivalent to the fraction shown by the arrow?
Select 3 answers.

3/6 ▪ **4/16** ▪ **5/20** ▪ 8/16 ▪ **25/100** ▪ 20/100 ▪ 3/18

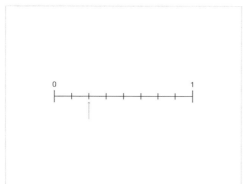

24. How many more parts of the circle need to be shaded to make it equivalent to the rectangle?

1 2 3 ▪ **5**

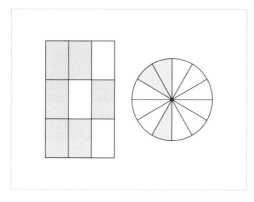

25. Which fraction is the odd one out?

▪ 4/6 ▪ 16/24 ▪ **9/12** ▪ 20/30 ▪ 12/18 ▪ 50/75

1/6

26. Which fractions are equivalent to the fraction shown by the arrow?
Select 4 answers.

4/7 ▪ **3/6** ▪ 8/12 ▪ **18/36** ▪ 15/20 ▪ 75/100 ▪ **50/100**
▪ **28/56**

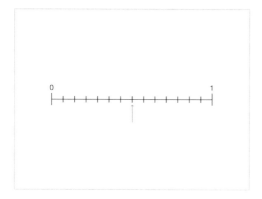

27. How many more parts of the rectangle need to be shaded to make it equivalent to the rhombus?

1 2 3 ▪ **11**

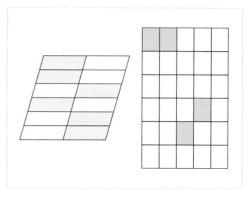

28. At the shop, Ben spends 1/4 of his money and Sadiq spends 25/100 of his money. Do they both spend the same amount of money?
Explain how you know.

a b c

Level 4:   Problem solving involving simplifying and equivalent fractions.

✸ **Required:** 6/6   ✸ **Student Navigation:** on
✸ **Randomised:** off

29. 60/80 = 3/x = y/z.
x + z = 20.
What is the value of y?

1 2 3 ▪ **12**

$$\frac{60}{80} = \frac{3}{x} = \frac{y}{z}$$

30. Sabina is thinking of a fraction that is equivalent to 80/100. The fraction has a denominator less than 30. How many possible answers are there?

1 2 3 ▪ **5**

Level 4: cont.

31. What is the missing number?

 ▪ 18

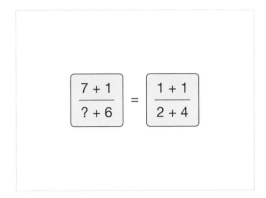

$$\frac{7+1}{?+6} = \frac{1+1}{2+4}$$

32. Norah is thinking of a fraction equivalent to 3/15.
 The numerator is an even number between 20 and
30. The sum of the denominator's digits is 4.
What is Norah's fraction?

▪ 26/130

33. Which **3** coloured parts are equivalent fractions?

 ▪ green (1) ▪ purple (2) ▪ pink (3) ▪ blue (4)
▪ orange (5) ▪ yellow (6) ▪ red (7)

3/7

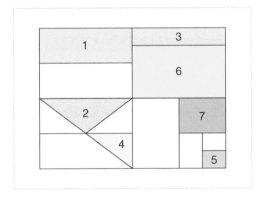

34. Ella gives Pedro 1/4 of her stickers and gives
Lennon 15/84. What fraction of her stickers must
Ella give to Scott, so that Scott and Lennon's total
is the same as Pedro's?

▪ 3/42 ▪ 6/84 ▪ 1/14

Convert between mixed numbers and improper fractions

Competency: Recognise mixed numbers and improper fractions and convert from one form to the other and write mathematical statements >1 as a mixed number [for example 2/5 + 4/5 = 6/5 = 1 1/5]

Quick Search Ref: 10278

Correct: Correct.   Wrong: Incorrect, try again.   Open: Thank you.

Level 1: Understanding - Terminology and the value of digits in mixed number and improper fractions.

✿ Required: 7/10   ✿ Student Navigation: on   ✿ Randomised: off

---

1. What is a **mixed number fraction**?

1/4

- **A whole number and a fraction combined to make one number.**
- The bottom number in a fraction, which shows how many equal parts the whole is divided into.
- The top number in a fraction, which shows how many parts are in the fraction.
- A fraction that is equal to or larger than one whole; the numerator is equal to or larger than the denominator.

2. What is an **improper fraction**?

1/4

- **A fraction that is equal to or larger than one whole; the numerator is equal to or larger than the denominator.**
- The top number in a fraction, which shows how many parts are in the fraction.
- The bottom number in a fraction, which shows how many equal parts the whole is divided into.
- A whole number and a fraction combined to make one mixed number.

3. How many **parts** make a whole in the following fraction?
7 3/5

1/3   ▪ 7 ▪ 3 ▪ **5**

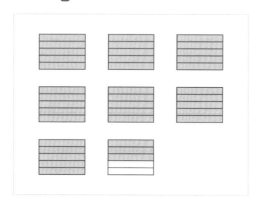

4. How many **wholes** are there in 4 6/7?

▪ **4** ▪ 6 ▪ 7

1/3

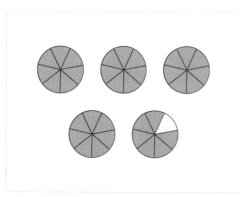

5. What is the **denominator** when 4 7/10 is written as an improper fraction?

1
2
3

▪ **10**

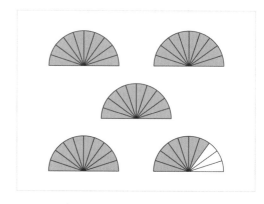

6. What is **83/10** as a mixed number fraction?

▪ 8 83/10 ▪ 83 1/10 ▪ 3 8/10 ▪ **8 3/10**

1/4

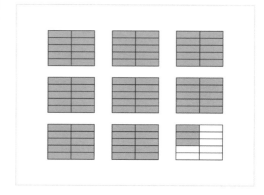

7. What is **6 2/5** as an improper fraction?

▪ **32/5** ▪ 62/5 ▪ 30/5 ▪ 12/5

1/4

---

8. What is **29/5** as a mixed number fraction?

 ▪ 5 4/5

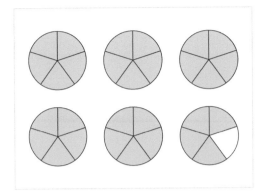

9. How many **parts** make a whole in the following fraction?
78/9

 ▪ 9

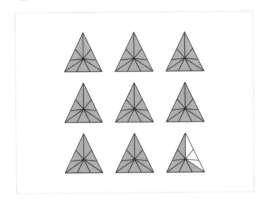

10. How many **wholes** are in the number 6 2/3?

▪ 6

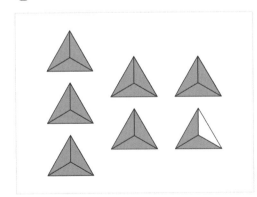

Level 2: Fluency - Recognising and converting between mixed number and improper fractions.

🌸 **Required:** 7/10   🌸 **Student Navigation:** on
🌸 **Randomised:** off

11. What is the **mixed number fraction** that represents the number of shaded parts?

 ▪ 4 5/8

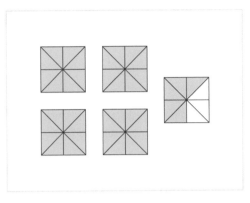

12. What is **16/3** as a mixed number fraction?

 ▪ 5 1/3

13. Express **7 4/5** as an improper fraction.

 ▪ 39/5

14. At a bakery, cakes are cut into **8** equal pieces. The bakery sells **4 whole cakes** and **7 pieces** in one day.
Write the amount of cake sold as an improper fraction.

▪ 39/8

15. What is the **improper fraction** that represents the number of shaded parts?

 ▪ 26/6 ▪ 13/3

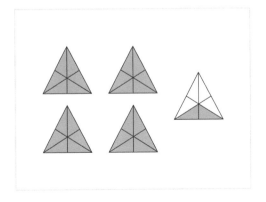

16. How many parts need to be shaded to represent 2 4/6?

 1 2 3

■ **16**

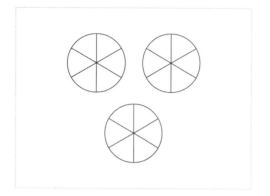

17. Biscuits come in packs of **12**. If Hannah has **18 biscuits,** how many **packets** of biscuits does she have?

a b c

Write the answer as a mixed number fraction.

■ **1 6/12** ■ **1 1/2**

18. Give **48/5** as a mixed number.

a b c

■ **9 3/5**

19. Convert **3 4/6** to an improper fraction.

a b c

■ **11/3** ■ **22/6**

20. Convert **45/10** to a mixed number.
Give your answer in the simplest form.

a b c

■ **4 1/2**

21. Which symbol makes the following statement true?

 9/4 ___ 2 1/2

1/3 ■ **<** ■ = ■ >

22. What is the missing numerator in the following equation?

 1 2 3 2/5 + ?/5 = 1 1/5.

■ **4**

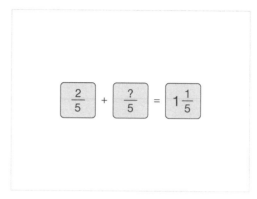

23. Ged and Naomi had two equal-sized sandwiches each.

a b c

Ged ate 1 1/2 of his sandwiches.
Naomi ate 5/4 of her sandwiches
How much did they eat altogether?
Give your answer as a **mixed number fraction**.

■ **2 3/4**

24. "A mixed number fraction is not a whole number".
Explain how you know that this statement is true.

a b c

25. What fraction is missing from the following equation?
Give your answer as a mixed number fraction.

a b c

■ **1 1/5**

26. Arrange the numbers in ascending order (smallest first).

■ **25/9** ■ **3** ■ **3 1/2** ■ **3 5/8** ■ **17/4**

27. Nadia writes: 17/5 = 3 7/5.
What mistake has she made?

a b c

28. Which symbol makes the statement true?

3/2 ___ 1 1/2

■ < ■ **=** ■ >

1/3

Level 4: Problem Solving - Converting between and adding mixed number and improper fractions.

✿ **Required:** 6/6   ✿ **Student Navigation:** on
✿ **Randomised:** off

29. The picture shows the amount of pizza left at the end of a party.
a
b   At the beginning of the party there were 7 pizzas.
c   How much pizza did the guests eat in total?
Give your answer as an improper fraction.

▪ **16/3** ▪ **32/6**

30. Convert the following mixed number fractions to
a   improper fractions and vice versa. Answers must
b   be in their simplest form.
c   Find your answers in the table to spell the 8-letter
word.

3/2, 2 3/10, 11/2, 17/5, 2 5/6, 2 3/5, 15/8, 7/3

▪ **triangle**

A	$3\frac{2}{5}$	H	$\frac{7}{4}$	O	$2\frac{1}{4}$	U	$2\frac{3}{5}$
B	$2\frac{4}{5}$	I	$5\frac{1}{2}$	P	$\frac{10}{3}$	V	$4\frac{1}{4}$
C	$\frac{19}{12}$	J	$4\frac{2}{3}$	Q	$\frac{14}{11}$	W	$\frac{13}{4}$
D	$1\frac{5}{7}$	K	$\frac{16}{7}$	R	$\frac{23}{10}$	X	$3\frac{2}{7}$
E	$2\frac{1}{3}$	L	$1\frac{7}{8}$	S	$\frac{22}{5}$	Y	$\frac{14}{9}$
F	$\frac{18}{7}$	M	$2\frac{7}{8}$	T	$1\frac{1}{2}$	Z	$\frac{11}{8}$
G	$\frac{13}{5}$	N	$\frac{17}{6}$						

31. A cafe sells fruit juice in 250 ml cups for 50 pence.
a   The cafe starts the day with **18** litres of juice.
b   At the end of the day there is **3 3/4** litres left. How
c   much money has the cafe made?
Include the £ sign in your answer.

▪ **£28.50**

32. The fractions are arranged in ascending order.
1   What is the missing denominator?
2
3   ▪ **3**

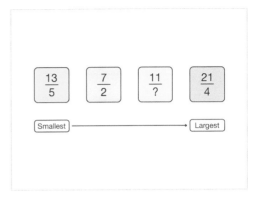

33. Elijah is trying to make the smallest improper
a   fraction using two of his number cards.
b   What is his fraction as a **mixed number fraction**?
c
▪ **1 4/17**

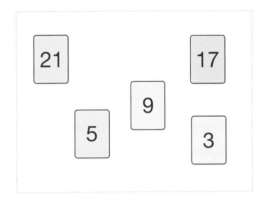

34. What mixed number fraction is Julia thinking of?
a   The number of **wholes** is an even digit less than 4.
b   The **numerator** is double the value of the digit
c   representing the wholes.
The **fraction part** is equivalent to 1/3.

▪ **2 4/12**

Mathematics **Y5**

Decimals and Percentages

Decimals

Equivalence

2 Times Table Decimal Multiplication Practice

Competency: Quick recall of decimal multiplication facts related to the 2 times table (numbers with 1 d.p.).

Quick Search Ref: 10393

Correct: Correct. **Wrong:** Incorrect, try again. **Open:** Thank you.

Level 1: Mixed multiplication facts.

✿ **Required:** 13/13   ✿ **Student Navigation:** off   ✿ **Randomised:** on

1. 0×0.2

[1 2 3] ▪ 0

2. 0.1×2

[1 2 3] ▪ 0.2

3. 0.2×2

[1 2 3] ▪ 0.4

4. 0.2×3

[1 2 3] ▪ 0.6

5. 0.2×4

[1 2 3] ▪ 0.8

6. 0.2×5

[1 2 3] ▪ 1

7. 0.2×6

[1 2 3] ▪ 1.2

8. 7×0.2

[1 2 3] ▪ 1.4

9. 8×0.2

[1 2 3] ▪ 1.6

10. 9×0.2

[1 2 3] ▪ 1.8

11. 10×0.2

[1 2 3] ▪ 2

12. 0.2×11

[1 2 3] ▪ 2.2

13. 0.2×12

[1 2 3] ▪ 2.4

3 Times Table Decimal Multiplication Practice

Competency: Quick recall of decimal multiplication facts related to the 3 times table (numbers with 1 d.p.).

Quick Search Ref: 10394

Correct: Correct.   **Wrong:** Incorrect. Try again.   **Open:** Thank you.

Level 1: Mixed multiplication facts.

Required: 13/13   **Student Navigation:** off   **Randomised:** on

1. 0.3 × 0 ▪ 0

2. 0.1 × 3 ▪ 0.3

3. 0.2 × 3 ▪ 0.6

4. 0.3 × 3 ▪ 0.9

5. 0.3 × 4 ▪ 1.2

6. 0.3 × 5 ▪ 1.5

7. 0.3 × 6 ▪ 1.8

8. 0.3 × 7 ▪ 2.1

9. 8 × 0.3 ▪ 2.4

10. 9 × 0.3 ▪ 2.7

11. 10 × 0.3 ▪ 3

12. 11 × 0.3 ▪ 3.3

13. 12 × 0.3 ▪ 3.6

4 Times Table Decimal Multiplication Practice

Competency: Quick recall of decimal multiplication facts related to the 4 times table (numbers with 1 d.p.).

Quick Search Ref: 10395

Correct: Correct.   **Wrong:** Incorrect, try again.   **Open:** Thank you.

Level 1:   Decimal multiplication facts.

✿ **Required:** 13/13   ✿ **Student Navigation:** off   ✿ **Randomised:** on

1. 0.4×0

[123] ▪ [0]

2. 0.1×4

[123] ▪ [0.4]

3. 0.2×4

[123] ▪ [0.8]

4. 0.3×4

[123] ▪ [1.2]

5. 0.4×4

[123] ▪ [1.6]

6. 0.4×5

[123] ▪ [2]

7. 0.4×6

[123] ▪ [2.4]

8. 0.4×7

[123] ▪ [2.8]

9. 0.4×8

[123] ▪ [3.2]

10. 9×0.4

[123] ▪ [3.6]

11. 10×0.4

[123] ▪ [4]

12. 11×0.4

[123] ▪ [4.4]

13. 12×0.4

[123] ▪ [4.8]

5 Times Table Decimal Multiplication Practice

Competency: Quick recall of decimal multiplication facts related to the 5 times table (numbers with 1 d.p.).

Quick Search Ref: 10396

Correct: Correct.   **Wrong:** Incorrect, try again.   **Open:** Thank you.

Level 1: Mixed decimal multiplication facts.

⚙ **Required:** 13/13   ⚙ **Student Navigation:** off   ⚙ **Randomised:** on

1. 0.5×0
$\frac{1}{2}$ ▪ **0**

2. 0.1×5
$\frac{1}{2}$ ▪ **0.5**

3. 0.2×5
$\frac{1}{2}$ ▪ **1**

4. 0.3×5
$\frac{1}{2}$ ▪ **1.5**

5. 0.4×5
$\frac{1}{2}$ ▪ **2**

6. 0.5×5
$\frac{1}{2}$ ▪ **2.5**

7. 0.5×6
$\frac{1}{2}$ ▪ **3**

8. 0.5×7
$\frac{1}{2}$ ▪ **3.5**

9. 0.5×8
$\frac{1}{2}$ ▪ **4**

10. 9×0.5
$\frac{1}{2}$ ▪ **4.5**

11. 10×0.5
$\frac{1}{2}$ ▪ **5**

12. 11×0.5
$\frac{1}{2}$ ▪ **5.5**

13. 12×0.5
$\frac{1}{2}$ ▪ **6**

6 Times Table Decimal Multiplication Practice

Competency: Quick recall of decimal multiplication facts related to the 6 times table (numbers with 1 d.p.).

Quick Search Ref: 10397

Correct: Correct.   **Wrong:** Incorrect, try again.   **Open:** Thank you.

Level 1:   Mixed decimal multiplication facts.

 Required: 13/13   **Student Navigation:** off   **Randomised:** on

1. 0.6×0

 ▪ 0

2. 6×0.1

▪ 0.6

3. 0.2×6

▪ 1.2

4. 0.3×6

▪ 1.8

5. 0.4×6

▪ 2.4

6. 0.5×6

▪ 3

7. 0.6×6

▪ 3.6

8. 0.6×7

▪ 4.2

9. 0.6×8

▪ 4.8

10. 0.6×9

 ▪ 5.4

11. 10×0.6

 ▪ 6

12. 11×0.6

▪ 6.6

13. 12×0.6

▪ 7.2

7 Times Table Decimal Multiplication Practice

Competency: Quick recall of decimal multiplication facts related to the 7 times table (numbers with 1 d.p.).

Quick Search Ref: 10398

Correct: Correct.   **Wrong:** Incorrect, try again.   **Open:** Thank you.

Level 1: Mixed decimal multiplication facts.

Required: 13/13   **Student Navigation:** off   **Randomised:** on

1. 0×0.7
123 ▪ 0

2. 7×0.1
123 ▪ 0.7

3. 7×0.2
123 ▪ 1.4

4. 0.3×7
123 ▪ 2.1

5. 0.4×7
123 ▪ 2.8

6. 0.5×7
123 ▪ 3.5

7. 0.6×7
123 ▪ 4.2

8. 0.7×7
123 ▪ 4.9

9. 0.7×8
123 ▪ 5.6

10. 9×0.7
123 ▪ 6.3

11. 10×0.7
123 ▪ 7

12. 0.7×11
123 ▪ 7.7

13. 0.7×12
123 ▪ 8.4

8 Times Table Decimal Multiplication Practice

Competency: Quick recall of decimal multiplication facts related to the 8 times table (numbers with 1 d.p.).

Quick Search Ref: 10399

Correct: Correct.   **Wrong:** Incorrect, try again.   **Open:** Thank you.

Level 1:   Decimal multiplication facts.

✿ **Required:** 13/13   ✿ **Student Navigation:** off   ✿ **Randomised:** on

---

1. 0 × 0.8

[123] ▪ 0

2. 8 × 0.1

[123] ▪ 0.8

3. 8 × 0.2

[123] ▪ 1.6

4. 8 × 0.3

[123] ▪ 2.4

5. 0.4 × 8

[123] ▪ 3.2

6. 0.5 × 8

[123] ▪ 4

7. 0.6 × 8

[123] ▪ 4.8

8. 0.7 × 8

[123] ▪ 5.6

9. 0.8 × 8

[123] ▪ 6.4

10. 9 × 0.8

[123] ▪ 7.2

11. 0.8 × 10

[123] ▪ 8

12. 0.8 × 11

[123] ▪ 8.8

13. 12 × 0.8

[123] ▪ 9.6

---

9 Times Table Decimal Multiplication Practice

Competency: Quick recall of decimal multiplication facts related to the 9 times table (numbers with 1 d.p.).

Quick Search Ref: 10400

Correct: Correct. Wrong: Incorrect, try again. Open: Thank you.

Level 1: Mixed decimal multiplication facts.

❖ **Required:** 13/13   ❖ **Student Navigation:** off   ❖ **Randomised:** on

1. 0×0.9
   123 ▪ 0

2. 9×0.1
   123 ▪ 0.9

3. 0.9×2
   123 ▪ 1.8

4. 9×0.3
   123 ▪ 2.7

5. 9×0.4
   123 ▪ 3.6

6. 9×0.5
   123 ▪ 4.5

7. 0.6×9
   123 ▪ 5.4

8. 9×0.7
   123 ▪ 6.3

9. 9×0.8
   123 ▪ 7.2

10. 0.9×9
    123 ▪ 8.1

11. 0.9×10
    123 ▪ 9

12. 11×0.9
    123 ▪ 9.9

13. 12×0.9
    123 ▪ 10.8

10 Times Table Decimal Multiplication Practice

Competency:	Quick recall of decimal multiplication facts related to the 10 times table (numbers with 1 d.p.).
Quick Search Ref:	10390

Correct: Correct.   **Wrong:** Incorrect, try again.   **Open:** Thank you.

Level 1: Mixed decimal multiplication facts.

✿ **Required:** 11/11   ✿ **Student Navigation:** off   ✿ **Randomised:** on

1. 10×0.1

[1/2/3] ▪ [1]

11. 10×1.2

[1/2/3] ▪ [12]

2. 10×0.2

[1/2/3] ▪ [2]

3. 10×0.3

[1/2/3] ▪ [3]

4. 10×0.4

[1/2/3] ▪ [4]

5. 10×0.5

[1/2/3] ▪ [5]

6. 10×0.6

[1/2/3] ▪ [6]

7. 10×0.7

[1/2/3] ▪ [7]

8. 0.8×10

[1/2/3] ▪ [8]

9. 0.9×10

[1/2/3] ▪ [9]

10. 1.1×10

[1/2/3] ▪ [11]

11 Times Table Decimal Multiplication Practice

Competency: Quick recall of decimal multiplication facts related to the 11 times table (numbers with 1 d.p.).

Quick Search Ref: 10391

Correct: Correct. **Wrong:** Incorrect, try again. **Open:** Thank you.

Level 1: Mixed decimal multiplication facts.

Required: 13/13   **Student Navigation:** off   **Randomised:** on

1. 0.1×11
   [123] ▪ 1.1

2. 0.2×11
   [123] ▪ 2.2

3. 1.1×3
   [123] ▪ 3.3

4. 11×0.4
   [123] ▪ 4.4

5. 11×0.5
   [123] ▪ 5.5

6. 11×0.6
   [123] ▪ 6.6

7. 0.7×11
   [123] ▪ 7.7

8. 0.8×11
   [123] ▪ 8.8

9. 11×0.9
   [123] ▪ 9.9

10. 1.1×10
    [123] ▪ 11

11. 11×1.1
    [123] ▪ 12.1

12. 11×1.2
    [123] ▪ 13.2

13. 1.1×0
    [123] ▪ 0

12 Times Table Decimal Multiplication Practice

| **Competency:** | Quick recall of decimal multiplication facts related to the 12 times table (numbers with 1 d.p.). |

| **Quick Search Ref:** | 10392 |

Correct: Correct.   **Wrong:** Incorrect, try again.   **Open:** Thank you.

Level 1:   Mixed decimal multiplication facts.

✸ **Required:** 13/13   ✸ **Student Navigation:** off   ✸ **Randomised:** on

1. 0.1×12

[123] ▪ 1.2

2. 0.2×12

[123] ▪ 2.4

3. 12×0.3

[123] ▪ 3.6

4. 12×0.4

[123] ▪ 4.8

5. 12×0.5

[123] ▪ 6

6. 12×0.6

[123] ▪ 7.2

7. 0.7×12

[123] ▪ 8.4

8. 12×0.8

[123] ▪ 9.6

9. 12×0.9

[123] ▪ 10.8

10. 10×1.2

[123] ▪ 12

11. 11×1.2

[123] ▪ 13.2

12. 1.2×12

[123] ▪ 14.4

13. 1.2×0

[123] ▪ 0

1 to 12 Times Tables Decimal Multiplication Facts (no correct feedback)

Competency: Quick recall of decimal multiplication facts related to times tables (numbers with 1 d.p.).

Quick Search Ref: 10348

Correct: Correct.   **Wrong:** Incorrect, try again.   **Open:** Thank you.

Level 1:   Mixed decimal multiplication facts.

✿ **Required:** 88/88   ✿ **Student Navigation:** off   ✿ **Randomised:** on

1. 0.1×1

`123` ▪ `0.1`

2. 0.1×2

`123` ▪ `0.2`

3. 0.1×3

`123` ▪ `0.3`

4. 0.1×4

`123` ▪ `0.4`

5. 0.1×5

`123` ▪ `0.5`

6. 6×0.1

`123` ▪ `0.6`

7. 7×0.1

`123` ▪ `0.7`

8. 8×0.1

`123` ▪ `0.8`

9. 9×0.1

`123` ▪ `0.9`

10. 10×0.1

`123` ▪ `1`

11. 0.1×11

`123` ▪ `1.1`

12. 0.1×12

`123` ▪ `1.2`

13. 0.2×2

`123` ▪ `0.4`

14. 0.2×3

`123` ▪ `0.6`

15. 0.2×4

`123` ▪ `0.8`

16. 0.2×5

`123` ▪ `1`

17. 0.2×6

`123` ▪ `1.2`

18. 7×0.2

`123` ▪ `1.4`

19. 8×0.2

`123` ▪ `1.6`

20. 9×0.2

`123` ▪ `1.8`

21. 10×0.2

`123` ▪ `2`

22. 0.2×11

`123` ▪ `2.2`

23. 0.2×12

[1 2 3] ▪ 2.4

24. 0.3×3

[1 2 3] ▪ 0.9

25. 0.3×4

[1 2 3] ▪ 1.2

26. 0.3×5

[1 2 3] ▪ 1.5

27. 0.3×6

[1 2 3] ▪ 1.8

28. 0.3×7

[1 2 3] ▪ 2.1

29. 8×0.3

[1 2 3] ▪ 2.4

30. 9×0.3

[1 2 3] ▪ 2.7

31. 10×0.3

[1 2 3] ▪ 3

32. 11×0.3

[1 2 3] ▪ 3.3

33. 12×0.3

[1 2 3] ▪ 3.6

34. 0.4×4

[1 2 3] ▪ 1.6

35. 0.4×5

[1 2 3] ▪ 2

36. 0.4×6

[1 2 3] ▪ 2.4

37. 0.4×7

[1 2 3] ▪ 2.8

38. 0.4×8

[1 2 3] ▪ 3.2

39. 9×0.4

[1 2 3] ▪ 3.6

40. 10×0.4

[1 2 3] ▪ 4

41. 11×0.4

[1 2 3] ▪ 4.4

42. 12×0.4

[1 2 3] ▪ 4.8

43. 0.5×5

[1 2 3] ▪ 2.5

44. 0.5×6

[1 2 3] ▪ 3

45. 0.5×7

[1 2 3] ▪ 3.5

46. 0.5×8

[1 2 3] ▪ 4

47. 9×0.5

[1 2 3] ▪ 4.5

48. 10×0.5

[1 2 3] ▪ 5

Level 1: cont.

49. 11×0.5

= 5.5

50. 12×0.5

= 6

51. 0.6×6

= 3.6

52. 0.6×7

= 4.2

53. 0.6×8

= 4.8

54. 0.6×9

= 5.4

55. 10×0.6

= 6

56. 11×0.6

= 6.6

57. 12×0.6

= 7.2

58. 0.7×7

= 4.9

59. 0.7×8

= 5.6

60. 9×0.7

= 6.3

61. 10×0.7

= 7

62. 0.7×11

= 7.7

63. 0.7×12

= 8.4

64. 0.8×8

= 6.4

65. 9×0.8

= 7.2

66. 0.8×10

= 8

67. 0.8×11

= 8.8

68. 12×0.8

= 9.6

69. 0.9×9

= 8.1

70. 0.9×10

= 9

71. 11×0.9

= 9.9

72. 12×0.9

= 10.8

73. 1.1×10

= 11

74. 10×1.2

= 12

Level 1: *cont.*

75. 11×1.1

$\begin{smallmatrix}1\\2\\3\end{smallmatrix}$ ▪ 12.1

76. 11×1.2

$\begin{smallmatrix}1\\2\\3\end{smallmatrix}$ ▪ 13.2

77. 1.2×12

$\begin{smallmatrix}1\\2\\3\end{smallmatrix}$ ▪ 14.4

78. 0×0.1

$\begin{smallmatrix}1\\2\\3\end{smallmatrix}$ ▪ 0

79. 0×0.2

$\begin{smallmatrix}1\\2\\3\end{smallmatrix}$ ▪ 0

80. 0.3×0

$\begin{smallmatrix}1\\2\\3\end{smallmatrix}$ ▪ 0

81. 0.4×0

$\begin{smallmatrix}1\\2\\3\end{smallmatrix}$ ▪ 0

82. 0.5×0

$\begin{smallmatrix}1\\2\\3\end{smallmatrix}$ ▪ 0

83. 0.6×0

$\begin{smallmatrix}1\\2\\3\end{smallmatrix}$ ▪ 0

84. 0×0.7

$\begin{smallmatrix}1\\2\\3\end{smallmatrix}$ ▪ 0

85. 0×0.8

$\begin{smallmatrix}1\\2\\3\end{smallmatrix}$ ▪ 0

86. 0×0.9

$\begin{smallmatrix}1\\2\\3\end{smallmatrix}$ ▪ 0

87. 1.1×0

$\begin{smallmatrix}1\\2\\3\end{smallmatrix}$ ▪ 0

88. 1.2×0

$\begin{smallmatrix}1\\2\\3\end{smallmatrix}$ ▪ 0

Read, write, order and compare numbers with up to 3 decimal places

Competency: Read, write, order and compare numbers with up to 3 decimal places.

Quick Search Ref: 10036

Correct: Correct.   Wrong: Incorrect. Try again.   Open: Thank you.

Level 1:   Understanding the value of digits in decimals.

🏵 Required: 7/10   🏵 Student Navigation: on   🏵 Randomised: off

---

1. In the number 45.17 what place value column is represented by the 5?

 ■ **Ones** ■ Tens ■ Hundredths ■ Tenths

1/4

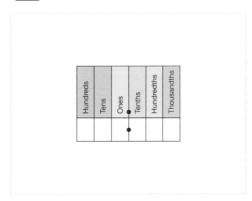

2. What digit is in the **hundredths column** in the number 5.971?

■ 9 ■ **7** ■ 5 ■ 1

1/4

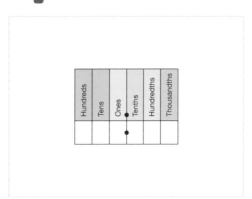

3. What is the value of the digit in the **hundredths column** in the number 483.019?

■ 0.04 ■ 0.08 ■ 0.03 ■ 0.00 ■ **0.01** ■ 0.09 ■ 1

1/7

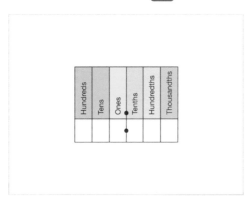

4. Write seventy-two, eight tenths and four hundredths in figures.

 ■ **72.84**

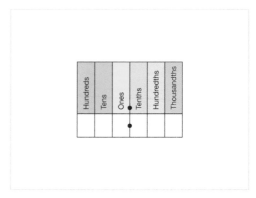

5. What is **one less** than 52.64?

■ 53.64 ■ **51.64** ■ 52.63 ■ 52.54 ■ 42.64

1/5

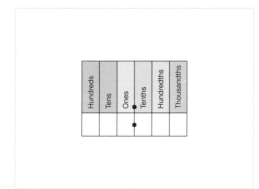

6. Put these numbers in ascending order (smallest at the top to largest at the bottom).

■ **2.7** ■ **5.6** ■ **6.5** ■ **7.2** ■ **8.9** ■ **10.3** ■ **13.5**

7. Write the number made by these place value cards.

■ **8.402**

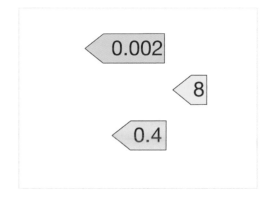

Level 1: *cont.*

8. Select the option that shows 3.461 written in words.

■ three ones, four hundred and sixty-one thousandths
1/3 ■ three point four hundred and sixty-one
■ three thousand, four hundred and sixty-one

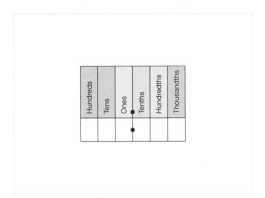

9. Write the number made by these place value cards.

■ 3.501

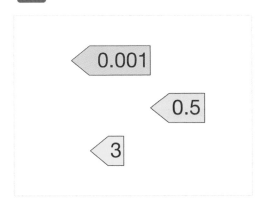

```
0.001
    0.5
  3
```

10. What is a **thousandth** more than 57.123?

■ 57.124 ■ 57.122 ■ 67.123 ■ 58.123 ■ 57.223
■ 57.133

1/6

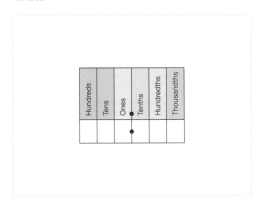

Level 2: Reading and writing decimals and understanding the value of digits after a decimal point.

❋ **Required:** 8/10   ❋ **Student Navigation:** on
❋ **Randomised:** off

11. How many **tenths** are in **2 ones**?

■ 20 ■ 10 ■ 2 ■ 200 ■ 0

1/5

12. The base ten blocks represent ones, tenths, hundredths and thousandths. What number is being represented?

■ 2.469

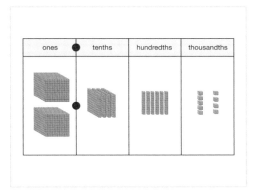

13. How many hundredths are there in this number?

■ 0

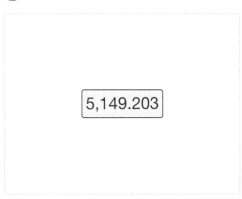

```
5,149.203
```

14. What is a **tenth** less than 628.714?

■ 628.614

15. What is the place value of 2 in the number 40.962?
There is more than one correct answer.

2/6 ■ 0.02 ■ two hundredths ■ two thousandths ■ two
■ 2 ■ 0.002

16. What digit represents **hundredths** in the number 6,132.895?

■ 9

17. Put these numbers in **descending** order (largest at the top to smallest at the bottom).

■ 432.970 ■ 429.764 ■ 427.355 ■ 426.010
■ 420.736 ■ 411.499

Level 2: *cont.*

18. What is the **value** of the digit in the **thousandths** column in the number 836.537?

a
b
c

Write your answer as a decimal (e.g. 0.02).

▪ 0.007

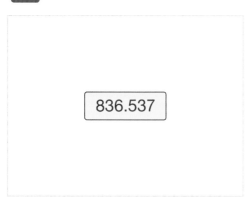

836.537

19. How many **hundredths** are in 9 tenths?

☐
☒
☐

1/5

▪ 0.9 ▪ 90 ▪ 900 ▪ 9,000 ▪ 0

20. What is a **thousandth** more than 276.462?

1
2
3

▪ 276.463

Level 3: Reasoning - Interpreting, comparing and ordering decimals.

❋ **Required:** 6/7   ❋ **Student Navigation:** on
❋ **Randomised:** off

21. Which symbol makes the statement true?

27.13 ____ 27.099

☐
☒
☐

1/3

▪ < ▪ = ▪ >

22. The table shows the number of visitors to a museum (in thousands) for each year from 2010 to 2015. Which **year** had the most visitors?

☐
☒
☐

1/6

▪ 2010 ▪ 2011 ▪ 2012 ▪ 2013 ▪ 2014 ▪ 2015

year	average number of visitors (thousands)
2010	321.569
2011	315.713
2012	321.801
2013	314.998
2014	318.004
2015	321.089

23. Using the cards, make the smallest number possible. You can only use each card once.

a
b
c

▪ 0.579

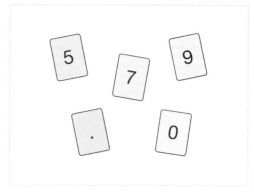

24. What number is halfway between 2.5 and 3.6? Explain how you worked it out.

a
b
c

25. Which of the following statements is false?

☐
☒
☐

1/4

▪ 1.009 < 1.09 ▪ 21.249 > 21.25 ▪ 4.35 > 4.053
▪ 85.023 < 85.2

26. Shamal has put the following numbers in ascending order (smallest to largest). Which **two** numbers need to be swapped around?

☐
☒
☐

2/7

▪ 834.014 ▪ 834.09 ▪ 834.12 ▪ 834.3 ▪ 834.9
▪ 834.607 ▪ 834.9001

27. Which of these numbers is closest in value to 7.5? Explain your answer.

a
b
c

7.05
7.15
7.55
7.6
7.49

Level 4: Multi-step problems using decimals to find a solution.

❋ **Required:** 6/6   ❋ **Student Navigation:** on
❋ **Randomised:** off

28. Here are two number lines. Find the difference between the values of *x* and *y*.

1
2
3

▪ 5.16

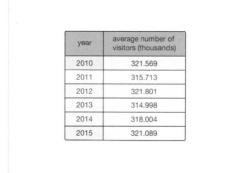

Level 4: *cont.*

29. Ahmed puts some numbers in order. Select all the possible values of the missing digit.

■ 3 ■ 1 ■ **7** ■ **9** ■ 2 ■ **5** ■ **4**

4/7

87.01, 87.24, 87.2 ? 8, 87.313

30. 6.15 < _._ _ > 6.27

1
2
3

The missing decimal has 3 digits.
The digits have a sum of 13.
All the digits are different.
What is the missing decimal number?

■ **6.25**

31. Chiara is thinking of 2 numbers that have a difference of 3.487.

1
2
3

One of the numbers is 11.665.
The other number is less than 10.
What is Chiara's other number?

■ **8.178**

32. Using the digit cards, make the number closest to 2. You must use all of the cards but can only use each card once.

1
2
3

■ **1.8742**

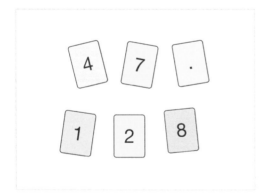

33. Arabella is thinking of a number.

1
2
3

-The number is greater than 6.34 and smaller than 7.56.
-The number has **3 digits** and all of the digits are odd.
-The same digit can be used more than once.

How many possible numbers could Arabella be thinking of?

■ **13**

Recognise place value in decimal numbers

Competency: Recognise and use thousandths and relate them to tenths, hundredths and decimal equivalents.

Quick Search Ref: 10184

Correct: Correct. Wrong: Incorrect. Try again. Open: Thank you.

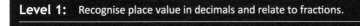

Level 1: Recognise place value in decimals and relate to fractions.

🌸 **Required:** 7/10 🌸 **Student Navigation:** on 🌸 **Randomised:** off

---

1. In a decimal number the digits after the decimal point represent...

1/3
- single digit whole numbers.
- a whole number with multiple digits.
- **parts of a whole number.**

2. 0.982 is less than 1. True or false?

1/2
- **True** ■ False

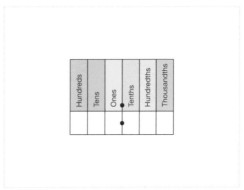

3. In the number 59.341 which digit represents the tenths?

1/5
- 5 ■ 9 ■ **3** ■ 4 ■ 1

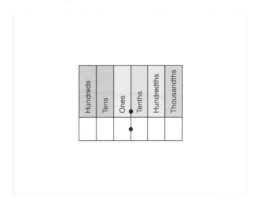

4. What is one hundredth when written as a fraction and a decimal?
You must select 2 answers.

2/6
- 1/10 ■ **1/100** ■ 1/1,000 ■ 0.1 ■ **0.01** ■ 0.001

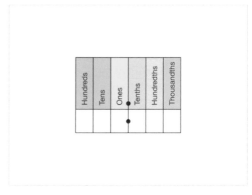

5. In the number 47.182 there are 8 hundredths. What is 8 hundredths written as a fraction?

1/5
- 8/10 ■ 100/8 ■ 8/1,000 ■ 800/1 ■ **8/100**

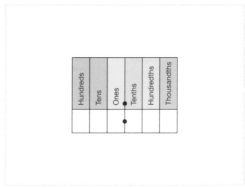

6. What is one thousandth as a fraction and a decimal?
Select 2 answers.

2/6
- 1/10 ■ 1/100 ■ **1/1,000** ■ 0.1 ■ 0.01 ■ **0.001**

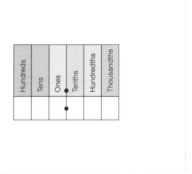

Level 1: *cont.*

7. Which numbers could be in the tenths column to make the number less than 0.5?
You must select 4 answers.

4/7   ▪ **3** ▪ **4** ▪ 8 ▪ 6 ▪ **1** ▪ **2** ▪ 5

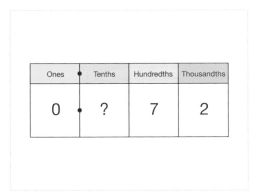

Ones	Tenths	Hundredths	Thousandths
0	?	7	2

8. In the number 3.964 there are 9 tenths. What is 9 tenths as a decimal?

1/4   ▪ 0.009 ▪ 9.0 ▪ **0.9** ▪ 0.09

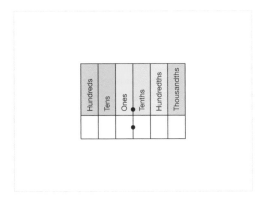

9. What is one tenth written as a fraction and a decimal?
You must select 2 answers.

2/6   ▪ **1/10** ▪ 1/100 ▪ 1/1,000 ▪ **0.1** ▪ 0.01 ▪ 0.001

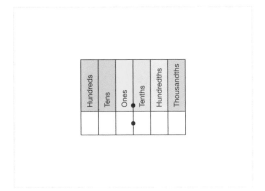

10. In the number 328.974 which digit represents the thousandths?

1
2
3   ▪ **4**

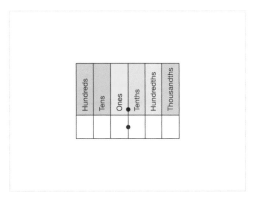

Level 2:   Converting between fractions and decimals.

✿ **Required:** 9/10   ✿ **Student Navigation:** on
✿ **Randomised:** off

11. What is 0.052 as a fraction?

a
b
c   ▪ **52/1000** ▪ **52/1,000**

12. What is the value of the digit 6 in 18.256?
Select all the correct answers.

3/7   ▪ **6 thousandths** ▪ 6/100 ▪ **6/1,000** ▪ 6 ones ▪ 0.6
▪ **0.006** ▪ 6 hundredths

13. What is 7/100 as a decimal?

a
b
c   ▪ **0.07**

14. What number is missing from the calculation?

a
b
c   ▪ **0.001**

$$3 + 0.7 + 0.09 + \boxed{?} = \boxed{3.791}$$

15. Place these numbers in ascending order (smallest at the top to largest at the bottom).

↑
↓   ▪ **7/1,000** ▪ **1 hundredth** ▪ **0.05** ▪ **4 tenths**

16. Write 0.942 as a fraction.

a
b
c   ▪ **942/1,000** ▪ **942/1000**

Level 2: *cont.*

17. Find 9/10 and 0.2 on the number line. Which is closest to 0.5?

■ 9/10 ■ 0.2

1/2

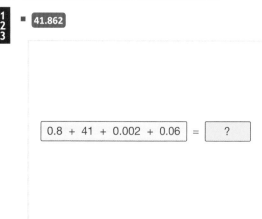

18. What is the answer to this calculation?

■ 41.862

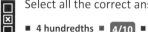

$$0.8 + 41 + 0.002 + 0.06 = \boxed{?}$$

19. What does the 4 represent in 92.481? Select all the correct answers.

■ 4 hundredths ■ 4/10 ■ 4/1,000 ■ 4 ones ■ 0.4

3/7 ■ 0.004 ■ 4 tenths

20. What is 0.307 as a fraction?

a
b
c

■ 307/1000 ■ 307/1,000

Level 3: Ordering and comparing with decimals and fractions.

✿ Required: 7/8   ✿ Student Navigation: on
✿ Randomised: off

21. Which sign makes the equation true?

■ < ■ = ■ >

1/3

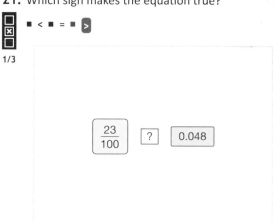

$$\frac{23}{100} \quad \boxed{?} \quad 0.048$$

22. Select all the numbers that are greater than 0.7.

■ 0.692 ■ 0.71 ■ 0.098 ■ 8/10 ■ 9/100 ■ 3/1,000

■ 0.9

3/7

23. Order these number in descending order (largest at the top to smallest at the bottom).

■ 7 ■ 0.901 ■ 0.51 ■ 4/10 ■ 32/100 ■ 0.235

■ 8/1,000

24. What number is missing from the equation?

1
2
3

■ 1000

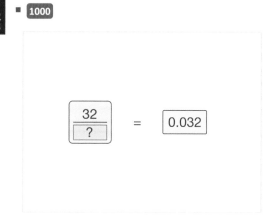

$$\frac{32}{\boxed{?}} = 0.032$$

25. Milly says '4.009 is bigger than 4.101 because 9 is bigger than 1. Is she correct? Explain your answer.

a
b
c

26. What needs to be added to 5.346 to get 5.7?

a
b
c

■ 0.354

27. Which is greater, 1/6 or 1/900? Explain your answer.

a
b
c

Level 3: cont.

28. Which sign makes the equation true?

⬚
☒ 4/10 __ 1.001
⬚
1/3

■ < ■ = ■ >

Level 4: Using knowledge of place value in decimals and the fractional equivalents to solve problems.

❋ **Required:** 6/6   ❋ **Student Navigation:** on
❋ **Randomised:** off

29. Using the digit cards make the number closest to
1
2 65.
3 You must use every card only once.

■ **64.951**

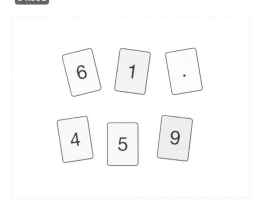

30. Pablo has written 4 decimal numbers that contain
a the digits 0, 1, 3 and 5. He has represented each
b number with a letter.
c

d . a a a is a whole number.
b . d a c is the number with the greatest value.
c . a d b is the number closest to 1.
a . d d b's digits have a sum of 11.

What is the value of **a.bcd?**

■ **0.513**

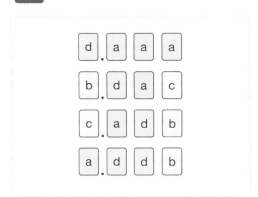

31. The table shows the times (in seconds) that
1 representatives from different countries ran
2 100 m. Some times are missing.
3 The USA is 8/100 slower than Jamaica.
France is 0.1 slower than the USA.
The USA's time is exactly halfway between
Jamaica's and Canada's.
What is Canada's time in seconds?

■ **9.97**

country	time (seconds)
Jamaica	9.81
USA	
Canada	
South Africa	
France	
China	

32. Jemma has replaced decimal numbers with
a symbols.
b 4/10 = circle
c 8/100 = star
2/1,000 = triangle
What number is represented in the image?

■ **1.282**

33. Virginia is thinking of a number.
a
b There is a 4 in the thousandths column.
c The ones column has the smallest possible odd
digit.
The number is bigger than 28.1 and smaller than
35.8.
The tenths column is equal to 6/10.
To find the digit in the hundredths column you
must add together all the other digits in the
number and divide by 2.

What is Virginia's number?

■ **31.674**

Level 4: *cont.*

34. Using the digit cards, work out how many numbers
 you can make that are less than 0.5.
You must use each digit card only once in every
number you make.

- 4

Round decimals with 2 decimal places to the nearest whole number and to one decimal place

Competency: Round decimals with two decimal places to the nearest whole number and to one decimal place.

Quick Search Ref: 10133

Correct: Correct.   Wrong: Incorrect. Try again.   Open: Thank you.

Level 1: Understanding of rounding to the nearest whole number and one decimal place, including which columns and digits determine whether to round up or down.

✿ **Required:** 7/10   ✿ **Student Navigation:** on   ✿ **Randomised:** off

---

1. Which definition best describes **rounding**?

1/3
- **Making a number simpler but keeping its value close to what it was so that it makes calculating easier.**
- Putting numbers in a sequence from the smallest to the largest.
- A number less than zero.

2. When rounding a digit of **5 or above** would you round up or down?

1/2
- **Up** ■ Down

3. Which of these digits show that a number needs to be rounded **down**?

3/6   Select **all** that would be rounded down.

- 6 ■ **1** ■ 9 ■ **4** ■ 7 ■ **2**

4. If rounding 27.43 to the nearest **one,** which column will determine whether to round up or down?

1/4   ■ **Tenths** ■ Tens ■ Hundredths ■ Ones

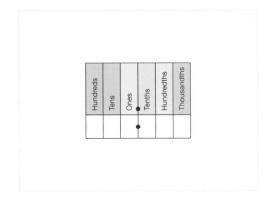

5. Amir says 'When rounding a number to the nearest tenth the digit in the ones column determines whether to round up or down.'

1/2   True or false?

- True ■ **False**

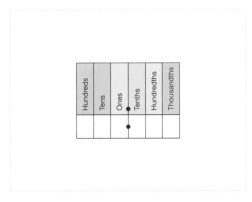

6. What is 8.2 rounded to the nearest whole number?

1/2
- **8** ■ 9

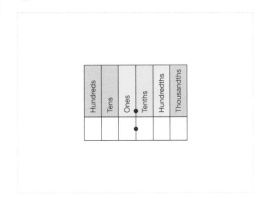

Level 1: *cont.*

7. If rounding to the nearest 0.1, which of these numbers would be rounded up?

4/7

▪ 9.06 ▪ 2.31 ▪ 3.17 ▪ 1.82 ▪ 4.54 ▪ 7.79 ▪ 9.46

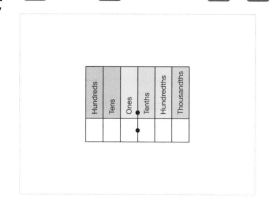

8. Tom is rounding numbers to the nearest 10.

34_

Which digits - when placed in the ones column - would show that Tom needs to round up?

You must select 4 answers.

▪ 6 ▪ 0 ▪ 9 ▪ 4 ▪ 7 ▪ 3 ▪ 8

9. When rounding 83.06 to the nearest whole number, which column will determine whether to round it up or down?

1/4   ▪ Tens ▪ Tenths ▪ Ones ▪ Hundredths

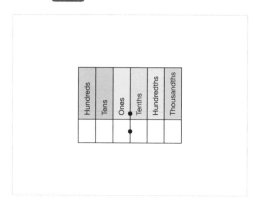

10. What is 6.80 rounded to the nearest 1/10?

1/4

▪ 7 ▪ 6.8 ▪ 6.9 ▪ 6

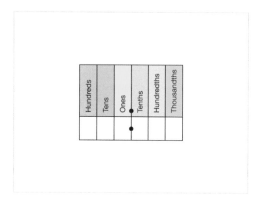

Level 2: Rounding to the nearest whole and tenth including misconceptions when rounding.

✱ **Required:** 7/10   ✱ **Student Navigation:** on
✱ **Randomised:** off

11. 17.64 rounded to the nearest _____ is 18.

1/4   ▪ ten ▪ one ▪ tenth ▪ hundredth

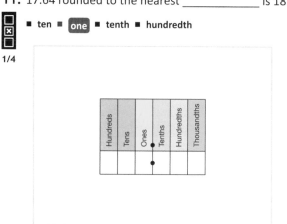

12. What is 34.62 rounded to the nearest whole number (nearest one)?

1 2 3   ▪ 35

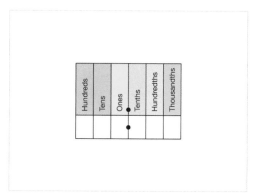

13. What is 5.49 rounded to the nearest **1 decimal place** (nearest tenth)?

1 2 3   ▪ 5.5

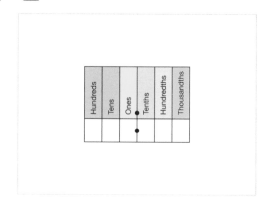

Level 2: *cont.*

14. Which numbers could be rounded to 5 when rounded to the nearest whole number? There are 5 correct answers.

5/7 ▪ `5.12` ▪ 5.50 ▪ `4.70` ▪ `5.39` ▪ `4.58` ▪ 4.49 ▪ `5.04`

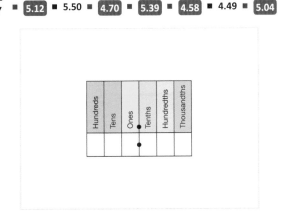

15. Robert scores 87.26% on a test. Round his percentage to the nearest tenth. Do not include the % sign in your answer.

▪ `87.3`

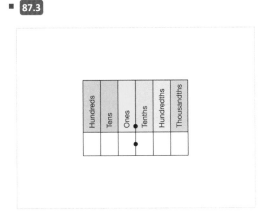

16. When rounding to the nearest whole number which of these numbers would be rounded to 3? There are 4 correct answers.

4/7

▪ `3.09` ▪ 3.80 ▪ `3.23` ▪ 2.46 ▪ 4.00 ▪ `2.60` ▪ `2.57`

17. What is 1,534.42 rounded to the nearest **tenth**?

 ▪ `1,534.4` ▪ `1534.4`

18. When rounding to 1 d.p. (decimal place) which of these numbers would be rounded down?

3/6 ▪ `13.23` ▪ `760.22` ▪ 1,290.35 ▪ 77.08 ▪ 544.98
▪ `902.72`

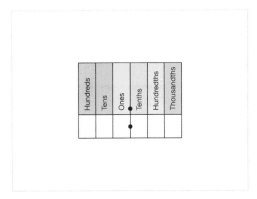

19. Which numbers could be rounded to 84 when rounded to the nearest whole number? There are 4 correct answers.

4/7 ▪ 84.5 ▪ `83.5` ▪ `83.71` ▪ 83.08 ▪ `84.29` ▪ `84.41`
▪ 83.49

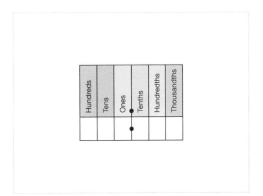

20. A pencil is 8.27 centimetres in length. What is this rounded to the nearest **1** cm? Give your answer in cm.

▪ `8`

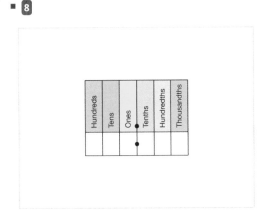

Level 3: Using knowledge of rounding to compare decimal numbers.

✻ **Required:** 6/7   ✻ **Student Navigation:** on
✻ **Randomised:** off

21. A mystery number with 2 decimal places is rounded to the nearest tenth to give the answer 75.4.

What is the **largest** number it could be?

▪ 75.44

22. When rounding 29.832 to the nearest 1 the answer will be 30. True or false? Select the answer with the correct reasoning.

1/4 ▪ True. The digit in the ones column is 9 so you must round up to 30.

▪ False. The digit in the thousandths column is 2 so you must round down to 29.

▪ True. The digit in the tenths column is 8 so you must round up to 30.

▪ False. The digit in the hundredths column is 3 so you must round down to 29.

23. Ryan says, 'I'm thinking of a number. When I round it to the nearest tenth I get the same answer as when I round it to the nearest whole number'. Is this possible? Explain your answer.

24. Claudia is measuring her textbook. She measures it as 24 centimetres, to the nearest centimetre. What is the greatest length it can be, to 2 decimal places? Give your answer in cm.

▪ 24.49

25. Round the numbers 63.23 and 1.54 to the nearest 1 d.p. and add the values together.
Then add 63.23 and 1.54 and round the answer to 1 d.p.

1/3 Which answer is more **accurate**?

▪ Rounding both numbers then adding.

▪ Adding the numbers then rounding.

▪ They are both the same.

26. A runner sets off on a 1 mile run. After 0.47 miles she stops. Is she closer to her starting point or her destination?
Explain how you know.

27. Harry is thinking of a number with 2 decimal places.
When rounded to the **nearest tenth** the number is 42.4.
What is the **lowest** possible value of Harry's number?

▪ 42.35

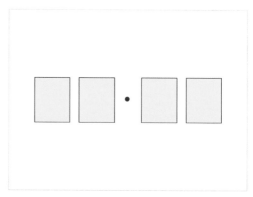

Level 4: Using knowledge of rounding to solve problems.

✻ **Required:** 5/6   ✻ **Student Navigation:** on
✻ **Randomised:** off

28. A company sells 182.21 kg of brown rice, 92.64 kg of white rice and 32.04 kg of basmati rice. How many kg of rice do they sell altogether to the nearest whole number?

▪ 307

29. Rounded to the nearest tenth x = 8.1 and y = 4.9. What is the largest possible difference between x and y?

▪ 3.29

30. Using **all** these digit cards there are 2 different numbers that can be made which **rounded to the nearest whole number** make **39**.
What is the sum of these 2 numbers?

▪ 78.42

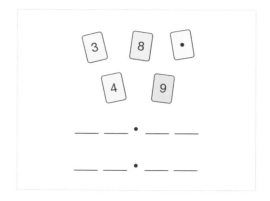

31. A number with 2 decimal places has different digits in each column. All its digits are even. When rounded to the nearest 1 it equals 85. What is the highest number it can be?

▪ 84.62

32. Jayden is thinking of a number with 2 decimal
places. When rounded to the nearest whole
number it equals 3.
All the digits in the number are even.
The sum of the digits is 18.
What is Jayden's number?

- 2.88

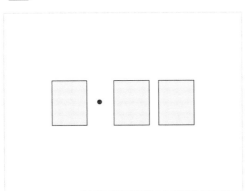

33. Two dice with faces 1 to 6 are rolled. They can be
combined in 2 different ways to make a number
less than 7 with 1 d.p. and then rounded to a
whole number.

For example, rolling a 3 and 4 = 4.3 which rounds
to 4 **or** 3.4 which rounds to 3.

Do this for every possible set of numbers. How
many times do the 2 numbers you make **round to
the same number?**

- 8

Solve problems involving numbers up to three decimal places

Competency: Solve problems involving number up to three decimal places.

Quick Search Ref: 10038

Correct: Correct.   **Wrong:** Incorrect, try again.   **Open:** Thank you.

Level 1: Problem Solving - Involving numbers up to three decimal places.

✿ **Required:** 8/8   ✿ **Student Navigation:** on   ✿ **Randomised:** off

---

1. When rounded to one decimal place, what is the difference between the smallest and largest numbers?

■ 1.7

2. Using each digit card **once**, make the closest possible number to 5.

■ 4.951

3. In an addition pyramid, each box is the sum of the two boxes directly below it. What number goes in the highlighted box?
Give your answer to two decimal places.

■ 10.6

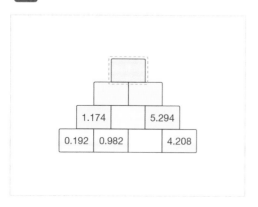

4. What does it cost to buy **one milk**, **one bread** and **one cheese**?

■ £2.20

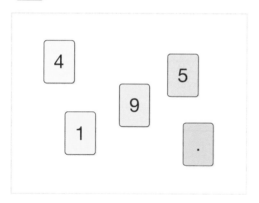

5. The table shows the finishing times of five children in a 100 metre race. If Gary came 3rd, what is his fastest possible finishing time?
Give your answer to two decimal places.

■ 10.88

name	time (seconds)
Lexie	11.98
Aleksandra	10.64
Lewis	11.05
Timmy	10.87
Gary	?

---

6. Libby is thinking of a number between 4 and 5.

`1` `2` `3` Her number has **3 decimal places** and the digits in the tenths, hundredths and thousandths columns are **consecutive numbers**. How many possible numbers could Libby be thinking of?

▪ **8**

7. Four decimal numbers contain the digits 0, 1, 3, 5.

`a` `b` `c` Each digit has been replaced with a letter. What is the value of **a.bcd**?

d.aaa is a **whole number**.
b.dac is the number with the **greatest value**.
c.adb is the number **closest to 1**.
a.ddb has digits that **total 11**.

▪ **0.513**

8. Rounded to the nearest tenth *x* = **6.4** and *y* =

`1` `2` `3` **9.9**. What is the **smallest possible difference** between *x* and *y* ?
Give your answer to two decimal places.

▪ **3.41**

Read and write decimal numbers as fractions

Competency: Read and write decimal numbers as fractions [for example 0.71 = 71/100].

Quick Search Ref: 10246

Correct: Correct.   Wrong: Incorrect, try again.   Open: Thank you.

Level 1: Understanding - Fraction and decimal equivalents, halves, quarters and tenths.

✿ **Required:** 10/10   ✿ **Student Navigation:** on   ✿ **Randomised:** off

---

1. Is the following statement true or false?
A decimal is part of a whole.

▪ True ▪ False

1/2

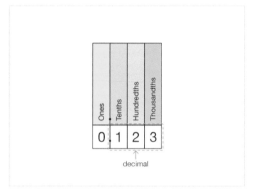

2. Which decimal has the same value as **1/2**?

▪ 0.10 ▪ 0.2 ▪ 0.12 ▪ 0.5

1/4

$$\frac{1}{2} = \frac{?}{10} = 0.\square$$

3. What is **0.3** as a fraction?

▪ 3/10 ▪ 3/100 ▪ 3/1000

1/3

$$0.3 = \frac{?}{?}$$

4. Which decimal has the same value as **1/4**?

▪ 0.4 ▪ 1.4 ▪ 0.5 ▪ 0.25

1/4

$$\frac{1}{4} = \frac{?}{100} = 0.\square$$

5. Which **three** of the fractions are **equal** to 1?

▪ 3/3 ▪ 40/60 ▪ 1/2 ▪ 24/24 ▪ 55/100 ▪ 1/1

3/6

6. Which fraction has the same value as **0.2**?

▪ 1/10 ▪ 1/4 ▪ 1/5 ▪ 1/2 ▪ 2/10

1/5

$$0.2 = \frac{2}{?} = \frac{?}{?}$$

7. The fraction 4/10 means 4 ÷ 10, which equals 0.4.
What is **7/10** as a decimal?

▪ 0.7

$$\frac{7}{10} = 0.\square$$

Level 1: *cont.*

8. What decimal is equal to **2/10**?

a
b
c   ▪ 0.2

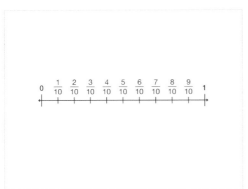

9. Which fraction is equal to **0.5**?

▪ 1/2 ▪ 1/5 ▪ 5/100 ▪ 5/50 ▪ 1/10 ▪ 5/10

1/6

$$0.5 = \frac{5}{?} = \frac{?}{?}$$

10. What is **1/4** as a decimal?

a
b
c   ▪ 0.25

$$\frac{1}{4} = \frac{?}{100} = 0.\boxed{}$$

Level 2: Fluency - Converting between fractions and decimals including hundredths and thousandths.

✿ **Required:** 10/10   ✿ **Student Navigation:** on
✿ **Randomised:** off

11. The fraction 74/100 = 74 ÷ 100 = 0.74.
     What is **82/100** as a decimal?

a
b
c   ▪ 0.82

12. What decimal is equal to 58/100?

a
b
c   ▪ 0.58

13. What is **0.44** as a fraction?

a
b   ▪ 44/100 ▪ 11/25 ▪ 22/50
c

14. What fraction of the 100 square is shaded?

a
b   ▪ 45/100 ▪ 9/20
c

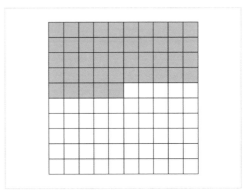

15. Which fractions are equivalent to **0.1**?

▪ 1/10 ▪ 1/100 ▪ 10/100 ▪ 2/20 ▪ 5/10 ▪ 30/300
▪ 10/10

4/7

16. What is **43/1,000** as a decimal?

a
b   ▪ 0.043
c

17. How much of the diagram is shaded?
     Give your answer as a decimal.

a
b
c   ▪ 0.4

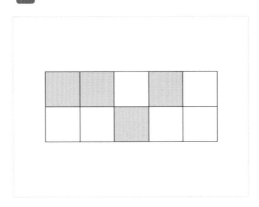

18. Which **three** fractions are equal to **0.75**?

▪ 3/4 ▪ 7/5 ▪ 50/70 ▪ 75/100 ▪ 75/10 ▪ 60/80

3/6

19. Express **65/100** as a decimal.

a
b   ▪ 0.65
c

Level 2: cont.

20. What fraction of the 100 square is shaded?

a b c ▪ 12/100 ▪ 3/25 ▪ 6/50

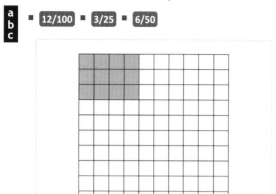

Level 3: Reasoning - Comparing and reasoning with fraction and decimal equivalents.

✷ Required: 8/8   ✷ Student Navigation: on
✷ Randomised: off

21. Which symbol makes the following statement true?
4/10 ___ 0.42

 1/3 ▪ < ▪ = ▪ >

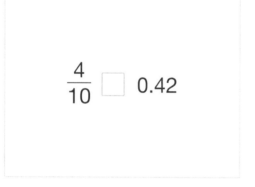

$$\frac{4}{10} \quad \square \quad 0.42$$

22. Which **five** colours represent a value **greater than** 0.1?

 5/7 ▪ purple ▪ white ▪ yellow ▪ blue ▪ pink ▪ black
▪ red

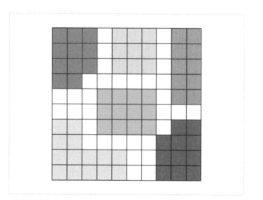

23. Charlie says that 0.30 = 30/100 and Becca says 0.30 = 3/10.
a b c Who is correct? Explain your answer.

24. What **fraction** does the arrow represent?

a b c ▪ 80/100 ▪ 4/5 ▪ 8/10

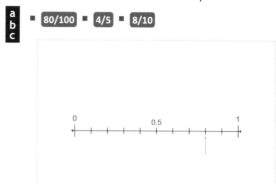

25. What is the missing **decimal**?

a b c ▪ 0.007

$\frac{7}{10}$	0.7
$\frac{7}{100}$	0.07
$\frac{7}{1,000}$	

26. Write the **decimal number** represented by shaded squares.

a b c ▪ 0.3

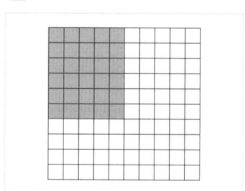

27. Matt says, "5/25 can't be simplified any further because 25 is not divisible by 10".
a b c Is Matt correct? Explain your answer.

Level 3: *cont.*

28. 1/4 __ 0.24.
Which symbol makes the statement true?

■ < ■ = ■ >

1/3

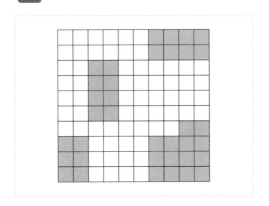

$$\frac{1}{4} \quad \square \quad 0.24$$

Level 4: Problem Solving - Problem Solving with fraction and decimal equivalents.

✸ **Required:** 6/6   ✸ **Student Navigation:** on
✸ **Randomised:** off

29. Work out how much of the 100 square is shaded.
What is **half** of this as a **decimal**?

a
b
c   ■ 0.18

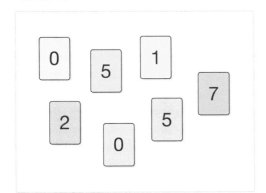

30. Using every digit card **once**, complete the
following statement:

a
b
c   __ . __ __ = __ __/__ __

■ 0.75 = 15/20

0   5   1
7
2   5
0

31. Arrange the fractions and decimals in **ascending**
order (smallest first).

↑
↓   ■ 12/100 ■ 0.24 ■ 1/4 ■ 5/10 ■ 0.55 ■ 0.7
     ■ 0.81

32. Three children each have a pack of raisins.
a   Bret eats 0.7 of his raisins.
b   Cara eats 28/100 of her raisins.
c   Celina eats 0.04 of her raisins.
If the child with the most raisins left over gives 1/2
of their raisins to Riaz, what **fraction of a pack**
does he get?
Give your answer as a fraction.

■ 12/25 ■ 48/100 ■ 24/50

33. Dale is thinking of a fraction.
a   The numerator is an **even number** between 0 and
b   5, but **is not** a prime number.
c   The denominator is **four times larger** than the
numerator.
What is Dale's number?
Give your answer as a decimal.

■ 0.25

34. 50 children were invited to a party and there were
a   50 cupcakes for after the disco.
b   9 children couldn't come to the party.
c   3 children didn't like cupcakes.
4 children left before the end of the disco.
The rest of the children ate one cupcake each.
If half of the **remaining** children were girls, what
proportion of the cupcakes were eaten by **boys**?
Give your answer as a decimal.

■ 0.34

Recognise and understand percentages including fraction and decimal equivalents

Competency: Recognise the per cent symbol (%) and understand that per cent relates to 'number of parts per hundred', and write percentages as a fraction with denominator 100, and as a decimal. Solve problems which require knowing percentage and decimal equivalents.

Quick Search Ref: 10034

Correct: Correct.   **Wrong:** Incorrect, try again.   **Open:** Thank you.

Level 1: Understanding - Terminology and percentages of shapes.

✿ **Required: 7/10**   ✿ **Student Navigation:** on   ✿ **Randomised:** off

1. What is a **percentage**?

1/3

- ▪ An amount expressed as a number out of 100.
- ▪ A whole number that divides exactly into another whole number without a remainder.
- ▪ A comparison of two or more values.

2. Select the symbol that is used to indicate a **percentage**.

1/4

- ▪ ÷ ▪ % ▪ ° ▪ >

3. What is **1%** as a fraction?

- ▪ 1/100

4. **1/4** is equal to ___%

- ▪ 25

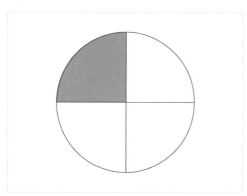

5. What percentage of the circle is shaded?

- ▪ 50 ▪ 50%

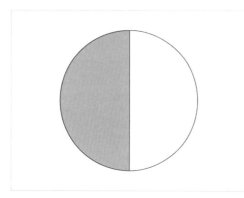

6. What **percentage** of the rectangle is shaded?

- ▪ 75 ▪ 75%

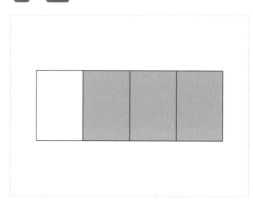

7. **One-tenth** is equal to ___%

- ▪ 10

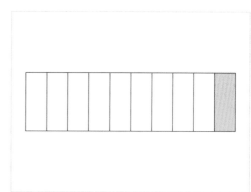

8. What percentage of the 100 square is shaded?

- ▪ 46% ▪ 46

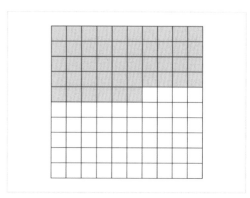

9. What percentage of the rectangle is shaded?

■ 7%   ■ **70%**   ■ 30%

1/3

10. What percentage of the 100 square is shaded?

  ■ **72** ■ **72%**

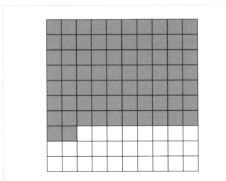

11. There were 100 grapes in a pack and Gilly
 ate 48 of them.
What percentage of the grapes are left?

■ **52%**   ■ **52**

12. What number makes the following statement
true?
 __% = 2/10 = 0.2

■ **20**

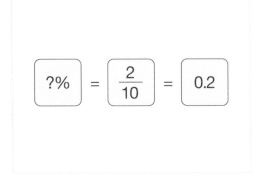

13. There are **200** building blocks in a box.
 Mabz uses **126** of them to make a model house.
What **percentage** of the blocks does he use?

■ **63%**   ■ **63**

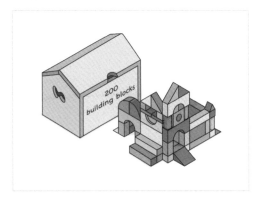

14. What is **25%** of 84?

  ■ **21**

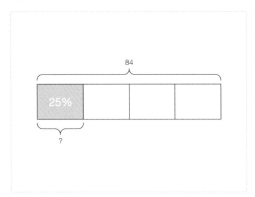

15. What **percentage** of the quilt is patterned?

  ■ **68%**   ■ **68**

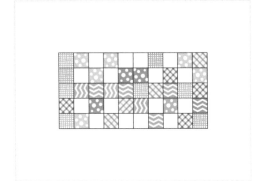

Level 2: *cont.*

16. What is **10%** of 32?

 ▪ 3.2

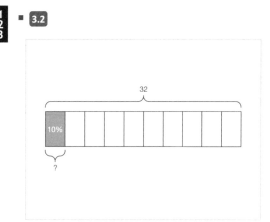

17. There are **50** people at a party and **27** are children. What percentage are adults?

▪ 46

18. What is **40%** of 60?

▪ 24 ▪ 6 ▪ 40 ▪ 15

1/4

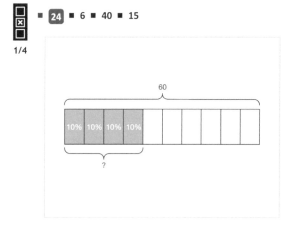

19. **0.3** is ___%.

▪ 30

20. What is **20%** of 174?

▪ 34.8

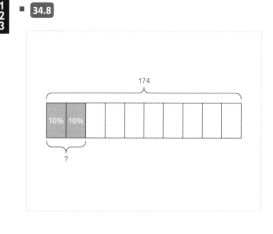

Level 3: Reasoning - Ordering, comparing and reasoning with percentages, fractions and decimals.

✿ **Required:** 5/6   ✿ **Student Navigation:** on
✿ **Randomised:** off

21. Which **two** percentages have a value **greater than** 0.7?

▪ 7% ▪ 6% ▪ 13% ▪ 98% ▪ 70% ▪ 81%

2/6

22. What sign makes the following statement true?
38% __ 1/4

▪ >

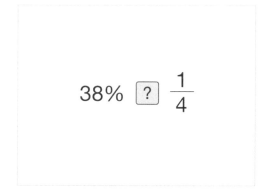

23. Logan has 8 books and reads 2 of them. What **percentage** of his books has he left to read?

▪ 75 ▪ 75%

24. Arrange the values in **descending order** (largest at the top, smallest at the bottom).

▪ 75/100 ▪ 68% ▪ 0.5 ▪ 4/10 ▪ 25%

25. Which is greater, 20% of 300, or 25% of 260? Explain your answer.

26. Select **three** options that have the same value.

▪ 50% ▪ 20% ▪ 0.5 ▪ 0.02 ▪ 55/100 ▪ 1/4 ▪ 1/2

3/7

27. Arrange the calculations in **ascending** order (smallest at the top, largest at the bottom).

▪ 1/10 of 70 ▪ 1/5 of 55 ▪ 20% of 65 ▪ 0.25 of 80
▪ 75% of 100

28. Ashley has **30** magnets.

[1 2 3] He gives **2/5** of the 30 to his friend.
He loses **30%** of the 30 under the fridge.
He throws **0.1** of the 30 away because they're damaged.
How many magnets does he have left?

▪ [6]

29. Shazia uses **1/25** of a pack of paper for her maths

[a b c] homework and **0.4** of the pack for her English homework.
What **percentage** of the pack does she have left?

▪ [56] ▪ [56%]

30. **32 children** in Year 5 are voting for where they

[1 2 3] want to go for their school trip.
25% vote for the castle.
The theme park gets twice as many votes as the farm.
How many votes does the winning option get?

▪ [16]

Year 5 School Trip
Tick (✓) the box next to your choice.

Theme park	☐
Castle	☐
Farm	☐

31. The watch has been **reduced by** ___% in the sale.

[1 2 3] ▪ [25]

price: £96.00
sale price: £72.00

SALE

Mathematics

Properties of Number

Multiples and Factors

Prime Numbers

Squares and Cubes

Understand Prime Factors

Competency: Recognise, understand and solve problems with prime numbers, composite numbers and prime factors.

Quick Search Ref: 10062

Correct: Correct.   Wrong: Incorrect, try again.   Open: Thank you.

Level 1: Understanding - Identifying prime factors of numbers less than 20.

✹ Required: 7/10   ✹ Student Navigation: on   ✹ Randomised: off

1. What is a prime number?

1/4
- A whole number which exactly divides into another whole number.
- A number that can only be divided by itself and 1.
- A number that can be divided evenly by numbers other than itself and 1.
- A number which is multiplied by itself.

2. What is a factor?

1/4
- A whole number which exactly divides into another whole number.
- A number that can only be divided by itself and 1.
- A number that can be divided evenly by numbers other than itself and 1.
- A number which is multiplied by itself.

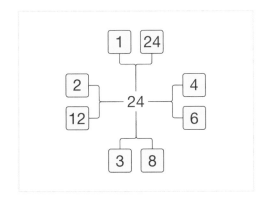

3. What is a prime factor?

1/4
- A whole number which exactly divides into another whole number.
- A number that can only be divided by itself and 1.
- A number that can be divided evenly by numbers other than itself and 1.
- A factor that is a prime number.

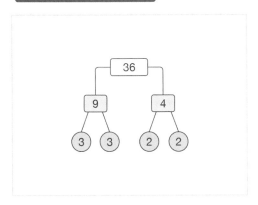

4. Select the two prime factors of 6.

2/4   ■ 1 ■ 2 ■ 3 ■ 6

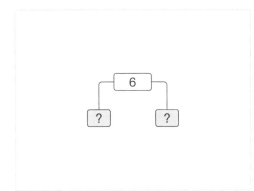

5. Select the two prime factors of 15.

2/4   ■ 1 ■ 3 ■ 5 ■ 15

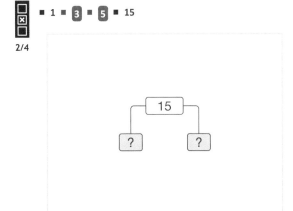

6. What number is a prime factor of 9?

1 2 3   ■ 3

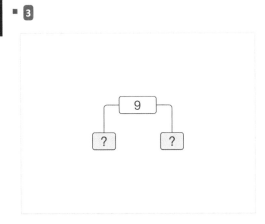

7. What number is a prime factor of 7?

1 2 3   ■ 7

Level 1: cont.

8. Select the two prime factors of 21.

 ■ 1 ■ **3** ■ **7** ■ 21

2/4

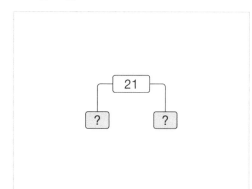

9. What number is a prime factor of 25?

 ■ **5**

10. Select the two prime factors of 33.

 ■ 1 ■ **3** ■ **11** ■ 33

2/4

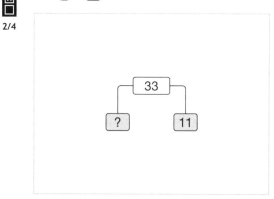

Level 2: Fluency - Identifying prime factors.

✹ **Required:** 7/10 ✹ **Student Navigation:** on
✹ **Randomised:** off

11. The prime factors of 48 are 2 and ___.

 ■ **3**

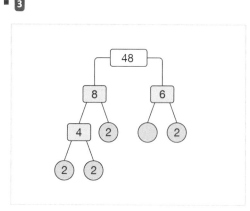

12. Use the factor tree to find the **two prime factors** of 36.

 ■ **3** ■ 4 ■ 6 ■ **2** ■ 12 ■ 9

2/6

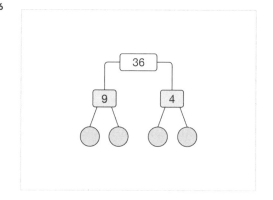

13. Use the factor tree to find the **three prime factors** of 30.

 ■ 15 ■ **3** ■ **2** ■ 6 ■ 10 ■ **5**

3/6

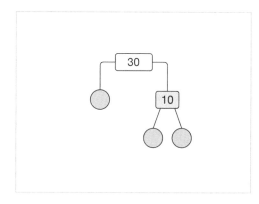

14. Which **two** numbers are **prime factors** of 20?

 ■ 1 ■ **2** ■ 4 ■ **5** ■ 10 ■ 20

2/6

15. What is the missing prime factor?

■ **7**

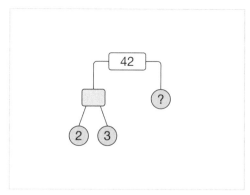

Level 2: *cont.*

16. The prime factors of 56 are 2 and ___ .

 ▪ **7**

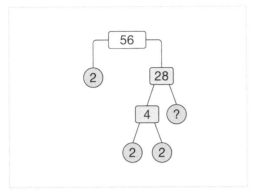

17. Which **two** numbers are **prime factors** of 35?

 ▪ 1 ▪ **5** ▪ **7** ▪ 35

2/4

18. The prime factors of 60 are 2, 3 and ___ .

 ▪ **5**

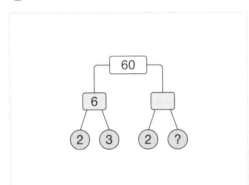

19. Which number is a prime factor of 16?

 ▪ 1 ▪ **2** ▪ 4 ▪ 8 ▪ 16

1/5

20. What is the missing prime factor?

 ▪ **7**

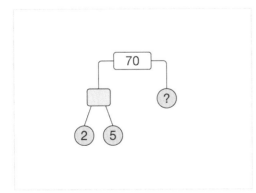

Level 3: Reasoning - Use reasoning to identify prime factors.

❋ **Required:** 5/5 ❋ **Student Navigation:** on
❋ **Randomised:** off

21. Alex says that all even numbers have a prime factor.
Is he correct? Explain your answer.

a
b
c

22. The number 24 is written as a product of its **prime factors**. Which one of the following is correct?

 ▪ 24 = 3 × 8 ▪ 24 = 4 × 6 ▪ **24 = 2 × 2 × 2 × 3**
1/4 ▪ 24 = 2 × 3 × 4

23. What is the **smallest** number which has **two** different prime factors?

 ▪ **6**

24. All numbers in the 6 times table have at least two prime factors. Explain why this is true.

a
b
c

25. The number 84 is written as a product of its **prime factors**. Which one of the following is correct?

▪ 84 = 2 × 2 × 21 ▪ 84 = 12 × 7 ▪ 84 = 2 × 42
1/6 ▪ **84 = 2 × 2 × 3 × 7** ▪ 84 = 4 × 21 ▪ 84 = 2 × 6 × 7

Level 4: Problem Solving - Calculate prime numbers up to 100.

❋ **Required:** 5/5 ❋ **Student Navigation:** on
❋ **Randomised:** off

26. Which number has the **most prime factors**?

 ▪ 21 ▪ 45 ▪ **66** ▪ 63 ▪ 85 ▪ 91
1/6

27. Which number has the **fewest prime factors**?

 ▪ 30 ▪ 42 ▪ 60 ▪ **99**
1/4

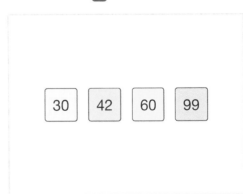

28. Which square number less than 100 has more than one prime factor?

 ▪ **36**

Level 4: *cont.*

29. Identify which prime number is a common factor
of the following numbers:
63, 70, 105.

▪ **7**

30. What is the highest prime factor of 156?

▪ **13**

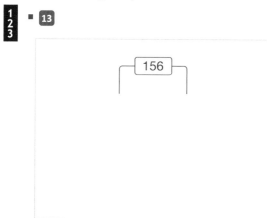

Understand prime numbers, composite numbers and prime factors

Competency: Recognise, understand and solve problems with prime numbers, composite numbers and prime factors.

Quick Search Ref: 10231

Correct: Correct.   Wrong: Incorrect, try again.   Open: Thank you.

Level 1: Understanding - Prime numbers, composite numbers and prime factors.

⚙ **Required:** 7/10   ⚙ **Student Navigation:** on   ⚙ **Randomised:** off

---

1. What is a prime number?

 1/4

- A whole number which exactly divides into another whole number.
- A number that can only be divided by itself and 1.
- A number that can be divided evenly by numbers other than itself and 1.
- A number which is multiplied by itself.

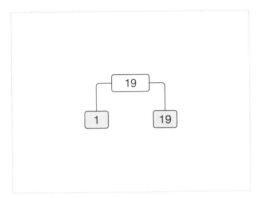

2. What is a composite number?

 1/4

- A whole number which exactly divides into another whole number.
- A number that has exactly 2 factors.
- A number that can be divided evenly by numbers other than itself and 1.
- A number which is multiplied by itself.

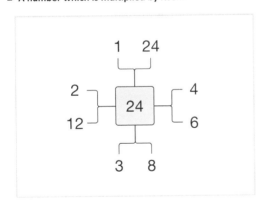

3. What is a factor?

 1/4

- A whole number which exactly divides into another whole number.
- A number that can only be divided by itself and 1.
- A number that can be divided evenly by numbers other than itself and 1.
- A number which is multiplied by itself.

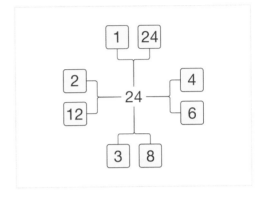

4. Is 19 a prime or composite number?

- composite number   ■ prime number

 1/2

5. 49 is a _____ number.

 1/2

- composite   ■ prime

173

Level 1: cont.

6. What is a prime factor?

1/4

- A whole number which exactly divides into another whole number.
- A number that can only be divided by itself and 1.
- A number that can be divided evenly by numbers other than itself and 1.
- A factor that is a prime number.

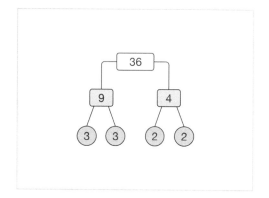

7. Which number is neither prime or composite?

1/4

- 15 ▪ 41 ▪ **1** ▪ 18

8. Select the two composite numbers.

2/5

- 11 ▪ **12** ▪ 13 ▪ **15** ▪ 19

9. Select the **two** prime numbers.

2/5

- **5** ▪ 6 ▪ **7** ▪ 8 ▪ 9

10. Is 7 a prime or composite number?

1/2

- composite number ▪ **prime number**

Level 2: Fluency - Identifying prime numbers, composite numbers and prime factors.

 Required: 6/8   Student Navigation: on
 Randomised: off

11. What is a prime number between 12 and 16?

1
2
3

- **13**

12. Use the factor tree to find the **two prime factors** of 36.

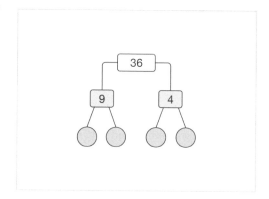
2/6

- **3** ▪ 4 ▪ 6 ▪ **2** ▪ 12 ▪ 9

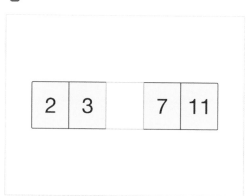

13. What is the missing number in the sequence?

1
2
3

- **5**

| 2 | 3 | | 7 | 11 |

14. Use the factor tree to find the **three prime factors** of 30.

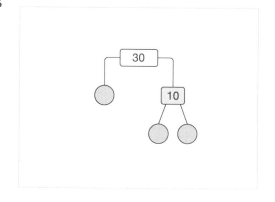
3/6

- 15 ▪ **3** ▪ **2** ▪ 6 ▪ 10 ▪ **5**

Level 2: *cont.*

15. Complete the number sequence.

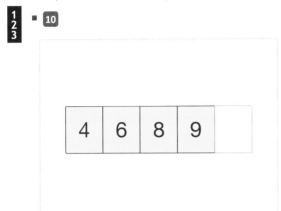

16. The prime factors of 48 are 2 and ___.

· 3

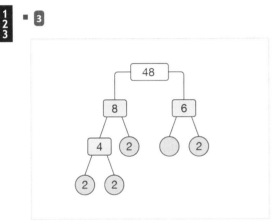

17. What is the missing number in the sequence?

· 13

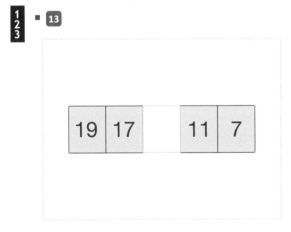

18. Which two numbers are prime factors of 20?

■ 1 ■ 2 ■ 4 ■ 5 ■ 10 ■ 20

2/6

Level 3: Reasoning - Use reasoning to identify prime numbers, composite numbers and prime factors.

❋ **Required:** 6/8   ❋ **Student Navigation:** on
❋ **Randomised:** off

19. How many prime numbers are there between 1 and 20?

· 8

20. The sum of three prime numbers is 20. One of the numbers is 13. What are the other **two** numbers?

■ 1 ■ 2 ■ 3 ■ 4 ■ 5 ■ 6

2/6

21. Other than 2 and 3, are there any other consecutive prime numbers between 1 and 100? *Explain your answer.*

22. The number 24 is written as a product of its **prime factors**. Which one of the following is correct?

■ 24 = 3 × 8 ■ 24 = 4 × 6 ■ 24 = 2 × 2 × 2 × 3
1/4 ■ 24 = 2 × 3 × 4

23. What is the **smallest** number which has **two** different prime factors?

· 6

24. Jamila says, "If you multiply two prime numbers, the answer will always be a prime number." Is she correct? Explain your answer.

25. Which of these numbers is the odd one out?

· 10

Level 3: cont.

26. What is the only **prime** number between 90 and
100?

1
2
3

▪ 97

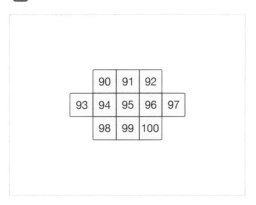

Level 4: Problem Solving - Calculate prime numbers up
to 100.

🌸 **Required:** 5/5   🌸 **Student Navigation:** on
🌸 **Randomised:** off

27. Derek collects football cards. The number of cards
he has in the morning is a **prime** number **between
90 and 100**. On the way to school he buys
3 packets which each contain 6 cards.
When Derek gets to school, he gives Keon some
cards (the **greatest prime factor of 33**).
How many cards does Derek have left?

1
2
3

▪ 104

28. I am a **prime** number between 70 and 100.
My **tens** digit is **greater** than my **ones** digit.
The **sum** of my digits is 10.
What number am I?

1
2
3

▪ 73

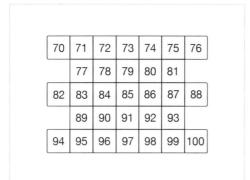

29. The two missing numbers in the equation are
prime numbers between 2 and 60. What number
goes in the **answer** box?

1
2
3

▪ 2

$? - 11 = \boxed{}$

30. Sam adds together two consecutive **composite**
numbers between 40 and 45 (inclusive). He then
adds a number which only has the **prime factors** 5,
3 and 2. What answer does Sam get?

1
2
3

▪ 119

31. Which number has the **most prime factors**?

▪ 21 ▪ 45 ▪ 66 ▪ 63 ▪ 85 ▪ 91

1/6

Identify multiples and factors

Competency: Identify multiples and factors, including finding all factor pairs of a number, and common factors of two numbers.

Quick Search Ref: 10216

Correct: Correct.   **Wrong:** Incorrect, try again.   **Open:** Thank you.

Level 1: Understanding - Identifying factors and multiples

🌼 **Required:** 7/10   🌼 **Student Navigation:** on   🌼 **Randomised:** off

---

1. A **factor** is:

1/4

- A whole number that divides exactly into another whole number without a remainder. It will pair with another number.
- A number that can be made by multiplying two whole numbers.
- A pair of numbers which result in a product when multiplied together.
- The ratio between two similar sets of measurements.

2. A **multiple** is:

1/4

- A whole number that divides exactly into another whole number without a remainder.
- A pair of numbers which result in a product when multiplied together.
- The ratio between two similar sets of measurements.
- The result of multiplying a whole number by another whole number.

3. What is the next multiple of 6?

1/4

6, 12, 18, 24, 30, ___.

■ 34 ■ 35 ■ **36** ■ 37

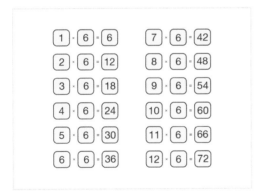

1 · 6 = 6		7 · 6 = 42	
2 · 6 = 12		8 · 6 = 48	
3 · 6 = 18		9 · 6 = 54	
4 · 6 = 24		10 · 6 = 60	
5 · 6 = 30		11 · 6 = 66	
6 · 6 = 36		12 · 6 = 72	

4. Select the number which is a **factor** of 12.

1/4

■ 5 ■ **6** ■ 7 ■ 8

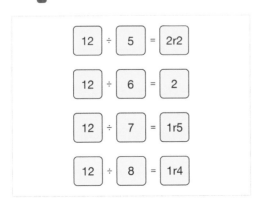

12 ÷ 5 = 2r2

12 ÷ 6 = 2

12 ÷ 7 = 1r5

12 ÷ 8 = 1r4

5. Select the **factor pair** (2 factors) of 24 which will make the following equation complete:

2/5

_ x _ = 24.

■ 3 ■ **4** ■ 5 ■ **6** ■ 7

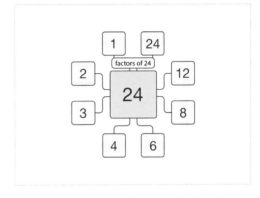

factors of 24: 1, 24, 2, 12, 3, 8, 4, 6 — **24**

6. Select the number which is a **multiple** of 5.

1/4

■ 13 ■ 14 ■ **15** ■ 16

1 · 5 = 5		7 · 5 = 35	
2 · 5 = 10		8 · 5 = 40	
3 · 5 = 15		9 · 5 = 45	
4 · 5 = 20		10 · 5 = 50	
5 · 5 = 25		11 · 5 = 55	
6 · 5 = 30		12 · 5 = 60	

7. Which number is a **factor** of 21?

1/4

■ 4 ■ 5 ■ 6 ■ **7**

21 ÷ 4 = 5r1

21 ÷ 5 = 4r1

21 ÷ 6 = 3r3

21 ÷ 7 = 3

Level 1: *cont.*

8. Select the **next** multiple of 4 in the following sequence:

4, 8, 12, 16, 20, 24, __.

1/4

■ **25** ■ **26** ■ **27** ■ 28

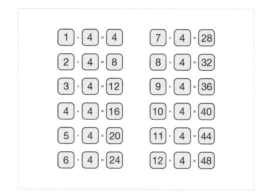

9. Select all the **multiples** of 4.

■ 12 ■ **13** ■ **14** ■ **15** ■ 16 ■ 48

3/6

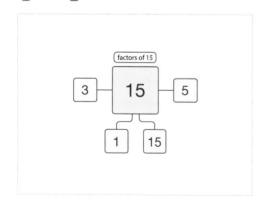

10. Select the **factor pair** (2 factors) of 15 which will make the following equation complete:

_ x _ = 15.

2/5

■ 3 ■ **4** ■ 5 ■ **6** ■ **7**

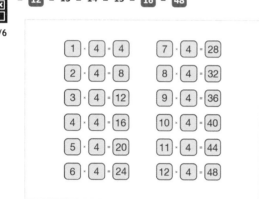

Level 2: Fluency - Identifying missing factors and multiples

✿ **Required:** 7/10   ✿ **Student Navigation:** on
✿ **Randomised:** off

11. Which **factor** of 18 is missing from the list?

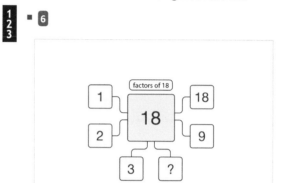 ■ 6

12. Write the number which is **missing** from the sequence:

8, 16, 24, __, 40.

■ 32

13. If two or more numbers have the same factor, this is called a **common factor**.
Select the common factors of **15 and 21**.

2/4   ■ 3 ■ **5** ■ **7** ■ 1

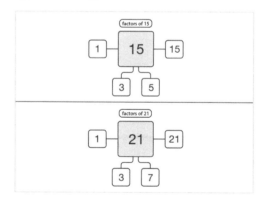

14. Which **factor** of 28 is missing from the list?

 ■ 7

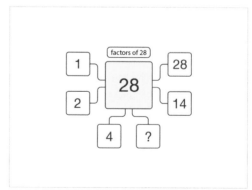

Level 2: *cont.*

15. What is the largest factor of 20 **not including** itself?

▪ 10

16. If two or more numbers have the same factor, this is called a **common factor.** 1 is a common factor of all numbers.

Not including 1, what is the only other common factor of **22 and 33?**

▪ 11

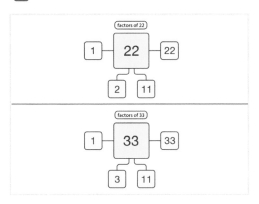

17. Below is a sequence of multiples of 6. Which number is missing?

6, 12, __, 24, 30.

▪ 18

18. What is the largest factor of 35 **not including** itself?

▪ 7

19. Select all the factors of 24 from the list.

5/7

▪ 2 ▪ 3 ▪ 4 ▪ 5 ▪ 6 ▪ 7 ▪ 8

20. Carlos is trying to find **all** the factors of 48.

Which factor has he missed?

▪ 8

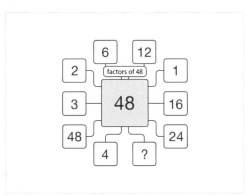

Level 3: Reasoning - Finding missing multiples and common factors

❋ **Required:** 5/5   ❋ **Student Navigation:** on
❋ **Randomised:** off

21. Select the number which goes in **box C.**

▪ 3 ▪ 5 ▪ 6 ▪ 7 ▪ 14

1/5

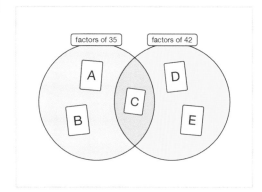

22. William says, "In my diagram, there will never be a number in box B."

a
b
c

Is he correct? Explain your answer.

23. Which number goes in **box C**?

▪ 55 ▪ 56 ▪ 60 ▪ 64 ▪ 65

1/5

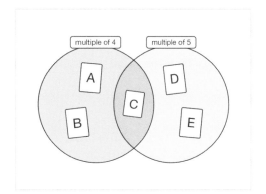

24. Layla says, 'When calculating factors of a number, there is always a factor pair. Therefore, every number contains an even number of factors.'

a
b
c

Is Layla correct? Explain your answer.

Level 3: *cont.*

25. What is the **largest multiple** of 7 between 1 and
 `1 2 3` 200?

 ▪ **196**

Level 4: Problem Solving - Use knowledge of multiples
and factors to answer questions

✳ **Required:** 5/5   ✳ **Student Navigation:** on
✳ **Randomised:** off

---

26. When two numbers next to each other are
 `1 2 3` multiplied together in a number tree, the answer
goes in the box above. Find all of the missing
values and write the value of *c*.

 ▪ **9**

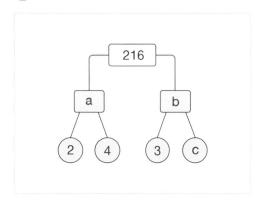

27. Suzy and her dad's age both have a **common**
 `1 2 3` **factor** of 6. Dad is **three times** older than Suzy and
between the age of 40 and 70. How old is Suzy?

 ▪ **18**

28. Year 5 are split into three groups for a P.E. game.
 `1 2 3` Each person in a group has to run 5 metres, drop a
beanbag in a bucket and return to their team for
the next person to go.

Team 1 drop a beanbag every **4 seconds**, team 2
every **6 seconds** and team 3 every **8 seconds**.

How many times do they all drop a beanbag at the
same time in 2 minutes?

 ▪ **5**

29. Numbered balls are dropped one at a time into a
 `1 2 3` multiple machine. A ball can only drop down a
tube that is a **multiple** of its number. Which
number ball ends up in box D?

 ▪ **9**

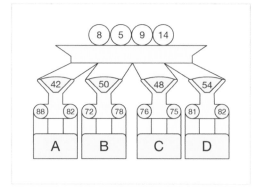

30. When two numbers next to each other are
 `1 2 3` multiplied together in a number tree, the answer
goes in the box above. Find all of the missing
values and write the value of **a**.

 ▪ **6**

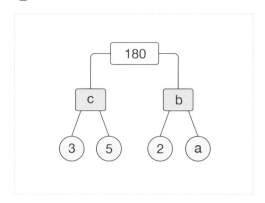

Recognising prime numbers - speed challenge (no correct feedback)

Competency: Children establish whether a number up to 100 is prime and recall prime numbers up to 19.

Quick Search Ref: 10026

Correct: Correct. **Wrong:** Incorrect, try again. **Open:** Thank you.

Level 1: Recognising prime numbers to 100.

✿ **Required:** 100/100   ✿ **Student Navigation:** off   ✿ **Randomised:** on

1. Is **1** a prime number?
■ Yes ■ No
1/2

2. Is **2** a prime number?
■ Yes ■ No
1/2

3. Is **3** a prime number?
■ Yes ■ No
1/2

4. Is **4** a prime number?
■ Yes ■ No
1/2

5. Is **5** a prime number?
■ Yes ■ No
1/2

6. Is **6** a prime number?
■ Yes ■ No
1/2

7. Is **7** a prime number?
■ Yes ■ No
1/2

8. Is **8** a prime number?
■ Yes ■ No
1/2

9. Is **9** a prime number?
■ Yes ■ No
1/2

10. Is **10** a prime number?
■ Yes ■ No
1/2

11. Is **11** a prime number?
■ Yes ■ No
1/2

12. Is **12** a prime number?
■ Yes ■ No
1/2

13. Is **13** a prime number?
■ Yes ■ No
1/2

14. Is **14** a prime number?
■ Yes ■ No
1/2

15. Is **15** a prime number?
■ Yes ■ No
1/2

16. Is **16** a prime number?
■ Yes ■ No
1/2

17. Is **17** a prime number?
■ Yes ■ No
1/2

18. Is **18** a prime number?
■ Yes ■ No
1/2

19. Is **19** a prime number?
■ Yes ■ No
1/2

20. Is **20** a prime number?
■ Yes ■ No
1/2

21. Is **21** a prime number?
■ Yes ■ No
1/2

22. Is **22** a prime number?
■ Yes ■ No
1/2

Level 1: *cont.*

23. Is **23** a prime number?

■ Yes ■ No

1/?

24. Is **24** a prime number?

■ Yes ■ No

1/?

25. Is **25** a prime number?

■ Yes ■ No

1/?

26. Is **26** a prime number?

■ Yes ■ No

1/?

27. Is **27** a prime number?

■ Yes ■ No

1/?

28. Is **28** a prime number?

■ Yes ■ No

1/?

29. Is **29** a prime number?

■ Yes ■ No

1/?

30. Is **30** a prime number?

■ Yes ■ No

1/?

31. Is **31** a prime number?

■ Yes ■ No

1/?

32. Is **32** a prime number?

■ Yes ■ No

1/?

33. Is **33** a prime number?

■ Yes ■ No

1/?

34. Is **34** a prime number?

■ Yes ■ No

1/?

35. Is **35** a prime number?

■ Yes ■ No

1/?

36. Is **36** a prime number?

■ Yes ■ No

1/?

37. Is **37** a prime number?

■ Yes ■ No

1/?

38. Is **38** a prime number?

■ Yes ■ No

1/?

39. Is **39** a prime number?

■ Yes ■ No

1/?

40. Is **40** a prime number?

■ Yes ■ No

1/?

41. Is **41** a prime number?

■ Yes ■ No

1/?

42. Is **42** a prime number?

■ Yes ■ No

1/?

43. Is **43** a prime number?

■ Yes ■ No

1/?

44. Is **44** a prime number?

■ Yes ■ No

1/?

45. Is **45** a prime number?

■ Yes ■ No

1/?

46. Is **46** a prime number?

■ Yes ■ No

1/?

47. Is **47** a prime number?

■ Yes ■ No

1/?

48. Is **48** a prime number?

■ Yes ■ No

1/?

49. Is **49** a prime number?

☐
☒
☐

■ Yes ■ No

1/2

50. Is **50** a prime number?

☐
☒
☐

■ Yes ■ No

1/2

51. Is **51** a prime number?

☐
☒
☐

■ Yes ■ No

1/2

52. Is **52** a prime number?

☐
☒
☐

■ Yes ■ No

1/2

53. Is **53** a prime number?

☐
☒
☐

■ Yes ■ No

1/2

54. Is **54** a prime number?

☐
☒
☐

■ Yes ■ No

1/2

55. Is **55** a prime number?

☐
☒
☐

■ Yes ■ No

1/2

56. Is **56** a prime number?

☐
☒
☐

■ Yes ■ No

1/2

57. Is **57** a prime number?

☐
☒
☐

■ Yes ■ No

1/2

58. Is **58** a prime number?

☐
☒
☐

■ Yes ■ No

1/2

59. Is **59** a prime number?

☐
☒
☐

■ Yes ■ No

1/2

60. Is **60** a prime number?

☐
☒
☐

■ Yes ■ No

1/2

61. Is **61** a prime number?

☐
☒
☐

■ Yes ■ No

1/2

62. Is **62** a prime number?

☐
☒
☐

■ Yes ■ No

1/2

63. Is **63** a prime number?

☐
☐
☐

■ Yes ■ No

1/2

64. Is **64** a prime number?

☐
☒
☐

■ Yes ■ No

1/2

65. Is **65** a prime number?

☐
☒
☐

■ Yes ■ No

1/2

66. Is **66** a prime number?

☐
☒
☐

■ Yes ■ No

1/2

67. Is **67** a prime number?

☐
☒
☐

■ Yes ■ No

1/2

68. Is **68** a prime number?

☐
☒
☐

■ Yes ■ No

1/2

69. Is **69** a prime number?

☐
☒
☐

■ Yes ■ No

1/2

70. Is **70** a prime number?

☐
☒
☐

■ Yes ■ No

1/2

71. Is **71** a prime number?

☐
☒
☐

■ Yes ■ No

1/2

72. Is **72** a prime number?

☐
☒
☐

■ Yes ■ No

1/2

73. Is **73** a prime number?

☐
☒
☐

■ Yes ■ No

1/2

74. Is **74** a prime number?

☐
☒
☐

■ Yes ■ No

1/2

75. Is **75** a prime number?

☐ ▪ Yes ▪ No
1/?

76. Is **76** a prime number?

☐ ▪ Yes ▪ No
1/?

77. Is **77** a prime number?

☐ ▪ Yes ▪ No
1/?

78. Is **78** a prime number?

☐ ▪ Yes ▪ No
1/?

79. Is **79** a prime number?

☐ ▪ Yes ▪ No
1/?

80. Is **80** a prime number?

☐ ▪ Yes ▪ No
1/?

81. Is **81** a prime number?

☐ ▪ Yes ▪ No
1/?

82. Is **82** a prime number?

☐ ▪ Yes ▪ No
1/?

83. Is **83** a prime number?

☐ ▪ Yes ▪ No
1/?

84. Is **84** a prime number?

☐ ▪ Yes ▪ No
1/?

85. Is **85** a prime number?

☐ ▪ Yes ▪ No
1/?

86. Is **86** a prime number?

☐ ▪ Yes ▪ No
1/?

87. Is **87** a prime number?

☐ ▪ Yes ▪ No
1/?

88. Is **88** a prime number?

☐ ▪ Yes ▪ No
1/?

89. Is **89** a prime number?

☐ ▪ Yes ▪ No
1/?

90. Is **90** a prime number?

☐ ▪ Yes ▪ No
1/?

91. Is **91** a prime number?

☐ ▪ Yes ▪ No
1/?

92. Is **92** a prime number?

☐ ▪ Yes ▪ No
1/?

93. Is **93** a prime number?

☐ ▪ Yes ▪ No
1/?

94. Is **94** a prime number?

☐ ▪ Yes ▪ No
1/?

95. Is **95** a prime number?

☐ ▪ Yes ▪ No
1/?

96. Is **96** a prime number?

☐ ▪ Yes ▪ No
1/?

97. Is **97** a prime number?

☐ ▪ Yes ▪ No
1/?

98. Is **98** a prime number?

☐ ▪ Yes ▪ No
1/?

99. Is **99** a prime number?

☐ ▪ Yes ▪ No
1/?

100. Is **100** a prime number?

☐ ▪ Yes ▪ No
1/?

Understand Prime Numbers and Composite Numbers

Competency: Recognise, understand and solve problems with prime numbers, composite numbers and prime factors.

Quick Search Ref: 10118

Correct: Correct.   Wrong: Incorrect, try again.   Open: Thank you.

Level 1:   Understanding - Prime numbers and composite numbers.

✿ Required: 7/10   ✿ Student Navigation: on   ✿ Randomised: off

1.   What is a prime number?

1/4

- A whole number which exactly divides into another whole number.
- **A number that can only be divided by itself and 1.**
- A number that can be divided evenly by numbers other than itself and 1.
- A number which is multiplied by itself.

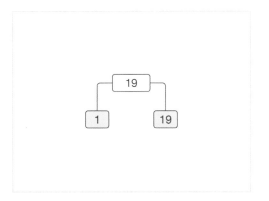

2.   What is a composite number?

1/4

- A whole number which exactly divides into another whole number.
- A number that has exactly 2 factors.
- **A number that can be divided evenly by numbers other than itself and 1.**
- A number which is multiplied by itself.

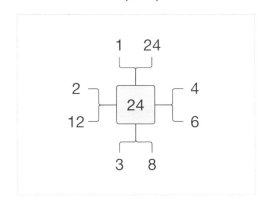

3.   What is a factor?

1/4

- **A whole number which exactly divides into another whole number.**
- A number that can only be divided by itself and 1.
- A number that can be divided evenly by numbers other than itself and 1.
- A number which is multiplied by itself.

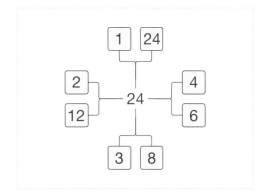

4.   Is 19 a prime or composite number?

1/2

- composite number ■ **prime number**

5.   49 is a _____ number.

1/2

- **composite** ■ prime

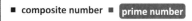 **Level 1:** *cont.*

6. Which number is neither prime or composite?

- 15 - 41 - **1** - 18

1/4

7. Is 7 a prime or composite number?

- composite number - **prime number**

1/2

8. Select the two composite numbers.

- 11 - **12** - 13 - **15** - 19

2/5

9. Select the **two** prime numbers.

- **5** - 6 - **7** - 8 - 9

2/5

10. Is 27 a prime or composite number?

- **composite number** - prime number

1/2

Level 2: Fluency - Identifying prime numbers and composite numbers.

✿ **Required:** 7/10   ✿ **Student Navigation:** on
✿ **Randomised:** off

11. What is a prime number between 12 and 16?

 ▪ **13**

12. What is the missing number in the sequence?

 ▪ **5**

13. What is the smallest prime number?

 ▪ **2**

14. Complete the number sequence.

 ▪ **10**

15. What is the missing number in the sequence?

 ▪ **13**

16. Complete the number sequence.

[1/2/3] ▪ [36]

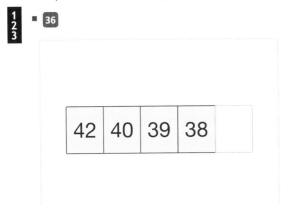

17. Select the composite number.

[▢/☒/▢] ▪ 47 ▪ [51] ▪ 53 ▪ 59

1/4

18. Complete the number sequence.

[1/2/3] ▪ [23]

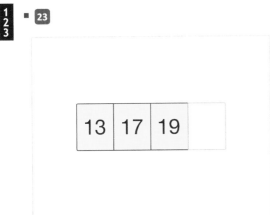

19. What is the smallest composite number?

[1/2/3] ▪ [4]

20. What is a prime number between 30 and 35?

[1/2/3] ▪ [31]

Level 3: Reasoning - Use reasoning to identify prime numbers and composite numbers.

✹ **Required:** 5/5   ✹ **Student Navigation:** on
✹ **Randomised:** off

21. How many prime numbers are there between 1 and 20?

[1/2/3] ▪ [8]

1	2	3	4	5
6	7	8	9	10
11	12	13	14	15
16	17	18	19	20

22. The sum of three prime numbers is 20. One of the numbers is 13. What are the other **two** numbers?

[▢/☒/▢] ▪ 1 ▪ [2] ▪ 3 ▪ 4 ▪ [5] ▪ 6

2/6

23. Jamila says, "If you multiply two prime numbers, the answer will always be a prime number." Is she correct? Explain your answer.

[a/b/c]

24. Which of these numbers is the odd one out?

[1/2/3] ▪ [10]

25. What is the only **prime** number between 90 and 100?

[1/2/3] ▪ [97]

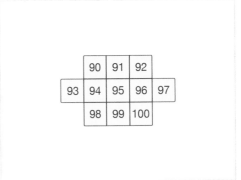

26. Derek collects football cards. The number of cards he has in the morning is a **prime** number **between 90 and 100**. On the way to school he buys 3 packets which each contain 6 cards.
When Derek gets to school, he gives Keon some cards (the **greatest prime factor of 33**).

How many cards does Derek have left?

▪ 104

27. I am a **prime** number between 70 and 100.
My **tens** digit is **greater** than my **ones** digit.
The **sum** of my digits is 10.
What number am I?

▪ 73

70	71	72	73	74	75	76
	77	78	79	80	81	
82	83	84	85	86	87	88
	89	90	91	92	93	
94	95	96	97	98	99	100

28. The two missing numbers in the equation are **prime** numbers between 2 and 60. What number goes in the **answer** box?

▪ 2

$$? \ - \ 11 \ = \ \boxed{}$$

29. Faizan adds together pairs of consecutive **composite** numbers between 50 and 55 (inclusive). How many **prime numbers** does he make?

▪ 3

30. Rule: square number - 2 = prime number.

There are five **square numbers** less than 100 which work for this rule. What is the total of these five square numbers?

▪ 168

$$\boxed{\text{square number}} \ - \ 2 \ = \ \boxed{\text{prime number}}$$

Practise Cube Numbers

Competency: Randomised 20 questions to identify and find cube numbers to 125.

Quick Search Ref: 10430

Correct: Correct. Wrong: Incorrect. Try again. Open: Thank you.

Level 1: I can identify and find square numbers.
❋ Required: 12/17   ❋ Student Navigation: off   ❋ Randomised: on

1. Is 8 a cube number?
■ [Yes] ■ No
1/2

2. Is 25 a cube number?
■ Yes ■ [No]
1/2

3. Is 64 a cube number?
■ [Yes] ■ No
1/2

4. Is 2 a cube number?
■ Yes ■ [No]
1/2

5. Is 125 a cube number?
■ [Yes] ■ No
1/2

6. Is 4 a cube number?
■ Yes ■ [No]
1/2

7. Is 100 a cube number?
■ Yes ■ [No]
1/2

8. Is 9 a cube number?
■ Yes ■ [No]
1/2

9. Is 16 a cube number?
■ Yes ■ [No]
1/2

10. Is 1 a cube number?
■ [Yes] ■ No
1/2

11. Is 50 a cube number?
■ Yes ■ [No]
1/2

12. Is 1,000 a cube number?
■ [Yes] ■ No
1/2

13. Is 27 a cube number?
■ [Yes] ■ No
1/2

14. Is 99 a cube number?
■ Yes ■ [No]
1/2

15. Is 3 a cube number?
■ Yes ■ [No]
1/2

16. Select **all** the cube numbers.
■ [1] ■ 2 ■ 4 ■ [8] ■ 16 ■ 32 ■ [64]
3/7

17. Select **all** the cube numbers.
■ [1] ■ 3 ■ 9 ■ [27] ■ 81 ■ [125] ■ 144
3/7

Level 2: I can use ^{3} notation.
❋ Required: 8/13   ❋ Student Navigation: off
❋ Randomised: on

18. What is 1^3?
1 2 3 ■ [1]

19. What is 2^3?
1 2 3 ■ [8]

20. What is 3^3?
1 2 3 ■ [27]

21. What is 4^3?
1 2 3 ■ [64]

Level 2: *cont.*

22. What is 5^3?

1
2
3   ▪ 125

23. Which cube number is between 120 and 130?

1
2
3   ▪ 125

24. Which cube number is between 0 and 5?

1
2
3   ▪ 1

25. Which cube number is between 6 and 20?

1
2
3   ▪ 8

26. Which cube number is between 20 and 40?

1
2
3   ▪ 27

27. Which cube number is between 50 and 70?

1
2
3   ▪ 64

28. $1^3 + 2^3 =$

1
2
3   ▪ 9

29. $2^3 + 10 = ?$

1
2
3   ▪ 18

30. $3^3 + 1^3 = ?$

1
2
3   ▪ 28

Practise Square Numbers

Competency: Randomised 20 questions to identify and find square numbers to 144.

Quick Search Ref: 10477

Correct: Correct.   Wrong: Incorrect. Try again.   Open: Thank you.

Level 1: I can identify and find square numbers.

✿ **Required:** 19/32   ✿ **Student Navigation:** off   ✿ **Randomised:** on

1. Is 49 a square number?
■ Yes ■ No
1/2

2. Is 2 a square number?
■ Yes ■ No
1/2

3. Is 1 a square number?
■ Yes ■ No
1/2

4. Is 25 a square number?
■ Yes ■ No
1/2

5. Is 50 a square number?
■ Yes ■ No
1/2

6. Is 100 a square number?
■ Yes ■ No
1/2

7. Is 77 a square number?
■ Yes ■ No
1/2

8. Is 31 a square number?
■ Yes ■ No
1/2

9. Is 81 a square number?
■ Yes ■ No
1/2

10. Is 12 a square number?
■ Yes ■ No
1/2

11. Is 4 a square number?
■ Yes ■ No
1/2

12. Is 5 a square number?
■ Yes ■ No
1/2

13. Is 9 a square number?
■ Yes ■ No
1/2

14. Is 10 a square number?
■ Yes ■ No
1/2

15. Is 13 a square number?
■ Yes ■ No
1/2

16. Is 16 a square number?
■ Yes ■ No
1/2

17. Is 20 a square number?
■ Yes ■ No
1/2

18. Is 30 a square number?
■ Yes ■ No
1/2

19. Is 36 a square number?
■ Yes ■ No
1/2

20. Is 43 a square number?
■ Yes ■ No
1/2

21. Is 64 a square number?
■ Yes ■ No
1/2

22. Is 55 a square number?
■ Yes ■ No
1/2

Level 1: *cont.*

23. Is 78 a square number?

■ Yes ■ No

1/2

24. Is 99 a square number?

■ Yes ■ No

1/2

25. Is 121 a square number?

■ Yes ■ No

1/2

26. Is 110 a square number?

■ Yes ■ No

1/2

27. Is 144 a square number?

■ Yes ■ No

1/2

28. Is 140 a square number?

■ Yes ■ No

1/2

29. Select **all** the square numbers.

■ 1 ■ 2 ■ 3 ■ 4 ■ 5 ■ 6 ■ 7

2/7

30. Select **all** the square numbers.

■ 9 ■ 11 ■ 13 ■ 14 ■ 16 ■ 20 ■ 25

3/7

31. Select **all** the square numbers.

■ 30 ■ 36 ■ 45 ■ 49 ■ 64 ■ 65 ■ 81

4/7

32. Select **all** the square numbers.

■ 100 ■ 110 ■ 121 ■ 125 ■ 130 ■ 140 ■ 144

3/7

Level 2: Using ² notation.

❋ **Required:** 5/12   ❋ **Student Navigation:** off
❋ **Randomised:** on

33. What is 1^2?

■ 1

34. What is 2^2?

■ 4

35. What is 3^2?

■ 9

36. What is 4^2?

■ 16

37. What is 5^2?

■ 25

38. What is 6^2?

■ 36

39. What is 7^2?

■ 49

40. What is 8^2?

■ 64

41. What is 9^2?

■ 81

42. What is 10^2?

■ 100

43. What is 11^2?

■ 121

44. What is 12^2?

■ 144

Recognise and use square numbers and cube numbers

Competency: Recognise and use square numbers and cube numbers and the notation for squared (²) and cubed (³).

Quick Search Ref: 10041

Correct: Correct.   **Wrong:** Incorrect, try again.   **Open:** Thank you.

Level 1: Understanding - Recognise square and cube numbers.

✸ **Required:** 7/10   ✸ **Student Navigation:** on   ✸ **Randomised:** off

---

1. A **square** number is found by:

1/4
- dividing a number by itself.
- multiplying a whole number by 2.
- **multiplying a whole number by itself.**
- multiplying a whole number by itself and then by itself again.

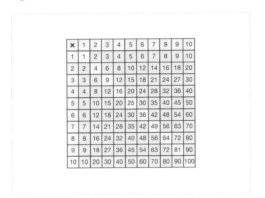

2. Which of these statements is correct?

1/4
- $7^2 = 7 \times 2$
- **$7^2 = 7 \times 7$**
- $7^2 = 7 + 7$
- $7^2 = 7 \times 7 \times 7$

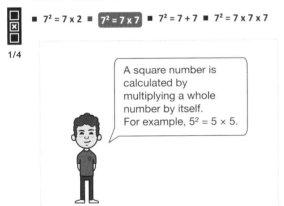

A square number is calculated by multiplying a whole number by itself. For example, $5^2 = 5 \times 5$.

3. Find the answer to **6^2**.

- **36**

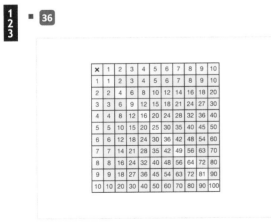

4. A **cube** number is found by:

1/4
- dividing a number by 3.
- multiplying a whole number by 3.
- multiplying a whole number by itself.
- **multiplying a whole number by itself and then by itself again.**

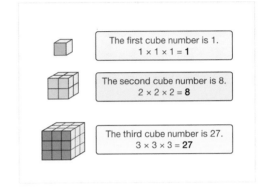

The first cube number is 1.
$1 \times 1 \times 1 = \mathbf{1}$

The second cube number is 8.
$2 \times 2 \times 2 = \mathbf{8}$

The third cube number is 27.
$3 \times 3 \times 3 = \mathbf{27}$

5. Which of these statements is true?

1/4
- $9^3 = 9 \times 3$
- $9^3 = 9 \times 9$
- **$9^3 = 9 \times 9 \times 9$**
- $9^3 = 9 + 9 + 9$

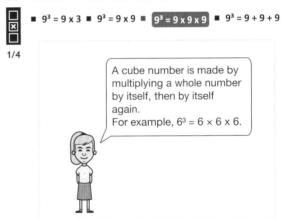

A cube number is made by multiplying a whole number by itself, then by itself again. For example, $6^3 = 6 \times 6 \times 6$.

6. What is **3 cubed**?

- **27**

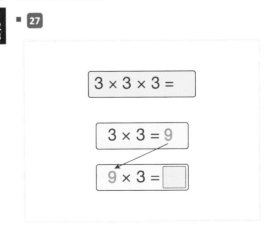

$3 \times 3 \times 3 =$

$3 \times 3 = 9$

$9 \times 3 = \boxed{}$

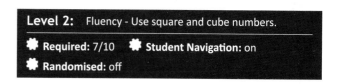

7. The answer to 8^2 is __.

 ▪ 64

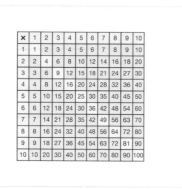

8. Select the statement which is true.

▪ $7^3 = 7 \times 3$ ▪ $7^3 = 7 \times 7$ ▪ $7^3 = 7 + 7 + 7$ ▪ $7^3 = 7 \times 7 \times 7$

1/4

A cube number is made by multiplying a whole number by itself, then by itself again.
For example, $6^3 = 6 \times 6 \times 6$.

9. Find the answer to 2^3.

▪ 8

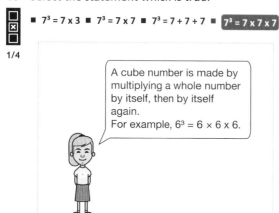

$2 \times 2 \times 2 =$

$2 \times 2 = 4$

$4 \times 2 = \boxed{}$

10. Select the statement which is correct.

▪ $5^2 = 5 \times 5 \times 5$ ▪ $5^2 = 5 \times 2$ ▪ $5^2 = 5 \times 5$ ▪ $5^2 = 5 + 5$

1/4

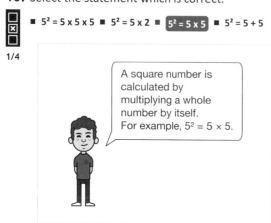

A square number is calculated by multiplying a whole number by itself.
For example, $5^2 = 5 \times 5$.

11. Which two square numbers add together to equal 74?

2/4 ▪ 5^2 ▪ 6^2 ▪ 7^2 ▪ 8^2

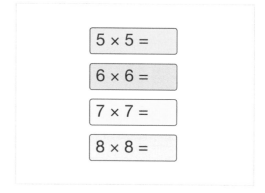

$5 \times 5 =$

$6 \times 6 =$

$7 \times 7 =$

$8 \times 8 =$

12. Find the **area** of a square, in square centimetres, where the sides all measure 9 centimetres.

Area = length x width.

▪ 81

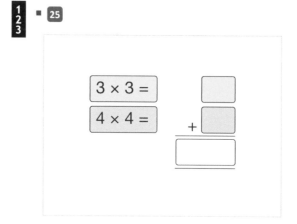

9 cm

9 cm

13. Find the answer to $3^2 + 4^2 =$.

▪ 25

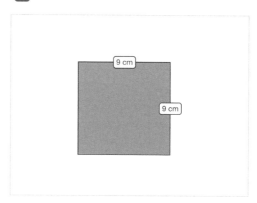

$3 \times 3 =$

$4 \times 4 =$

$+$

Level 2: *cont.*

14. Select the symbol which makes the following statement **true**:

5^2 __ 11^2.

1/3

■ < ■ > ■ =

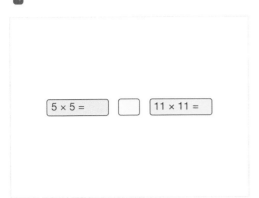

15. Jim highlights all square and cube numbers in a number grid between 1 and 100. Which **two numbers** has he forgotten to highlight?

2/5   ■ 24 ■ 25 ■ 26 ■ 27 ■ 28

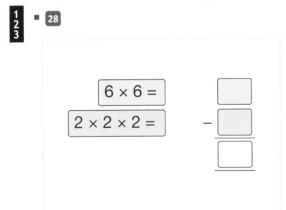

16. Complete the equation: $6^2 - 2^3$ = __.

■ 28

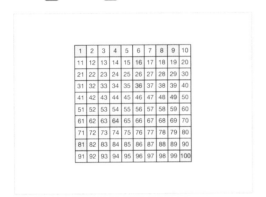

17. All sides of a square measure 7 metres. How many square metres is its **area**?

Area = length x width.

■ 49

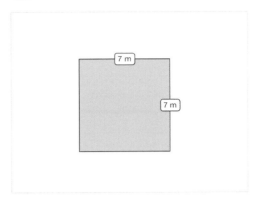

18. Select the pair of square numbers which **equal 20** when added together.

■ 1^2 ■ 2^2 ■ 3^2 ■ 4^2

2/4

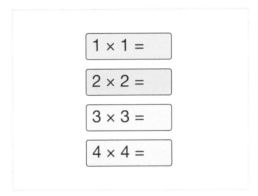

19. Complete the equation: $5^3 - 3^2$ = __.

■ 116

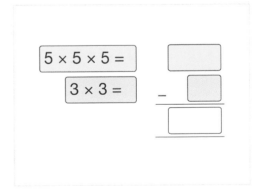

Level 2: *cont.*

20. Select the symbol which makes the following statement **true**:

7^2 ___ 4^3.

1/3

■ < ■ > ■ =

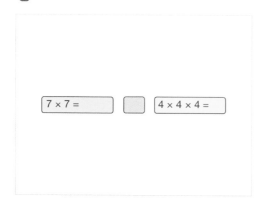

Level 3:   Reasoning - Comparing square and cube numbers.

✹ **Required:** 5/5   ✹ **Student Navigation:** on
✹ **Randomised:** off

21. Select the cube number that is also a **square number.**

■ 2^3 ■ 3^3 ■ 4^3 ■ 5^3

1/4

22. Pat is thinking of a number between 1 and 100. His number is **10 more** than one square number and **7 less** than another. What **number** is Pat thinking of?
The answer is **not** a square number.

■ 74

23. Find each **square or cube number** and sort from the **lowest to the highest** value.

 ■ 5^2 ■ 3^3 ■ 7^2 ■ 4^3 ■ 9^2 ■ 5^3

24. Orla says, *"The answer to 9 x 9^2 is the same as 9^3."*

Is Orla correct? Explain your answer.

25. Michael says, *"The answer to $7^2 + 8^2$ is the same as the answer to 15^2."*

Is Michael correct? Explain your answer.

Level 4:   Problem Solving - Using algebra to find square and cube numbers.

✹ **Required:** 5/5   ✹ **Student Navigation:** on
✹ **Randomised:** off

26. Fabrice's age is a **cube number**. Next year, his age will be a square number. How old is he?

■ 8

27. To find the **area** of a square, you multiply the **length** of one of the sides by the **width**.

This can be shown by the formula:
$A = lw$.

For this square, what is the width in metres?

■ 7

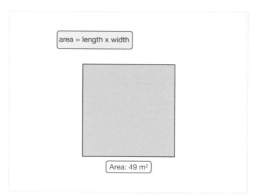

28. *a* stands for a missing whole number. a^2 means *a* x *a*.

$a^2 + 6^2 = 100$.

What is the value of **a**?

■ 8

29. What is the smallest number which - when squared - gives a three digit answer?

■ 10

30. The answer to *2 x b, then add 3* is a **square number**.

b is a missing number between **20 and 30**.

Find the value of *b*.

■ 23

Mathematics

Measurement

Metric and Imperial

Area and Perimeter

Length

Mass

Volume and Capacity

Time

Compare and Convert Imperial and Metric Units

Competency: Understand and use approximate equivalences between metric units and common imperial units such as inches, pounds and pints.

Quick Search Ref: 10071

Correct: Correct.   Wrong: Incorrect, try again.   Open: Thank you.

Level 1: Understanding - Recognise imperial units and simple one-to-one conversions.

⚙ **Required:** 7/10   ⚙ **Student Navigation:** on   ⚙ **Randomised:** off

1. Which **three** are imperial units of measure?

 ▪ inches ▪ feet ▪ kilograms ▪ centimetres ▪ pints

3/5

2. Which **two** imperial units are used to measure length?

▪ inches ▪ pounds ▪ pints ▪ feet ▪ stones

2/5

Imperial unit of measure	Approximate metric equivalent
1 inch	2.5 cm
1 pound	0.45 kg (approx 0.5 kg)
1 pint	570 ml (approx 0.5 l)
1 foot	30 cm
1 stone	6.5 kg

3. Which **two** imperial units are used to measure mass?

▪ inches ▪ pounds ▪ pints ▪ feet ▪ stones

2/5

Imperial unit of measure	Approximate metric equivalent
1 inch	2.5 cm
1 pound	0.45 kg (approx 0.5 kg)
1 pint	570 ml (approx 0.5 l)
1 foot	30 cm
1 stone	6.5 kg

4. Which imperial unit is used to measure capacity?

▪ inches ▪ pounds ▪ pints ▪ feet ▪ stones

1/5

Imperial unit of measure	Approximate metric equivalent
1 inch	2.5 cm
1 pound	0.45 kg (approx 0.5 kg)
1 pint	570 ml (approx 0.5 l)
1 foot	30 cm
1 stone	6.5 kg

5. One inch is approximately how many centimetres?

▪ 1 cm ▪ 2.5 cm ▪ 5 cm ▪ 10 cm

1/4

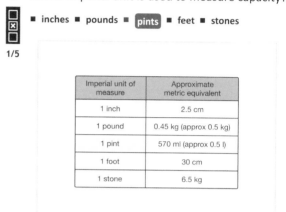

6. One pint is approximately how many litres?

▪ 0.5 litres ▪ 1 litre ▪ 2 litres ▪ 5 litres

1/4

Level 1: cont.

7. One foot is is approximately how many centimetres?

■ 10 cm ■ 30 cm ■ 60 cm ■ 100 cm

1/4

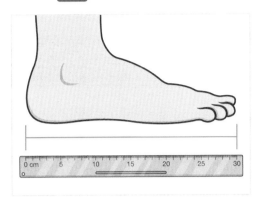

8. One pound is approximately how many kilograms?

■ 0.5 kg ■ 1 kg ■ 5 kg ■ 7 kg

1/4

9. One stone is approximately how many kilograms?

■ 1 kg ■ 5 kg ■ 6.5 kg ■ 10 kg

1/4

10. Which statement is correct?

■ One pint is approximately 2 litres.
■ One inch is approximately 2.5 centimetres.
■ One stone is approximately 10 kilograms.
■ One foot is approximately 10 centimetres.

1/4

Level 2: Fluency - Convert between and order imperial and metric units of measure.

✿ **Required:** 7/10   ✿ **Student Navigation:** on
✿ **Randomised:** off

11. Approximately how many inches are in ten cm?

1
2
3   ■ 4

? inches = 10 centimetres

12. Six pounds is approximately how many kilograms?

1
2
3   ■ 3

6 pounds = ? kilograms

13. How many full feet are there in one metre?

1
2
3   ■ 3

? feet = 1 metre

© Learning by Questions Ltd.   199   Ref:10071   Compare and Convert Imperial and Metr...

14. Four stone is roughly _____ kilograms.

 ▪ 26

4 stone = ? kilograms

15. which symbol is missing from this statement?
5 kilograms _____ 8 pounds

1/3   ▪ < ▪ **>** ▪ =

5 kilograms ? 8 pounds

16. Order the masses by weight, starting with the lightest.

↑
↓   ▪ 5 pounds ▪ 3 kilograms ▪ 1 stone ▪ 10 kilograms

17. Order the lengths by size, starting with the shortest.

↑
↓   ▪ 5 centimetres ▪ 10 centimetres ▪ 5 inches ▪ 1 foot

18. On average, there are eight pints of blood in the human body. Approximately how many litres is this?

▪ 4 ▪ 4.5

19. A fish tank can hold ten litres of water. Approximately how many pints is this?

▪ 20

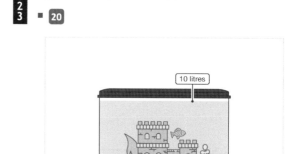

10 litres

20. Which symbol is missing from this statement?
20 centimetres _____ 10 inches

1/3   ▪ **<** ▪ > ▪ =

20 centimetres ? 10 inches

Level 3:   Reasoning - Use addition and subtraction to convert between multiple units of metric and imperial measure.

✹ **Required:** 8/8   ✹ **Student Navigation:** on
✹ **Randomised:** off

21. Amy says, "fifteen centimetres is approximately six inches". Is she correct? Explain your answer.

a
b
c

15 centimetres is approximately six inches.

Level 3: *cont.*

22. What is the approximate sum of the following measurements in **centimetres**?
3 inches, 35 centimetres, 0.2 metres

- 62.5

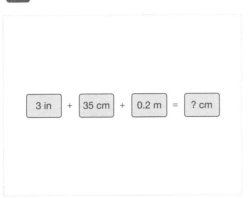

23. What is the sum of the following masses in **kilograms**?
14 pounds, 3 stone, 4 kilograms and 1,500 grams

- 32 - 31.5

24. Kay's motorbike has a fuel tank capacity of 18.5 litres. Jimmy's motorbike has a fuel tank capacity of 40 pints. Approximately how much more fuel does Jimmy's motorbike hold than Kay's in pints?

- 3

25. Aston says, "Ten pounds is heavier than one stone." Is he correct? Explain your answer.

a
b
c

26. A calf weighs 250 kilograms and a lamb weighs 100 pounds. If a farm trailer carries one calf and two lambs, what is the approximate mass it is carrying in **kilograms**?
Include the units kg (kilograms) in your answer.

- 350 kg - 350 kilograms

27. Three children throw paper planes.
Olivia throws her plane three feet.
Jade throws her plane 12 inches.
Jack throws his plane 20 centimetres.
1/3   Who throws their plane the furthest?

- Olivia - Jade - Jack

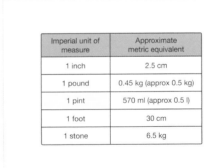

Imperial unit of measure	Approximate metric equivalent
1 inch	2.5 cm
1 pound	0.45 kg (approx 0.5 kg)
1 pint	570 ml (approx 0.5 l)
1 foot	30 cm
1 stone	6.5 kg

28. Three children are weighed.
Leanne has a mass of six stone.
Kyle has a mass of 35 kilograms.
John has a mass of 60 pounds.
What is their total combined mass in **kilograms**?
Include the units kg (kilograms) in your answer.

- 104 kg - 104 kilograms

Imperial unit of measure	Approximate metric equivalent
1 inch	2.5 cm
1 pound	0.45 kg (approx 0.5 kg)
1 pint	570 ml (approx 0.5 l)
1 foot	30 cm
1 stone	6.5 kg

29. A bakery uses 4.5 kilograms of butter and 6
pounds of sugar a day. In **pounds**, what is the
approximate combined mass of butter and sugar
used in a 3 day period?
Don't include the units in your answer.

▪ 45

30. A garden container is filled with 25 litres of water.
Rain water adds seven pints to the container. Jane
then uses 5,500 millilitres to water her plants.
How many **pints** of water are left in the container?
Don't include the units in your answer.

▪ 46

31. A supermarket sells potatoes for 70 pence per
kilogram. The local grocery sells potatoes for 26
pence per pound. Approximately how much
cheaper are potatoes in the local grocery per
kilogram **in pence**?
Include the units p (pence) in your answer.

▪ 18p ▪ 18 pence

32. Harry buys four feet of ribbon.
Julia buys twice as much.
Angela buys 5 inches more than Julia.
In **centimetres**, how much ribbon does Angela
buy?
Don't include the units in your answer.

▪ 252.5

33. A small container can hold a mass of 56 kilograms
and is three-quarters full. An item with a mass of
40 pounds is removed from the container and a
further 2 kilograms of items fall out when the
container is moved.
What is the approximate mass of the items
remaining in the container to the **nearest stone**?
Don't include the units in your answer.

▪ 3

Calculate the Perimeter of Composite Rectilinear Shapes

Competency: Measure and calculate the perimeter of composite rectilinear shapes in cm and m.

Quick Search Ref: 10048

Correct: Correct.   **Wrong:** Incorrect, try again.   **Open:** Thank you.

Level 1:   Understanding - Calculating the perimeter of regular and composite shapes with no missing lengths.

✹ **Required:** 6/8   ✹ **Student Navigation:** on   ✹ **Randomised:** off

---

1. To find the perimeter of a rectilinear shape you:

   1/3
   - Multiply the length by the width.
   - Add the length and the width.
   - Add the lengths of all the sides.

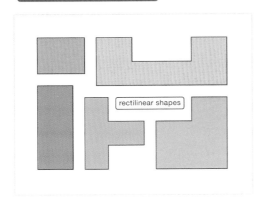

2. The perimeter of the square is ___ centimetres.

   - 28

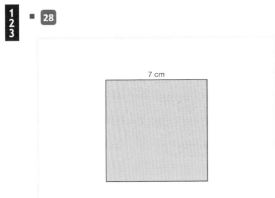

3. Harry draws a square on a sheet of 1 cm grid paper.

   1/4

   What is the perimeter of the square?

   - 12 cm² ■ 6 cm ■ **12 cm** ■ 9 cm²

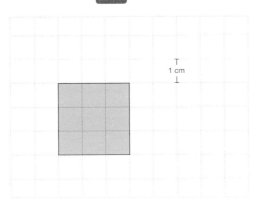

4. The perimeter of the rectangle is ___ metres.

   1 2 3
   - 32

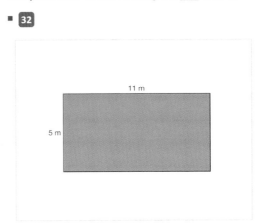

5. The perimeter of the **composite shape** is ___ metres.

   1 2 3
   - 48

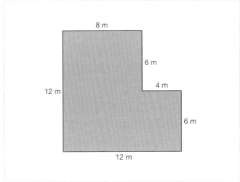

6. The perimeter of the **composite shape** is ___ centimetres.

   1 2 3
   - 52

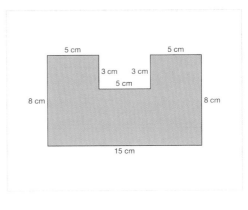

Level 1: *cont.*

7. The perimeter of the **composite shape** is ___
metres.

1
2
3

■ **44**

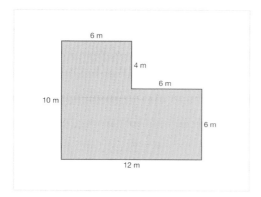

8. The perimeter of the **composite shape** is ___
metres.

1
2
3

■ **40**

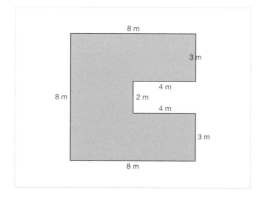

Level 2: Fluency - Composite shapes with missing
lengths and converting units.

✱ **Required:** 6/8   ✱ **Student Navigation:** on
✱ **Randomised:** off

9. The perimeter of the composite shape is
___metres.

1
2
3

■ **30**

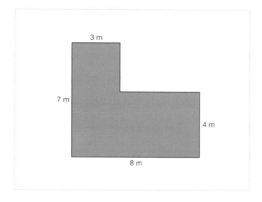

10. What is the perimeter of the composite shape?
a
b
c
Include the units m (metres) in your answer.

■ **48 m** ■ **48 metres.**

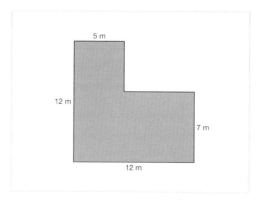

11. What is the perimeter of the composite rectilinear
a
b
c
shape?
Include the units cm (centimetres) in your answer.

■ **36 cm** ■ **36 centimetres**

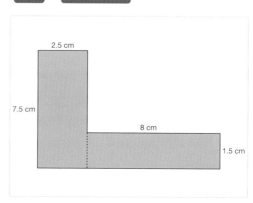

12. What is the perimeter of the composite rectilinear
a
b
c
shape in **metres**?
Include the units m (metres) in your answer.

■ **20 m** ■ **20 metres**

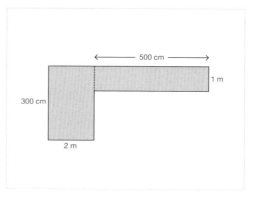

Level 2: *cont.*

13. What is the perimeter of the composite shape?
a
b   *Include the units m (metres) in your answer.*
c
   ■ 36 metres ■ 36 m

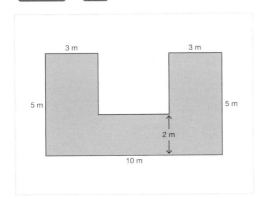

14. The **net** is made up of squares that each have a
a   side length of five centimetres.
b   What is the perimeter of the net?
c   *Include the units cm (centimetres) in your answer.*

   ■ 70 cm ■ 70 centimetres

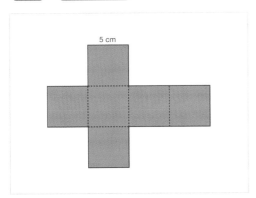

15. What is the perimeter of the composite shape?
a   *Include the units m (metres) in your answer.*
b
c   ■ 104 m ■ 104 metres

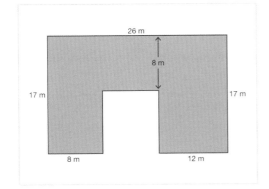

16. The net is made up of squares that each have a
a   side length of nine centimetres.
b   What is the perimeter of the net?
c   *Include the units cm (centimetres) in your answer.*

   ■ 126 centimetres ■ 126 cm

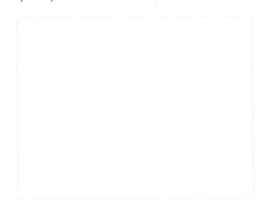

Level 3: Reasoning - Finding perimeter of composite
        rectilinear shapes in cm and m.

✿ **Required:** 5/5   ✿ **Student Navigation:** on
✿ **Randomised:** off

17. Order these shapes by their perimeter, starting
   with the **shortest**.

   ■ shape B ■ shape D ■ shape C ■ shape A

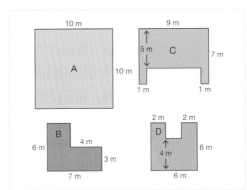

18. There are three rectilinear shapes with perimeters
a   of 12 cm, 20 cm and 16 cm.
b   The three shapes are joined together to create a
c   **composite rectilinear shape.**
   How do you know the perimeter of the composite
   rectilinear shape will measure less than 48 cm?
   Explain your answer.

Level 3: *cont.*

19. Shapes A, B and C are squares. Shape C has a
a perimeter of 32 centimetres and its length is twice
b the size of shape B. The length of shape B is twice
c the size of shape A.
All three shapes are joined together to make a
new shape. What is the perimeter of the
composite shape?
Include the units cm (centimetres) in your answer.

▪ 44 cm ▪ 44 centimetres

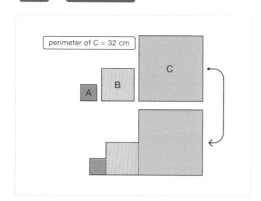

20. What is the length of the rectangle?
a *Include the units m (metres) in your answer.*
b
c ▪ 24 m ▪ 24 metres

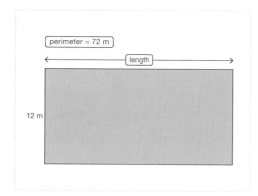

21. In the composite rectilinear shape, side x
a measures 3 metres.
b Explain how you would calculate this
c measurement.

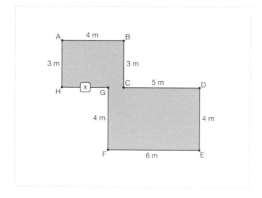

© Learning by Questions Ltd.   206   Ref:10048   Calculate the Perimeter of Composite R...

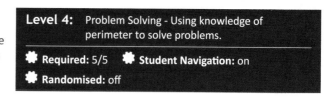

Level 4: Problem Solving - Using knowledge of
perimeter to solve problems.

✦ **Required:** 5/5   ✦ **Student Navigation:** on
✦ **Randomised:** off

22. In their PE lesson, the children in Year 5 are going
a to run around the perimeter of the playground
b and attached sports field.
c How many metres will they each run?
Include the units m (metres) in your answer.

▪ 336 m ▪ 336 metres

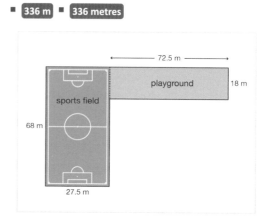

23. Toby's mum and dad are putting fairy lights around
a the outsides of three windows for Christmas.
b Each pane is 20 centimetres in length and each
c window has four panes.
How many centimetres of fairy lights do they need
to decorate all **three** windows?
Include the units cm (centimetres) in your answer.

▪ 480 centimetres ▪ 480 cm

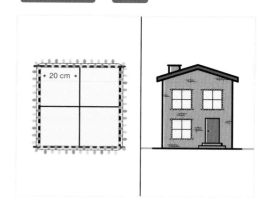

Level 4: *cont.*

24. At a fun run, Jack and Sarah are putting tape
a around the course so that everybody knows where
b to run. They have three boxes of tape: one
c containing 3.2 kilometres, one containing 900
metres of, and the other containing 3.12
kilometres.
How many **metres** of tape will they have left over?
Include the units m (metres) in your answer.

■ **20 metres** ■ **20 m**

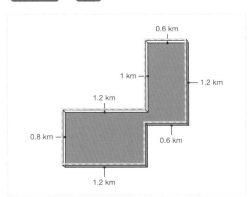

25. Use the following clues to find the perimeter of
shape A and shape B:
The perimeter of the composite shape is 24
metres.
1/5 The length of shape A is double the length of
shape B.
The width of each shape is the same.
Shape A is a rectangle.
Shape B is a square.

■ shape A = 20 m, shape B = 10 m
■ shape A = 16 m, shape B = 12 m
■ shape A = 12 m, shape B = 18 m
■ **shape A = 18 m, shape B = 12 m**
■ shape A = 16 m, shape B = 8 m

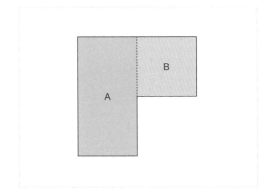

26. The area of the rectangle is 64 m² and the
a perimeter is 40 m. What is the length of the
b rectangle?
c *Include the units m (metres) in your answer.*

■ **16 m** ■ **16 metres**

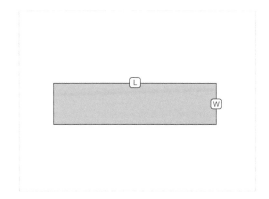

Find and compare the area of rectangles and squares

Competency: Calculate and compare the area of rectangles and squares including using standard units, square centimetres (cm²) and square metres (m²) and estimate the area of irregular shapes.

Quick Search Ref: 10117

Correct: Correct.   Wrong: Incorrect, try again.   Open: Thank you.

Level 1: Understanding - Finding the area of squares and rectangles.

✿ **Required:** 7/10   ✿ **Student Navigation:** on   ✿ **Randomised:** off

1. Which of the following statements describes **area**?

1/3
- ■ Area is the total distance around a 2D shape.
- ■ **Area is a measure of how much space there is on the surface of a 2D shape.**
- ■ Area is the amount that something can hold.

2. To find the area of a rectangle or square you need to perform which of the following calculations?

1/4
- ■ length + width ■ length ÷ width ■ **length x width**
- ■ length - width

3. **Area** is measured in:

1/4
- ■ Centimetres (cm) ■ Cubic units (³) ■ Metres (m)
- ■ **Square units (²)**

4. What is the area of the rectangle?

1/4
- ■ 16 cm ■ **15 cm²** ■ 15 cm ■ 8 cm²

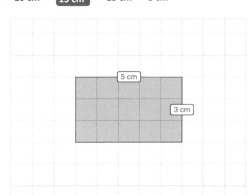

5. What is the area of the square?

1/3
- ■ 12 cm ■ **9 cm²** ■ 6 cm²

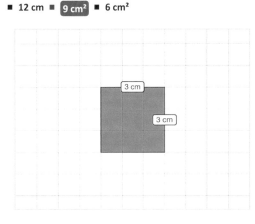

6. The area of the rectangle is _____ cm².

- ■ **70**

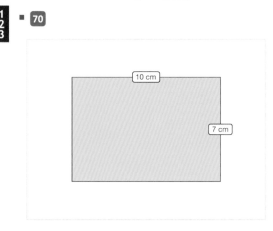

7. The area of the square is _____ cm².

- ■ **36**

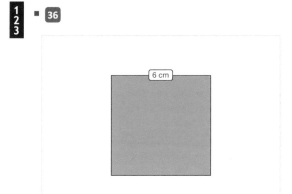

8. The area of the rectangle is _____ m².

- ■ **36**

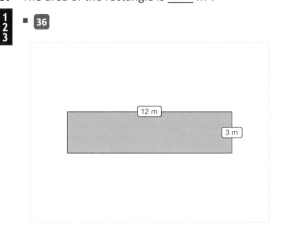

Level 1: *cont.*

9. The area of the rectangle is _____ m².

$\frac{1}{2}$ ▪ **48**

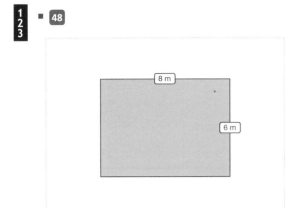

10. The area of the rectangle is _____ cm².

$\frac{1}{2}$ ▪ **54**

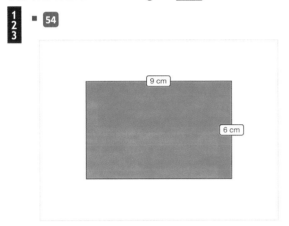

Level 2: Fluency - Comparing and estimating the area of squares, rectangles and composite shapes.

✿ **Required:** 7/10   ✿ **Student Navigation:** on
✿ **Randomised:** off

11. Select **three** shapes on the centimetre squared paper which have an area of 12 square centimetres.

3/5 ▪ [Shape A] ▪ Shape B ▪ Shape C ▪ [Shape D] ▪ [Shape E]

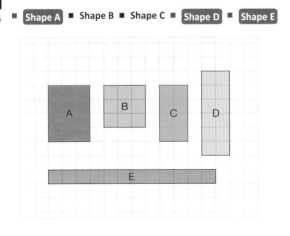

12. Find the area of each shape, then order them, **smallest** area first.

↑↓ ▪ [Shape B] ▪ [Shape E] ▪ [Shape A] ▪ [Shape D]
   ▪ [Shape C]

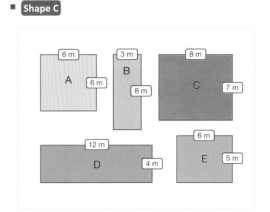

13. **Estimate** the area of the rectangle in square centimetres.

$\frac{1}{2}$ ▪ **18**

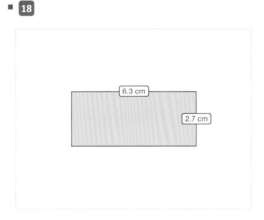

14. Calculate the **total area** of the composite rectilinear shape in square metres.

$\frac{1}{2}$ ▪ **28**

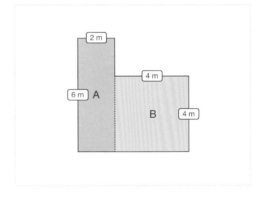

15. **Estimate** the area of the rectangle in square metres.

 ▪ 56

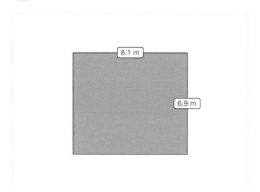

16. Select **two** shapes which have an area of 18 square centimetres.

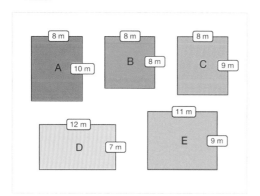

2/5

▪ Shape A ▪ Shape B ▪ Shape C ▪ Shape D ▪ Shape E

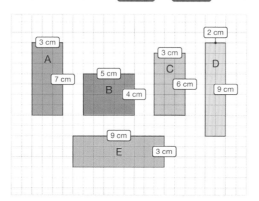

17. Find the area of each shape, then order them, **smallest** area first.

▪ Shape B ▪ Shape C ▪ Shape A ▪ Shape D
▪ Shape E

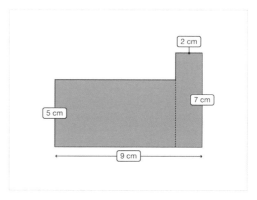

18. Calculate the **total area** of the composite rectilinear shape in square metres.

▪ 122

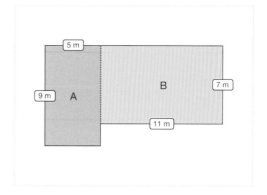

19. Calculate the **total area** of the composite rectilinear shape in square centimetres.

▪ 49

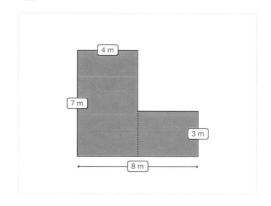

20. Find the **total area** of the composite rectilinear shape in square metres.

▪ 40

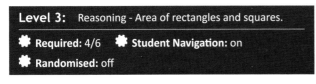

Level 3: Reasoning - Area of rectangles and squares.

✹ **Required:** 4/6   ✹ **Student Navigation:** on
✹ **Randomised:** off

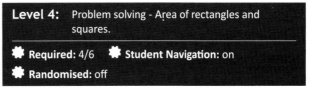

Level 4: Problem solving - Area of rectangles and squares.

✹ **Required:** 4/6   ✹ **Student Navigation:** on
✹ **Randomised:** off

21. The rectangle has a perimeter of 4,200 centimetres and width of seven metres.

What is the **surface area** of the rectangle in **square metres**?

- 98

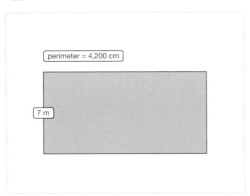

22. Sam says, "The area of a square will always be a square number."

Is he correct? Explain your answer.

23. A square has an area of 4 square metres. What is its area in **square centimetres**?

- 100,000 ■ 40,000 ■ 200 ■ 800 ■ 400

1/5

24. A page in a sticker book has a length and width of 12 centimetres and each sticker has an area of four square centimetres. What is the maximum number of stickers you could stick on one page?

- 36

25. Erica says, "The area of a rectangle will never be a square number."

Is she correct? Explain your answer.

26. A square has an area of 25 square metres. What is its area in **square centimetres**?

- 250,000 ■ 500 ■ 2,000 ■ 2,500

1/4

27. Highbury Primary School is having the netball court resurfaced. The court is 30 metres long and 15 metres wide.

It costs **£20.00** to resurface **one square metre** of the court. How much, in pounds, will it cost to resurface the full court?

- 9000

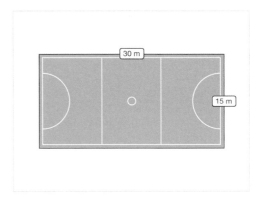

28. Diagram (a) shows a bathroom tile, which has the design of an **equilateral triangle** within a square. The tile has an area of **81 square centimetres**.

Diagram (b) shows four of the tiles laid out on the floor.

In **centimetres**, what is the **perimeter of the red shape** in diagram (b)?

- 72

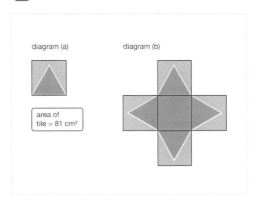

29. Salma's mum is decorating her living room and needs to buy some wallpaper for one wall. The wall measures five metres by three metres.

The wallpaper is sold in rolls of **two square metres**. How many **full rolls** will she need to buy to decorate the wall?

- 8

30. Highbury Primary School is having a gymnastics competition and needs to buy new mats to cover the gym floor.

What is the **total cost** of the gym mats in pounds if each mat costs £2.50?

- 80

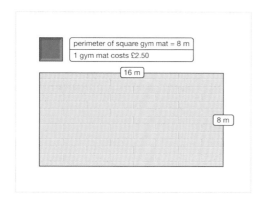

31. Jack puts a poster for his new band in the window of the local post office.

The window measures eight metres wide and has a length of six metres. The poster covers one quarter of the window.

What is the **area** of the poster in **square metres**?

- 12

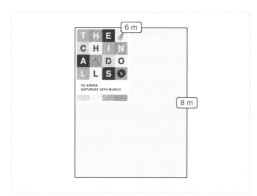

32. Bacup Cricket Club is having its field returfed for the new season.

The field is 60 metres wide and 140 metres long. The wicket area, which is **3 metres** wide and **20 metres** long, **does not** need to be returfed

If one square metre of turf costs **£2.00**, what will be the **total cost** in pounds to returf the cricket field excluding the wicket area?

- 16680

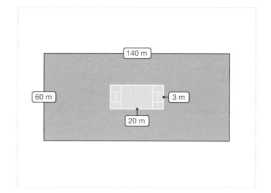

Convert Units of Measure: km and m, cm and m, cm and mm

Competency: Convert between different units of metric measure.

Quick Search Ref: 10029

Correct: Correct.   Wrong: Incorrect, try again.   Open: Thank you.

Level 1: Understanding - Use methods for converting between different units of metric measure.

✾ **Required:** 7/10   ✾ **Student Navigation:** on   ✾ **Randomised:** off

---

1. Arrange these metric units in ascending order according to size (smallest first).

- millimetre ▪ centimetre ▪ metre ▪ kilometre

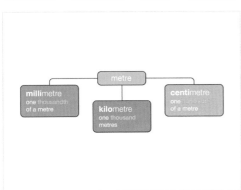

2. How many millimetres are there in one centimetre?

▪ **10** ▪ 100 ▪ 1000

1/3

3. How many centimetres are there in one metre?

 ▪ 10 ▪ **100** ▪ 1000

1/3

4. How many metres are there in one kilometre?

 ▪ 10 ▪ 100 ▪ **1,000**

1/3

5. To convert from centimetres to millimetres . . .

 ▪ **multiply by 10.** ▪ divide by 10. ▪ multiply by 100.
▪ divide by 100.

1/4

6. To convert from metres to centimetres . . .

 ▪ divide by 100. ▪ **multiply by 100.** ▪ divide by 1,000.
▪ multiply by 1,000.

1/4

---

7. To convert from kilometres to metres . . .

- multiply by 100. ■ divide by 100. ■ **multiply by 1,000.**
- divide by 1,000.

1/4

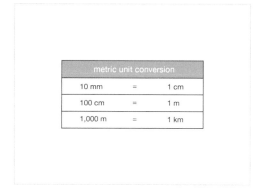

8. To convert from millimetres to centimetres . . .

- multiply by 10. ■ **divide by 10.** ■ multiply by 100.
- divide by 100.

1/4

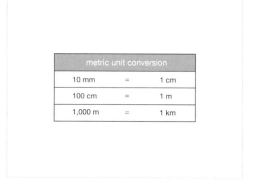

9. To convert from centimetres to metres . . .

- **divide by 100.** ■ multiply by 100. ■ divide by 1,000.
- multiply by 1,000.

1/4

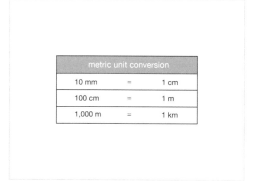

10. When converting from **metres** to **kilometres** you:

- multiply by 100. ■ divide by 100. ■ multiply by 1,000.
- **divide by 1,000.**

1/4

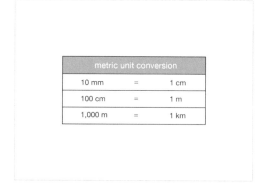

Level 2: Fluency - Convert between units of measure for values with up to 3 decimal places.

✹ **Required:** 8/8   ✹ **Student Navigation:** on
✹ **Randomised:** off

11. 65 centimetres is equal to 605 millimetres.

- true ■ **false**

1/2

12. A flower is 200 mm tall. What does it measure in **centimetres**?
Include the units cm (centimetres) in your answer.

- **20 cm**

13. Find the missing conversion to complete the table.

- **0.8**

centimetres (cm)	metres (m)
50	0.5
30	0.3
80	?
150	1.5

14. A farmer's fence is 2.542 kilometres long. What does it measure in metres?

- 25.42 m ■ **2,542 m** ■ 0.2542 m ■ 254.2 m

1/4

15. Tara's hair is 45 cm long. Her friend's hair is 37 cm long. How much longer is Tara's hair in metres?
Include the units m (metres) in your answer.

- **0.08 m**

Level 2: cont.

16. Cara is 1.22 m tall. Her sister is 32 cm taller. How tall is Cara's sister in centimetres?
Include the units cm (centimetres) in your answer.

a
b
c

- 154 cm

17. Rubik the robot can fly a distance of 1,200 m. Neera the robot can fly a distance of 800 m. How much further can Rubik fly than Neera in kilometers?
Include the unit km (kilometres) in your answer.

a
b
c

- 0.4 km

18. A large mat measures 1.2 m and a small mat measures 78 cm. When they are joined together, what is the combined length of the mats in centimetres?
Include the unit cm (centimetres) in your answer.

a
b
c

- 198 cm

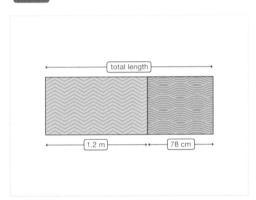

Level 3: Reasoning - Convert units of measure.

✿ **Required:** 6/6   ✿ **Student Navigation:** on
✿ **Randomised:** off

19. Which of the following sequences is ordered correctly from the longest measurement to smallest?

□
☒
□

1/3   - 0.4 km, 4 m, 3¾ m, 305 cm   - 305 cm, 0.4 km, 4 m, 3¾ m
- 4 m, 0.4 km, 305 cm, 3¾ m

20. Choose **two** calculations that equal 0.861 km.

□
☒
□

2/5

- 8.61 m × 10   - 0.86 km + 1 m   - 0.8 km + 61 km
- 1 km - 139 m   - 0.87 km - 1 m

21. What is the missing value in this equation?
43 cm + 1.08 m = 23 mm + _____ m

1
2
3

- 1.487

22. A tower of ten identical blocks is 400 centimetres tall. If three of the blocks fall down, how tall will the tower be in metres?
Include the units m (metres) in your answer.

a
b
c

- 2.8 m

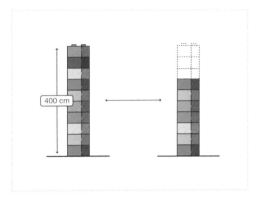

23. What symbol is missing from this equation?
24 mm ___ 3 cm - 6 mm

□
☒
□

1/3   - < ■ > ■ =

24. The table shows the average length of gardens in three cities. How many centimetres longer is the average garden in Preston than in London?
Include the units cm (centimetres) in your answer.

a
b
c

- 185 cm

average garden length	
city	length (m)
London	6.52
Edinburgh	7.13
Preston	8.37

Level 4: Problem Solving - Converting units of measure using the four operations.

✿ **Required:** 5/5   ✿ **Student Navigation:** on
✿ **Randomised:** off

25. At the seaside, a ride in a horse-drawn carriage costs £3.50 for 500 m. What is the cost in pounds to travel for 2 km?

1
2
3

- 14

26. Four children are comparing how far they live from school. Who lives the furthest away from school?

1/4

■ Sean ■ John ■ Ella ■ Ruth

27. A carpet shop sold three carpets on Saturday morning.
The first carpet measured 2.5 m in length.
The second carpet was twice as long as the first.
The third carpet measured 400 mm less than the second.
How many metres of carpet did the shop sell?
Include the units m (metres) in your answer.

a
b
c

■ **12.1 m**

28. Zoe needs a large piece of card for an art project.
She already has a 0.6 metre piece of card and a 45 centimetre piece of card. She decides to join them together by overlapping them. When joined together, the total length of the card is 90 centimetres. By how many centimetres do the pieces of card overlap?
Include the units cm (centimetres) in your answer.

a
b
c

■ **15 cm**

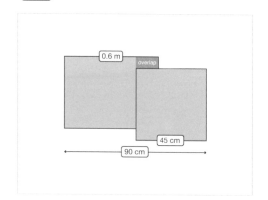

29. Jane is making a barrier by placing objects from her garden side by side. She has two bricks, one fishing rod, two bats and three skipping ropes. What is the longest barrier she can make?
Give your answer to the nearest metre. Include the units m (metres) in your answer.

a
b
c

■ **12 m**

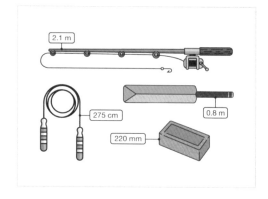

Convert Units of Measure: g and kg, l and ml

Competency: Convert between different units of metric measure (g and kg, l and ml).

Quick Search Ref: 10144

Correct: Correct.   **Wrong:** Incorrect, try again.   **Open:** Thank you.

Level 1:   Understanding - Methods for converting and identifying units of measure.

⚙ **Required:** 7/10   ⚙ **Student Navigation:** on   ⚙ **Randomised:** off

1. How many grams are in one kilogram?

▪ 10 ▪ 100 ▪ **1,000**

1/3

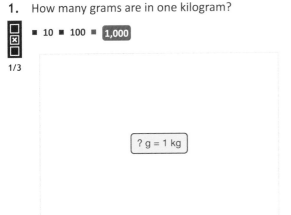

? g = 1 kg

2. How many millilitres are in one litre?

▪ 10 ▪ 100 ▪ **1,000**

1/3

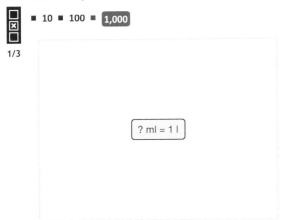

? ml = 1 l

3. To convert from kilograms to grams, . . .

▪ multiply by 100. ▪ divide by 100. ▪ **multiply by 1,000.**
▪ divide by 1,000.

1/4

metric unit conversion		
1 kg	=	1,000 g
1 l	=	1,000 ml

4. To convert from litres to millilitres, . . .

▪ **multiply by 1,000.** ▪ divide by 1,000. ▪ multiply by 100.
▪ divide by 100.

1/4

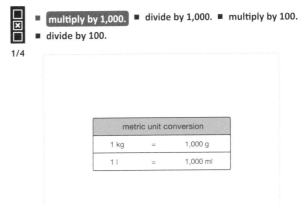

metric unit conversion		
1 kg	=	1,000 g
1 l	=	1,000 ml

5. To convert from grams to kilograms, . . .

▪ multiply by 100. ▪ divide by 100. ▪ multiply by 1,000.
▪ **divide by 1,000.**

1/4

metric unit conversion		
1,000 g	=	1 kg
1,000 ml	=	1 l

6. To convert from millilitres to litres, . . .

▪ **divide by 1,000.** ▪ multiply by 1,000. ▪ multiply by 100.
▪ divide by 100.

1/4

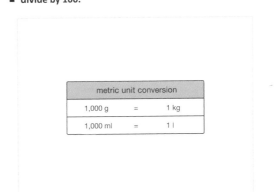

metric unit conversion		
1,000 g	=	1 kg
1,000 ml	=	1 l

Level 1: *cont.*

7. Which unit of measure are you likely to see on a small carton of apple juice?

■ litres ■ kilograms ■ millilitres ■ grams

1/4

8. Which unit of measure are you likely to see on a bag of sugar?

■ litres ■ kilograms ■ millilitres ■ grams

1/4

9. Which unit of measure are you likely to see on a small piece of cheese?

■ litres ■ kilograms ■ millilitres ■ grams

1/4

10. Which unit of measure are you likely to see on a large bottle of water?

■ litres ■ kilograms ■ millilitres ■ grams

1/4

Level 2: Fluency - Converting and ordering units of measure.

✱ **Required:** 10/10   ✱ **Student Navigation:** on
✱ **Randomised:** off

11. What is the amount shown in litres?
Include the units ml (millilitres) in your answer.

■ 0.35 ml

12. What is the weight shown converted to **grams**?
Include the units g (grams) in your answer.

■ 1,500 g ■ 1500 g

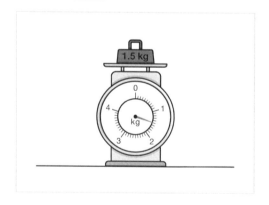

13. 6.425 litres = _____ millilitres

■ 6,425 ■ 6425

Level 2: *cont.*

14. 835 grams = _____ kilograms

 ▪ 0.835

15. Arrange the quantities into ascending order according to size (smallest first).

 ▪ half a litre ▪ 5,300 ml ▪ 8.5 l ▪ 8,750 ml

16. Choose the correct symbol to complete this statement.
three-quarters of a kilogram ___ 586 grams

 1/3 ▪ < ▪ > ▪ =

17. What is the total amount of liquid shown in litres?
Don't include the units in your answer.

▪ 3.22

18. Arrange the masses into descending order according to size (largest first).

 ▪ 5 kg ▪ 3,450 g ▪ 3.42 kg ▪ 2,500 g

19. 3.250 kg + 4,100 g = _____ kg

▪ 7.35

20. 3 litres - 2,250 millilitres = _____ millilitres

 ▪ 750

Level 3: Reasoning - Converting values to the same unit of measure and using four operations.

✿ **Required:** 7/8   ✿ **Student Navigation:** on
✿ **Randomised:** off

21. What is the combined weight of the three objects in kilograms?
Include the units in your answer.

▪ 5.795 kg

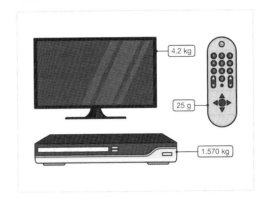

22. Marcel says, "Three-quarters of a kilogram is equal to 75 grams."
Is he correct? Explain your answer.

23. Kane has a jug containing 1.64 litres of juice.
Lara has a jug containing 2,120 millilitres of juice.
How many more millilitres of juice does Lara have than Kane?
Don't include the units in your answer.

▪ 480

Level 3: *cont.*

24. Jodie buys 2,500 grams of bird feed at 80 pence
per kilogram, and 1,500 grams of fish food at
£1.24 per kilogram. She pays with a £10 note. How
much change does she receive?
Include the £ sign in your answer.

- £6.14

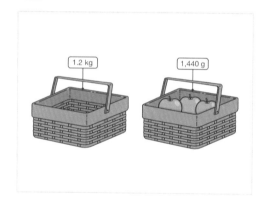

25. Choose **two** calculations that equal 0.684 kg.

- 342 g × 2 ■ 2 kg - 1.556 kg ■ 0.5 kg + 174 g
- 1 kg - 316 g ■ 0.5 kg + 0.084 g

2/5

26. A basket weighs 1.2 kilograms.
A basket containing three equal-sized apples
weighs 1,440 grams. How much does each apple
weigh in **grams**?
Include the units in your answer.

- 80 g

27. A plastic cup holds 200 millilitres of liquid.
Laura fills it with water and pours it into a large
jug. She repeats this process eight times. How
many litres of water will be in the large jug when
she has finished?
Don't include the units in your answer.

- 1.6

28. 3/4 of a litre - 0.03 litres = . . .

- 500 millilitres + 0.25 litres ■ half of 14,440 millilitres
- 753 millilitres ■ half of 1,440 millilitres ■ 7.200 litres
- 2/10 of a litre ■ 50% of a litre

1/7

Level 4: Problem Solving - Converting between
different units of measure (including fractions
and decimals).

✱ **Required:** 5/5   ✱ **Student Navigation:** on
✱ **Randomised:** off

29. Thomas and Ella each have a bag of seashells.
Thomas has 4/10 of a kilogram of shells. Ella has
1/5 of a kilogram of shells.
How much more does Thomas' bag of shells
weigh?
Include the units g (grams) in your answer.

- 200 g

30. Dennis, Tom and Adam are having a water fight.
a b c They fill a bucket with 3,580 millilitres of water. Dennis throws 1.05 litres of water. Tom throws twice as much water as Dennis. Adam throws 0.12 litres of water. How much water is left in the bucket in millilitres?
Include the units in your answer.

▪ 310 millilitres ▪ 310 ml

31. A family buys five 1 kilogram bags of pasta. On
a b c Monday, dad uses 1/10 of the pasta in a salad. On Wednesday, the twins each have a 750 gram bowl of pasta for lunch. On Thursday, friends come over and they eat three times the amount of pasta used on Monday. How many kilograms of pasta are left?
Include the units in your answer.

▪ 1.5 kilograms ▪ 1.5 kg

32. Carol's car has a fuel tank capacity of 52 litres.
1 2 3 She fills the tank **three-quarters full**. She uses half of the fuel travelling to a football match, 15 litres travelling to an art fair, and another 1500 millilitres travelling to the supermarket. How many litres of fuel does the car have left in its tank?
Don't include the units in your answer.

▪ **3**

33. Three equal-sized cakes have a combined weight
a b c of 1.2 kilograms. Jay eats 2/10 of one cake. His sister takes half of a cake to school. His grandma eats 250 grams of one cake. How many kilograms of cake are left?
Include the units in your answer.

▪ 0.670 kg ▪ 0.67 kg

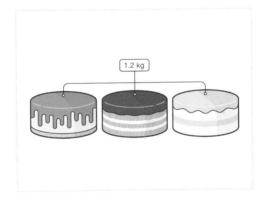

Estimate volume and capacity

Competency: Estimate volume. For example, using 1 cm³ blocks to build cuboids (including cubes) and capacity using water.

Quick Search Ref: 10154

Correct: Correct.   Wrong: Incorrect, try again.   Open: Thank you.

Level 1: Understanding - Units of measure for volume and capacity.

✿ Required: 6/7   ✿ Student Navigation: on   ✿ Randomised: off

1. **Capacity** is:

☐
☒
☐

1/3
- The amount of space that an object fills.
- How heavy or light an object is.
- **The amount of space in a container or the amount of liquid that it can hold.**

2. **Volume** is:

☐
☒
☐

1/3
- **The amount of space that an object fills.**
- How heavy or light an object is.
- The amount of space in a container or the amount of liquid that it can hold.

3. Which unit of measure would you use to measure water in a glass?

☐
☒
☐

1/4
- Litres ■ Kilograms ■ **Millilitres** ■ Metres

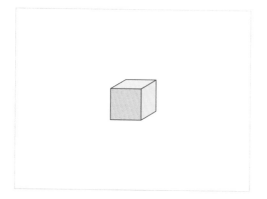

4. Which unit of measure would you use to measure the water in a swimming pool?

☐
☒
☐

1/4
- millilitres ■ grams ■ centimetres ■ **litres**

5. Which unit of measure would you use to measure the volume of a cube?

☐
☒
☐

1/4
- square centimetres (cm²) ■ millilitres
- **cubic centimetres (cm³)** ■ kilometres

6. In cubic centimetres (cm³), what is the volume of the model shown?

1
2
3
- **5**

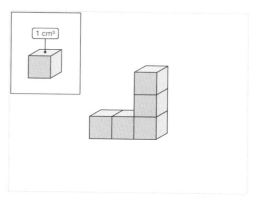

7. In cubic centimetres (cm³), what is the volume of the model shown?

1
2
3
- **8**

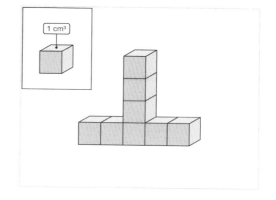

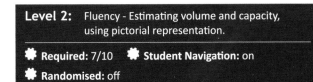

8. What is the most likely capacity of a small carton of fruit juice?

▪ 1 litre ▪ 300 millilitres ▪ 26 millilitres

1/3

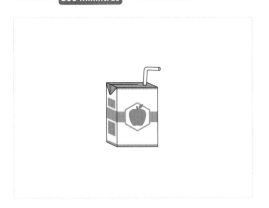

9. In cubic centimetres (cm³), estimate the volume of the cuboid.

▪ 40

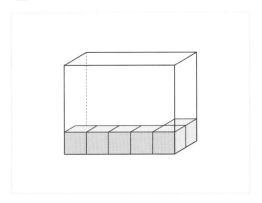

10. Estimate the total amount of liquid in both containers. Give your answer in **millilitres** (ml).

▪ 625

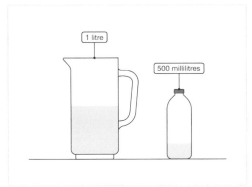

11. The water has been poured from the small bottle into an empty six litre cylinder. Estimate the capacity of the small bottle to the **nearest litre**.

▪ 3

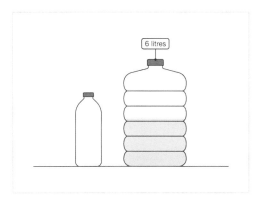

12. Which of the models are equal in volume?

▪ (b) and (c) ▪ (a) and (d) ▪ (a), (b), (c) and (d)
▪ (a), (b), (c), (d) and (e)

1/4

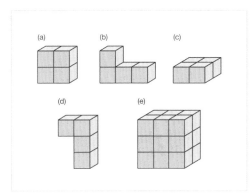

13. Estimate the **capacity** of the flask.

▪ 500 millilitres ▪ 1.5 litres ▪ 1 litre

1/3

14. What is the most likely capacity of an average-sized ketchup bottle?

▪ more than one litre ▪ less than one litre

1/2

15. The capacity of the container is two litres. What is the best estimate for the volume of liquid it is holding?

1/3 ■ **1,500 millilitres** ■ **250 millilitres** ■ **500 millilitres**

16. Which measurement is closest to the volume of **two jars** of honey?

■ **0.7 litres** ■ **500 milillitres** ■ **7 litres**

1/3

17. Gary has four identical glasses of water, each containing 0.315 litres of water. If he rounds each glass of water to the nearest 100 millilitre, approximately how much water will he have in total?

1/4

■ **1,200 ml** ■ **1,260 ml** ■ **1,300 ml** ■ **1,600 ml**

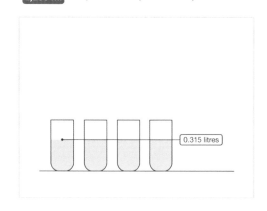

Level 3: Reasoning - Use rounding to estimate volume and capacity in various contexts.

✹ **Required:** 3/3   ✹ **Student Navigation:** on
✹ **Randomised:** off

18. Maya and Samuel pour water from a bottle into an empty plastic container. Who do you agree with?

1/2

■ **Maya** "I think the volume of water in the bottle is larger than the volume of water in the container."

■ **Samuel** "I think the volume of the water in the bottle is the same as the volume of water in the container."

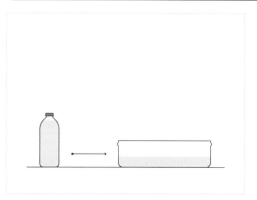

19. In millilitres, estimate how much more oil there is than water. Give your answer to the **nearest 100 millilitres**.
Don't include the units in your answer.

■ **1,600** ■ **1600ml** ■ **1600millilitres** ■ **1600**
■ **1,600millilitres** ■ **1,600ml**

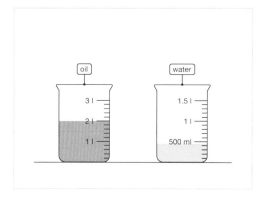

20. Round the capacities to the nearest 100 millilitres and estimate the **total capacity** of the items shown. Give your answer to the **nearest litre**.

■ **6**

21. Mr Lee is filling a **six litre bucket** with water for his gardening project. **Round to the nearest hundred** and find out approximately how many jugs of water he will need to fill his bucket if the capacity of one jug is **206 millilitres**.

- 30

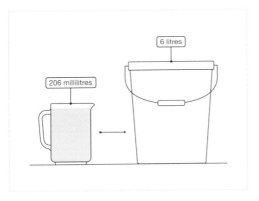

22. A can of juice has a capacity of **316 millilitres**. A bottle of juice has a capacity of **562 millilitres**. Round both to the **nearest 100 millilitres** and estimate in litres how much juice Hamad will have altogether if he buys **sixteen cans** and **four bottles** of juice.

- 7.2

23. A tennis ball has a **volume** of 130 cubic centimetres. The capacity of a tennis ball holder is 4,221 cubic centimetres. Round both to the **nearest 100 cubic centimetres** and estimate how many tennis balls can fit into **three** tennis ball holders.

- 126

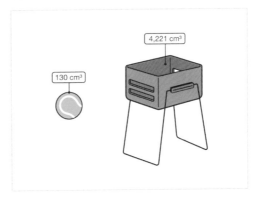

24. The capacity of a lemonade bottle is 1.5 litres. The capacity of a glass is 229 millilitres. Round the capacity of the glass to the **nearest 100 millilitres** and estimate how many **full glasses** can be filled by **three bottles** of lemonade.

- 22

25. A cereal box has a capacity of 1,872 cubic centimetres. A box of tea bags has a capacity of 1,238 cubic centimetres. Round both to the **nearest 100 cubic centimetres** and estimate the total capacity of **nine** cereal boxes and **five** tea bag boxes.

- 23100

Solve Problems Involving Converting Between Units of Time

Competency: Solve problems involving converting between units of time.

Quick Search Ref: 10280

Correct: Correct.   **Wrong:** Incorrect, try again.   **Open:** Thank you.

Level 1: Problem Solving - Converting between different units of time (seconds, minutes, hours, days, weeks, months and years).

✱ **Required:** 7/10   ✱ **Student Navigation:** on   ✱ **Randomised:** off

---

1. Harriet is 8 years, 45 weeks, 46 days and 72 hours old. How many years old is Harriet?

■ **9**

2. Farhana has a cat that is 62 months old.
Jade has a dog that is 4 years and 8 months old.
Safeera has a horse that is 45 months old.
Who has the oldest pet?

1/3

■ **Farhana** ■ Jade ■ Safeera

3. Two movies have a total running time of 3 hours and 30 minutes. The first film starts at 6.25 p.m. and finishes at 7.45 p.m.
How long is the second film in hours and minutes?

1/4

■ 1 hour 20 minutes ■ Two hours ■ **2 hours 10 minutes**
■ 2 hours 20 minutes

4. Jane takes 3 minutes and 14 seconds to plant a flower. She then takes three times as long to water her garden. How long in **seconds** does she spend watering her garden?
Don't include units in your answer.

■ **582**

5. It takes Mercury 88 days to orbit the Sun.
It takes Venus 225 days to orbit the Sun. What is the total duration of the two orbits to the **nearest week**?
Don't include units in your answer.

■ **45**

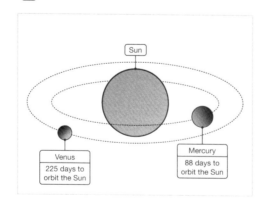

6. The table shows the gestation periods for different animals. What is the difference between the gestation periods of the red deer and the red fox?

1/4

■ 25 weeks ■ **25 weeks and 3 days**
■ 25 weeks and 5 days ■ 41 weeks and 5 days

animal	gestation period
mouse	20 days
red deer	236 days
sheep	147 days
chipmunk	31 days
red fox	58 days

7. The table shows the gestation periods for different animals. Which two animals have a combined gestation period of 25 weeks and 3 days?

1/4

■ mouse and red deer ■ red deer and sheep
■ **sheep and chipmunk** ■ chipmunk and red fox

animal	gestation period
mouse	20 days
red deer	236 days
sheep	147 days
chipmunk	31 days
red fox	58 days

8. A team of six builders each work 12 hours a day to repair a bridge. It takes them a total of five days to complete the work. How many hours does it take to repair the bridge in total?

■ **360**

9. The duration of a luxury cruise is 210 hours. It departs on the 14th of January at 9.00 a.m. On which date will the journey be completed?

1/4

■ 20th January ■ 21st January ■ 22nd January
■ **23rd January**

---

10. Jodie and Steph did a sponsored silence. Jodie raised 20 pence for every minute of silence and Steph raised 8 pence for every 20 seconds of silence. They raised a total of £2.32. Jodie was silent for 8 minutes. For how many seconds was Steph silent?
Don't include units in your answer.

▪ 180

Solve Problems Involving Measurements: All Four Operations

Competency: Use all four operations to solve problems involving measure. For example, length, mass, volume and money using decimal notation, including scaling.

Quick Search Ref: 10022

Correct: Correct.　**Wrong:** Incorrect, try again.　**Open:** Thank you.

Level 1: Understanding - Use all four operations to solve problems involving length, distance and height.

✱ **Required:** 4/6 　　✱ **Student Navigation:** on 　　✱ **Randomised:** off

---

1. What is the most suitable unit of measure for recording the length of a football pitch?

    ■ Kilometres ■ Litres ■ **Metres** ■ Kilograms

    1/4

    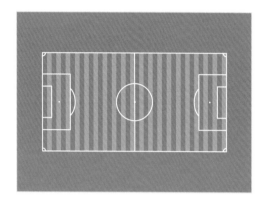

2. Kevin walked 43.8 kilometres on Saturday and 32.2 kilometres on Sunday. How many kilometres did he walk **in total** over the weekend?

    ■ **76**

3. A ribbon is 5.2 metres long. Three lengths are cut from the ribbon.
    - 1.5 metres
    - 168 centimetres
    - 39 centimetres
    How much ribbon is leftover in **metres**?

    ■ **1.63**

    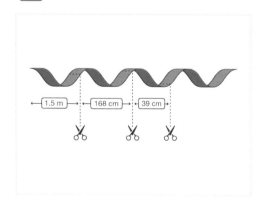

4. Shazad makes a tower from 70 pence worth of ten pence coins. If a ten pence coin is 1.9 millimetres thick, what is the height of the tower in **centimetres**?

    ■ **1.33**

    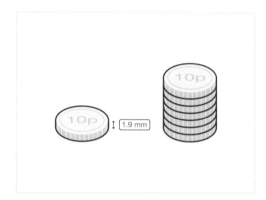

5. Usain Bolt is the only sprinter to win the **100 metre** and **200 metre** titles at **three** consecutive Olympics. What is the total distance in **kilometres** covered by Usain over the three Olympics?

    ■ **0.9**

6. Two long jumpers are practising their jumps for the athletic championships. They each take two attempts.

    Jade jumps 6.64 metres and 6.52 metres.
    Grace jumps 7.52 metres and 814 centimetres.

    In **centimetres**, how much further does Grace jump than Jade over the two attempts?

    ■ **250**

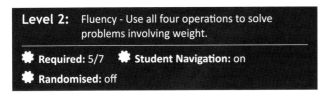

Level 2: Fluency - Use all four operations to solve problems involving weight.

✱ **Required:** 5/7   ✱ **Student Navigation:** on
✱ **Randomised:** off

7. What is the most suitable unit of measure for weighing a bag of cement?

■ **Kilograms** ■ **Kilometres** ■ **Grams** ■ **Litres** ■ **Metres**

1/5

8. A box of 17 dried apricots weighs 184 grams. The weight of the empty box is 14 grams. How much does **one dried apricot** weigh in **grams**?

■ 10

9. Mr. Brown asked the children in year 5 to keep a diary of how much sweets and chocolate they ate over the weekend.
8 children each ate 50 grams of sweets.
15 children each ate 45 grams of chocolate.
How much **chocolate**, to the **nearest kilogram**, did the children eat in total?

■ 1

10. Maria has a recipe for 12 pancakes. She wants to make 30 pancakes. How many grams of flour will she use?

■ 275

11. Mrs. Jolly the baker uses 125 grams of caster sugar to make thirty biscuits. A bag of caster sugar weighs one kilogram. How many biscuits can Mrs. Jolly make from **two bags** of caster sugar?

■ 480

12. Yasir places a 0.5 kilogram weight and a 150 gram weight on one side of the balance scales. Rashid places a 0.75 kilogram weight and a 350 gram weight on the other side.
How much more weight, in **grams**, does Yasir need to add to make the scales balance?

■ 450

Level 2: cont.

13. A basketball weighs 0.6 kilograms. **Two basketballs** weigh the same as **eight hockey balls**. How many **grams** does one hockey ball weigh?

- **150**

Level 3: Reasoning - Use all four operations to solve problems involving volume.

✿ **Required:** 4/5   ✿ **Student Navigation:** off
✿ **Randomised:** off

14. What is the most suitable unit of measure for recording the **volume** of water in the bottle?

1/4

- Metres ▪ Kilograms ▪ Millimetres ▪ **Millilitres**

15. Anna keeps a log of how much water she drinks in a week. How many **litres** of water did Anna drink in total on Monday, Tuesday and Wednesday?

- **2.45**

Day	Amount (ml, l)
Monday	200 ml
Tuesday	1.25 l
Wednesday	1 l
Thursday	350 ml
Friday	620 ml
Saturday	2.5 l
Sunday	468 ml

16. Sharon has to take 7.5 millilitres of medicine three times a day for a 30 days. How many millilitres of medicine will she consume in this time?

- **675**

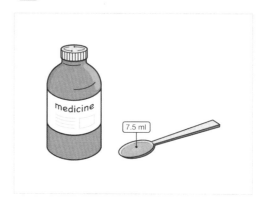

17. Tony makes a tropical fruit drink for breakfast. It contains the following:
One-tenth of a litre of pineapple juice.
Three-fifths of a litre of orange juice.
One-eighth of a litre of mango juice.
Which is the most suitable jug for Tony to serve his drink in?

1/3

- jug 1 ▪ jug 2 ▪ **jug 3**

18. One can holds 355 millilitres of pop. There are **24 cans** in one case. How many **litres** of pop are in **three cases**?

- **25.56**

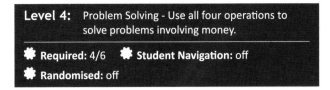

Level 4:   Problem Solving - Use all four operations to solve problems involving money.

❄ **Required:** 4/6   ❄ **Student Navigation:** off
❄ **Randomised:** off

19. How many pennies are equivalent to £8.00?

 ▪ 800

20. Shazia buys six books costing £5.99 each. She pays with a £50.00 note. How much change does she receive?

▪ £14.06

21. A family cinema ticket costs £8.67. Mr. Finch buys one family ticket and a drink for each of his two children. He spends a total of £15.07. How much does **one drink** cost?

▪ £3.20

22. Joseph was given £120 for his birthday. He spent one-quarter of the amount on a computer game, **and from the money left over** he spent two-fifths on gifts for his family. How much money did Joseph have left after buying the game and the gifts?

▪ £54.00 ▪ £54

23. Danny's dad works nine hours a day from Monday to Friday. He is paid £7.50 per hour. How much does Danny's dad earn in one week?

▪ £337.50

24. There is a sale at a department store offering a 25% discount on clothes. Sarah buys a coat that originally cost £58. How much does she pay?

▪ £43.50

Mathematics

Y5

Geometry

2D Shape

3D Shape

Angles

Coordinates

Recognise regular and irregular polygons

Competency: Distinguish between regular and irregular polygons based on reasoning about equal sides and angles.

Quick Search Ref: 10251

Correct: Correct.   Wrong: Incorrect, try again.   Open: Thank you.

Level 1: Understanding - Identifying polygons.

✿ Required: 7/10   ✿ Student Navigation: on   ✿ Randomised: off

1. A **polygon** is a:

1/4
- 2-dimensional closed shape with curved sides.
- 3-dimensional closed shape with three or more straight sides.
- **2-dimensional closed shape with three or more straight sides.**
- 2-dimensional open shape.

2. A polygon has the same number of sides and angles.

- **True** ■ False

3. Is a **circle** a polygon?

1/2
- Yes ■ **No**

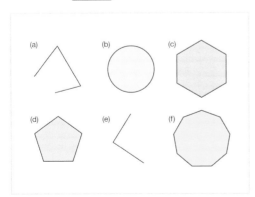

4. Which **three** shapes are polygons?

3/6
- shape (a) ■ shape (b) ■ **shape (c)** ■ **shape (d)**
- shape (e) ■ **shape (f)**

5. Sort the polygons by **number of sides**, from least to most sides.

- **Triangle** ■ **Quadrilateral** ■ **Pentagon** ■ **Hexagon**
- **Heptagon** ■ **Octagon**

6. Select the **two** properties of a **regular** polygon.

2/4
- Two sides are equal in length.
- **All sides are equal in length.**
- The total of all angles equal 180°. ■ **All angles are equal.**

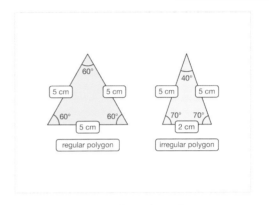

7. Which shape is a **regular** polygon?

1/4
- shape (a) ■ **shape (b)** ■ shape (c) ■ shape (d)

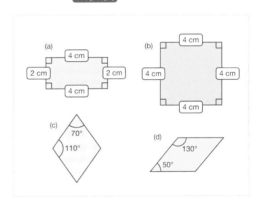

8. Is this shape a **polygon**?

1/2
- **Yes** ■ No

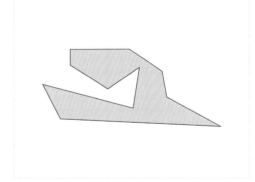

Level 1: *cont.*

9. Select the **three** shapes which are **not polygons**.

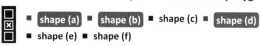

- shape (a) - shape (b) - shape (c) - shape (d)
- shape (e) - shape (f)

3/6

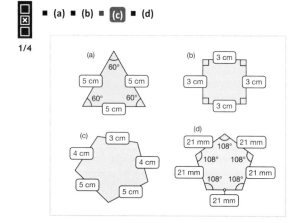

10. Select the **irregular** polygon.

- (a) - (b) - (c) - (d)

1/4

Level 2: Fluency - Recognise regular and irregular polygons.

✿ **Required:** 6/8   ✿ **Student Navigation:** on
✿ **Randomised:** off

11. Which **two** shapes are **regular** polygons.

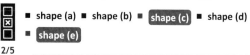

- shape (a) - shape (b) - shape (c) - shape (d)
- shape (e)

2/5

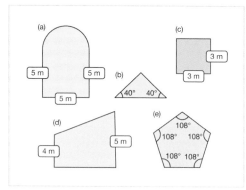

12. Which pair of shapes consists of a **regular** polygon and an **irregular** polygon?

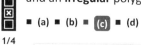

- (a) - (b) - (c) - (d)

1/4

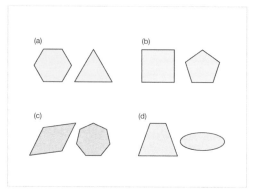

13. Which of the following is a **regular quadrilateral**?

- Kite - Rhombus - Parallelogram - Square
- Rectangle - Trapezium

1/6

14. Select two **irregular polygons**.

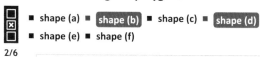

- shape (a) - shape (b) - shape (c) - shape (d)
- shape (e) - shape (f)

2/6

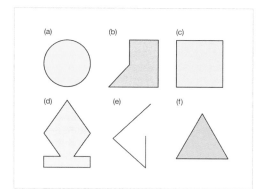

15. Which **two** shapes are **regular polygons**.

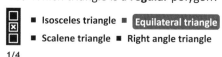

- Trapezium - Heptagon - Rhombus - Octagon
- Rectangle

2/5

16. Which triangle is a **regular** polygon?

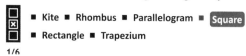

- Isosceles triangle - Equilateral triangle
- Scalene triangle - Right angle triangle

1/4

17. Select two **regular polygons**.

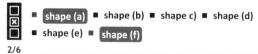

- shape (a) - shape (b) - shape c) - shape (d)
- shape (e) - shape (f)

2/6

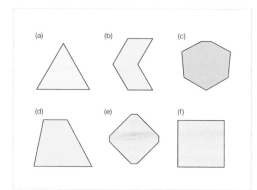

Level 2: cont.

18. Select the **regular polygon**.

■ shape (a) ■ shape (b) ■ shape (c) ■ shape (d)
■ shape (e)

1/5

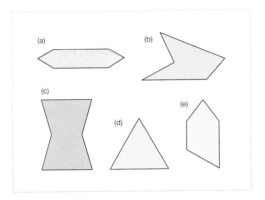

Level 3: Reasoning - Properties of polygons.

❄ **Required: 4/6** ❄ **Student Navigation: on**
❄ **Randomised: off**

19. "I am thinking of a polygon which has three short
sides and two long sides. It has two right angles,
two obtuse angles and one acute angle." What
polygon am I thinking of?

a
b
c

■ an irregular pentagon ■ a irregular pentagon
■ irregular pentagon

20. A triangle has two 40 degree angles. The triangle is
not a **regular polygon**. Explain why.

a
b
c

21. Which regular polygon's angles each measure **135
degrees**?

■ Equilateral triangle ■ Square ■ Pentagon ■ Hexagon
1/6 ■ Heptagon ■ Octagon

regular polygon	number of angles	total measurement of angles
equilateral triangle	3	180°
square	4	360°
pentagon	5	540°
hexagon	6	720°
heptagon	7	900°
octagon	8	1080°

22. A regular octagon has a perimeter of 76
centimetres (cm). What does **one side** of the
octagon measure in centimetres?

■ 9.5

23. What is the next number in the following
sequence:
60, 90, 108, ____

■ 120

regular polygon	number of angles	total measurement of angles
equilateral triangle	3	180°
square	4	360°
pentagon	5	540°
hexagon	6	720°
heptagon	7	900°
octagon	8	1080°

24. "I am thinking of a regular polygon. The polygon
only contains **acute angles**." What polygon am I
thinking of?

a
b
c

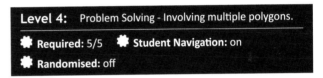

■ A Equilateral Triangle ■ Equilateral Triangle
■ An Equilateral Triangle

Level 4: Problem Solving - Involving multiple polygons.

❄ **Required: 5/5** ❄ **Student Navigation: on**
❄ **Randomised: off**

25. For his art project, Brad uses some wool to make a
pentagon, **hexagon** and **heptagon**. All of the
shapes are regular polygons with their sides
measuring 5 cm.
In centimetres, how much wool does he use in
total?

■ 90

26. Jamal is drawing a **regular polygon** onto a clock
face. He has drawn the first two sides.
What polygon is he drawing?

a
b
c

■ A Hexagon ■ Hexagon ■ An Hexagon

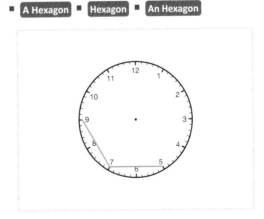

27. The composite shape is made up of **regular polygons** joined to rectangle (a). The perimeter of each square is 26 centimetres and the perimeter of each triangle is 10.5 centimetres. What is the perimeter of rectangle (a)?

 1 2 3

■ **20**

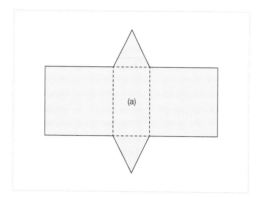

28. The composite shape is made up of **regular polygons.** The perimeter of each square is 18cm. What is the **perimeter** of the triangle?

1 2 3

■ **13.5**

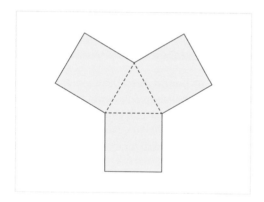

29. Eric needs to replace the turf in his new garden. His garden is a **4-sided regular polygon** which is **15 metres** wide. How many pieces of turf will Eric need?

1 2 3

■ **20**

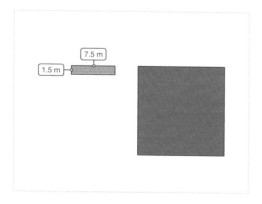

Use the properties of rectangles to find missing lengths and angles

Competency: Use the properties of rectangles to deduce related facts and find missing lengths and angles.

Quick Search Ref: 10116

Correct: Correct.   **Wrong:** Incorrect, try again.   **Open:** Thank you.

Level 1:   Understanding - Properties of a rectangle.

❋ **Required:** 7/10   ❋ **Student Navigation:** on   ❋ **Randomised:** off

---

1. Choose **three** statements which are **true**.

- All angles of a rectangle are equal.
- The angles of a rectangle add up to 180 degrees.

3/5
- All sides of a rectangle are equal in length.
- Opposite sides of a rectangle are parallel.
- Opposite sides of a rectangle are equal in length.

2. In a rectangle, how many degrees does each **angle** measure?

- 90

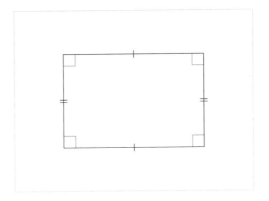

3. What is the measurement of **side b** in metres (m)?

- 8

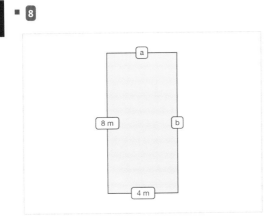

4. Which side of the rectangle is **parallel** to **side d**?

- Side a ■ Side b ■ Side c

1/3

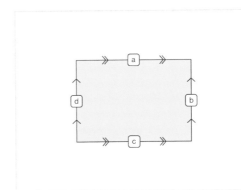

5. The rectangle has **two diagonal lines** running through it from corner to corner.
Select the statement which is **not true**.

1/4
- The two diagonals are equal in length.
- Opposite central angles are equal in size.
- All the central angles are equal in size.
- The four triangles created are isosceles triangles.

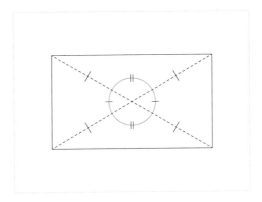

6. The rectangle has been divided by two diagonal lines. Which angle measures **70 degrees**?

- Angle (a) ■ Angle (b) ■ Angle (c)

1/3

---

7. The rectangle has been divided to make four **isosceles triangles**. Which angle measures **25 degrees**?

1/4 ■ Angle (a) ■ Angle (b) ■ Angle (c) ■ Angle (d)

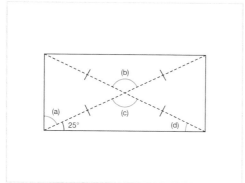

8. In the rectangle shown, which two angles are the same size?

■ Angles (a) and (d) ■ Angles (b) and (c)

1/2

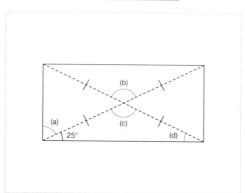

9. **Side a** measures ___ metres (m).

1
2
3 ■ 6

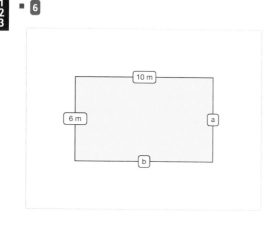

10. Which side of the rectangle is **parallel** to **side a**?

■ Side b ■ Side c ■ Side d

1/3

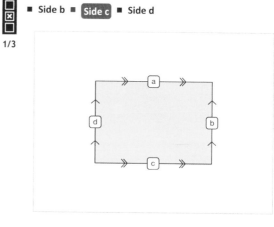

Level 2: Fluency - Use the properties of a rectangle to find missing lengths and angles.

✹ **Required:** 6/6   ✹ **Student Navigation:** on
✹ **Randomised:** off

11. In the rectangle shown, what is the size of **angle (a)** in degrees.

1
2
3 ■ 20

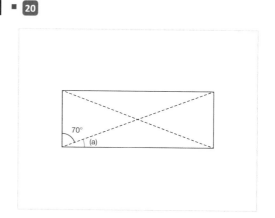

12. What is the value, in degrees of **(a) + (b)**?

1
2
3 ■ 180

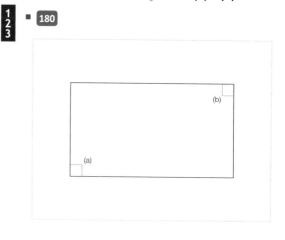

Level 2: *cont.*

13. The **perimeter** of the rectangle is **20 metres**. What is the **length** of **side b** in metres?

1
2
3 ▪ **3**

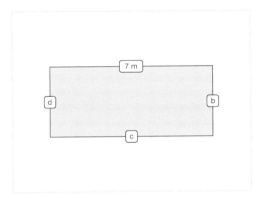

14. What is the total, in degrees of **(a) + (b) + (c)**?

1
2
3 ▪ **90**

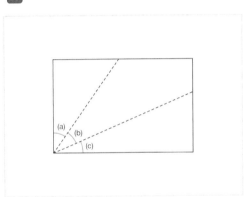

15. Two **diagonal lines** have been drawn onto the rectangle. Use them to calculate the measurement of **angle (a)** in degrees.

1
2
3 ▪ **30**

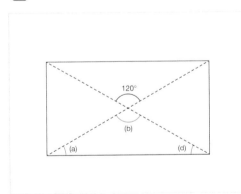

16. The diagram shows the width and length of an incomplete rectangle. The **perimeter** of the rectangle is **16 metres**. What is the **length** of **side x** in metres?

1
2
3 ▪ **5**

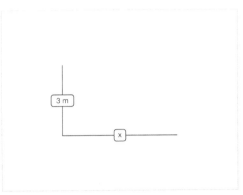

Level 3: Reasoning - Find missing lengths, angles and area.

✿ **Required:** 5/6   ✿ **Student Navigation:** on
✿ **Randomised:** off

17. Three crates are stacked on top of each other to create a composite rectilinear shape. What is the **total** of all **internal angles** of the new shape?

1
2
3 ▪ **360**

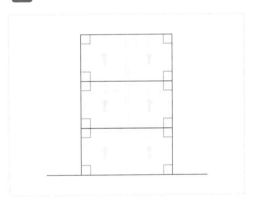

18. A rectangle has an **area** of 84 square centimetres and **perimeter** of 38 centimetres (cm). Its length and width are **both whole numbers.** What is the **length** of the rectangle in centimetres?

☐
☒
☐
1/4

▪ **21 cm** ▪ **42 cm** ▪ **7 cm** ▪ **12 cm**

19. The quadrilateral has been split into four identical isosceles triangles. How do you know the quadrilateral is a square?

a
b
c

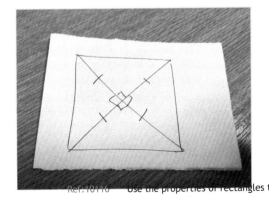

20. A **rectangular** piece of card has a **perimeter** of 40 centimetres and **width** of 8 centimetres. What is the **area** of the card in square centimetres (cm²)?

- 96

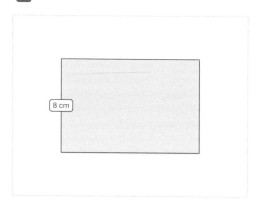

21. Find the measurement of **angle (c)** in degrees.

 - 270

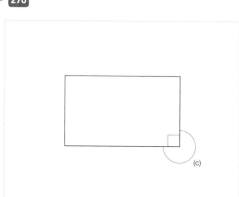

22. St John's school has a **rectangular** playground which is split into **two sections**; one for football and one for netball. In the football section, one of the angles measures **30 degrees**. What does angle (x) measure in degrees?

- 150

❋ **Required:** 3/3   ❋ **Student Navigation:** on
❋ **Randomised:** off

23. The rectangle has **two diagonal lines** running through it from corner to corner. Using the given angles, find the size of **angle (c)** in degrees.

 - 110

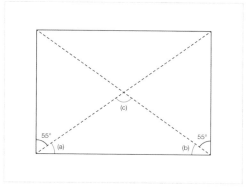

24. The children in year 5 have made a **rectangular** shaped postbox for Valentine's Day. The box is made from two pieces of card, which are a rectangle and a square. The **area** of the **square** is **144** square centimetres. The **perimeter** of the **postbox** is **88 centimetres**.
In square centimetres, what is the **area** of the postbox?

- 384

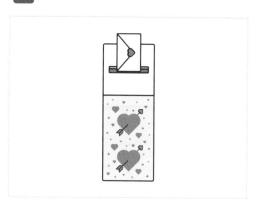

25. Two rectangles are joined together to make the letter T. Calculate the total of all **internal angles** of the new shape in degrees.

- 1080

Identify 3D shapes

Competency: Identify 3D shapes, including cubes and other cuboids, from 2D representations.

Quick Search Ref: 10193

Correct: Correct.   Wrong: Incorrect, try again.   Open: Thank you.

Level 1: Understanding - Properties of 3D shapes

✿ **Required:** 7/10   ✿ **Student Navigation:** on   ✿ **Randomised:** off

---

1. A **net** is:

1/4

- one of the surfaces of a 3D shape.
- a part of a 3D shape where three edges meet to form a point.
- a line where two faces of a 3D shape meet.
- ■ **a 2D shape that can be folded to form a 3D shape or a solid.**

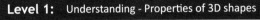

2. The **edge** of a 3D shape is:

1/4

- one its flat surfaces.
- a part of the shape where three edges meet to form a point.
- ■ **a line where two faces meet.**
- the flat shape it makes when unfolded.

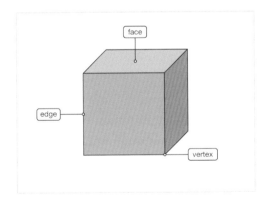

3. The **face** of a 3D shape is:

1/4

- ■ **one of its flat surfaces.**
- a part of a shape where three edges meet to form a point.
- a line where two flat surfaces meet.
- the flat shape it makes when unfolded.

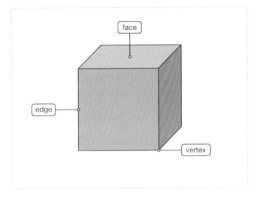

4. Select the **two** 3D shapes.

2/5

- ■ **(a)** ■ (b) ■ (c) ■ (d) ■ **(e)**

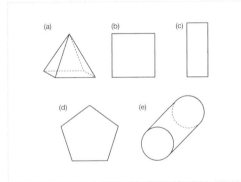

5. The net folds into a _____ .

1/4

- cylinder ■ cuboid ■ **cube** ■ pyramid

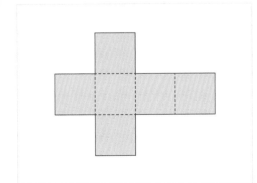

Level 1: *cont.*

6. The **vertex** of a 3D shape is:

1/4

- one of its flat surfaces.
- **a part of the shape where three edges meet to form a point.**
- a line where two flat surfaces meet.
- the flat shape it makes when unfolded.

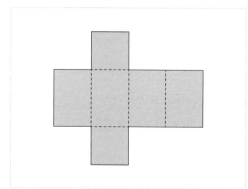

7. The net folds into a _____ .

1/4

- cylinder ▪ **cuboid** ▪ cube ▪ pyramid

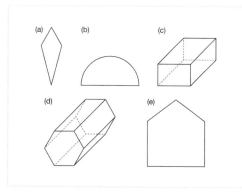

8. Select the **two** 3D shapes.

▪ (a) ▪ (b) ▪ **(c)** ▪ **(d)** ▪ (e)

2/5

9. The net folds into a _____ .

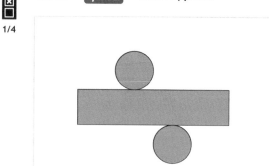
1/4

- cuboid ▪ **cylinder** ▪ cube ▪ pyramid

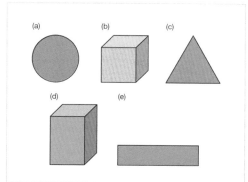

10. Select the **two** 3D shapes.

▪ (a) ▪ **(b)** ▪ (c) ▪ **(d)** ▪ (e)

2/5

Level 2: Fluency - Naming 3D shapes and identifying their properties

✿ **Required:** 4/6 ✿ **Student Navigation:** on
✿ **Randomised:** off

11. This **3D** shape is a _____ .

a
b
c

▪ **cuboid**

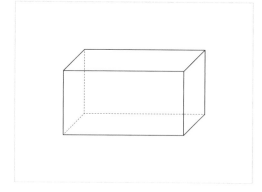

12. How many **vertices** does the prism have?

 ▪ **10**

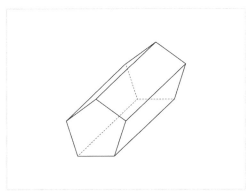

13. This **3D** shape is a _____ .

 ▪ **cube**

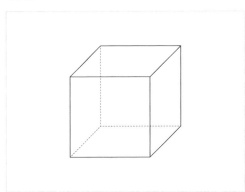

14. How many **edges** does the cuboid have?

 ▪ **12**

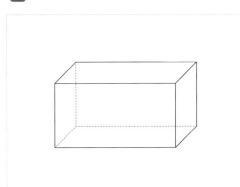

15. Which **two** shapes have the same number of faces, edges and vertices?

▪ **Cuboid** ▪ **Cylinder** ▪ **Cube**

2/4 ▪ **Triangular-based pyramid**

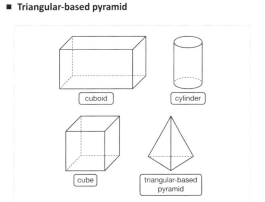

16. How many **faces** does the triangular prism have?

▪ **5**

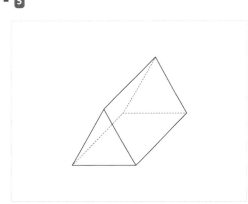

Level 3: Reasoning - Identifying 3D shapes

✸ **Required:** 5/7 ✸ **Student Navigation:** on
✸ **Randomised:** off

17. Here is the net of a dice. When it's folded and rolled, the letter showing on the **top** of the dice is **b**. What letter is on the bottom of the dice?

▪ **e**

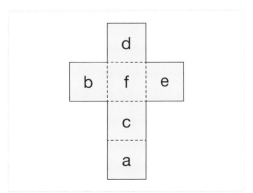

Level 3: *cont.*

18. A cube has **6 faces, 8 vertices and 12 edges**.

If two cubes are joined face to face to form a cuboid, the new shape will have **12 faces, 16 vertices** and **24 edges**.

Is this true? Explain your answer.

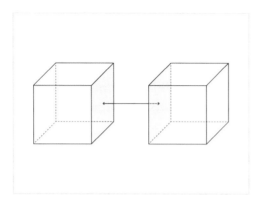

19. What 3D shape has **12 edges**, **eight vertices** and **six faces which are all square**?

1/5

- Square-based pyramid ■ Cuboid ■ Cylinder ■ **Cube**
- Tetrahedron

20. Sort the 3D shapes by their number of **edges**, from most edges to least.

- **cube** ■ **triangular prism** ■ **square-based pyramid**
- **triangular-based pyramid** ■ **cylinder**

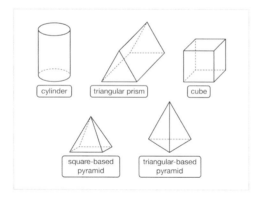

21. Jerry says "A hexagon has six sides, so a **hexagonal-based pyramid** must have six faces."

Is Jerry correct? Explain your answer.

22. Here is the **net** of a dice. When it's folded and rolled, the letter showing on the top of the dice is **f**. What letter is on the bottom of the dice?

- **a**

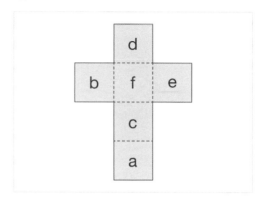

23. Which net folds into a cube?

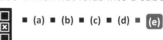

1/5

- (a) ■ (b) ■ (c) ■ (d) ■ **(e)**

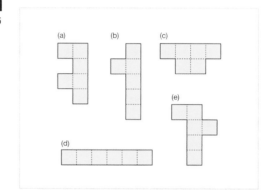

Level 4: Problem Solving - Combining and visualising 3D shapes.

✹ **Required:** 5/5   ✹ **Student Navigation:** on
✹ **Randomised:** off

24. Danny has a piece of card and he wants to make a **cuboid-shaped box** to hold a gift for his sister. He wants to work out how much card he needs so he can make a net.

What is the total area of the net in square centimetres (cm²)?

- **210**

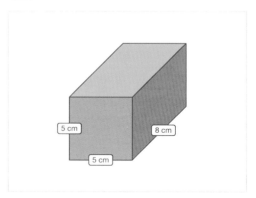

Level 4: cont.

25. How many **cubes** make up the 3D model?

 ▪ 20

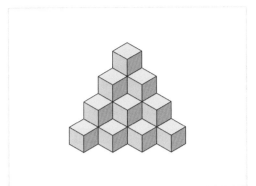

26. Each face of the dice contains a different mathematical symbol. The diagram shows the dice from three different angles. The missing symbol is the cubed (³) symbol.

1/5

Which symbol will the cubed (³) symbol be **opposite**? Use the blank net to help you work out the answer.

▪ x ▪ ² ▪ + ▪ ÷ ▪ -

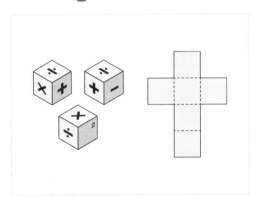

27. Peter is playing with some building blocks. He puts a **cube** on the table and places a **square-based pyramid** on top of it. If he walks around the table, how many **visible faces** will he be able to count?

 ▪ 8

28. Ben is making a rocket ship and places a **square-based pyramid** on top of a **cuboid.** How many **faces** does Ben's rocket ship have?

 ▪ 9

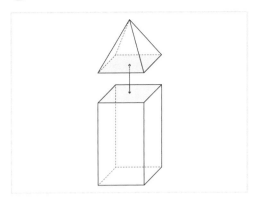

Estimate and Compare Acute, Obtuse and Reflex Angles

Competency: Estimate and compare acute, obtuse and reflex angles.

Quick Search Ref: 10076

Correct: Correct.   Wrong: Incorrect, try again.   Open: Thank you.

Level 1:   Understanding - Comparing acute, obtuse and reflex angles.

✿ **Required:** 7/9   ✿ **Student Navigation:** on   ✿ **Randomised:** off

---

1.   An **acute** angle is:

- equal to 90 degrees.
- between 90 degrees and 180 degrees.
1/4 ▪ less than 90 degrees. ▪ greater than 180 degrees.

2.   An **reflex** angle is:

- equal to 90 degrees.
- between 90 degrees and 180 degrees.
1/4 ▪ less than 90 degrees. ▪ greater than 180 degrees.

3.   An **obtuse** angle is:

- equal to 90 degrees.
- between 90 degrees and 180 degrees.
1/4 ▪ less than 90 degrees. ▪ greater than 180 degrees.

4.   Which **two** angles are **acute**?

- Angle (a) ▪ Angle (b) ▪ Angle (c) ▪ Angle (d)
- Angle (e) ▪ Angle (f)
2/6

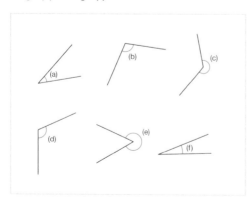

5.   Which **two** angles are **obtuse**?

- Angle (a) ▪ Angle (b) ▪ Angle (c) ▪ Angle (d)
- Angle (e) ▪ Angle (f)
2/6

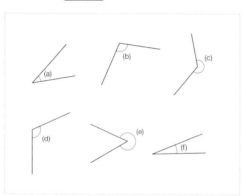

6.   Which **two** angles are **reflex**?

- Angle (a) ▪ Angle (b) ▪ Angle (c) ▪ Angle (d)
- Angle (e) ▪ Angle (f)
2/6

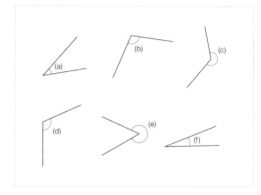

7.   What type of angle is shown?

- Right angle ▪ Obtuse ▪ Acute ▪ Reflex
1/4

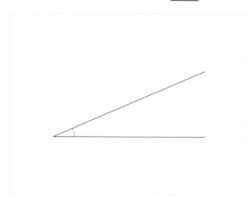

8.   What type of angle is shown?

- Obtuse ▪ Reflex ▪ Right angle ▪ Acute
1/4

Level 1: *cont.*

9. What type of angle is shown?

- Acute ■ Obtuse ■ Reflex ■ Right angle

1/4

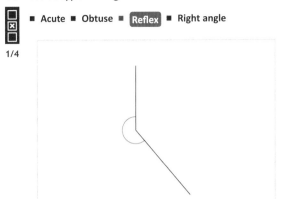

Level 2: Fluency - Comparing and estimating acute, obtuse and reflex angles.

✿ **Required:** 7/9   ✿ **Student Navigation:** on
✿ **Randomised:** off

10. Which angle is the **odd one out**?

■ 127° ■ 179° ■ 181° ■ 95° ■ 150°

1/5

11. If a triangle has one angle which measures **105** degrees and another which measures **32** degrees, what **type** of angle is the third angle?

a
b
c

■ Acute angle ■ Acute ■ An acute angle

12. What is the **maximum** possible size of an **acute** angle as a whole number?

1
2
3

■ 89

13. One of the triangle's angles has been covered. **Estimate** what type of angle it is.

■ Acute ■ Obtuse ■ Right angle ■ Reflex

1/4

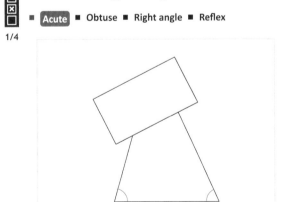

14. Estimate the size of angle (a) in degrees.

1
2
3

■ 46 ■ 43 ■ 45 ■ 47 ■ 44

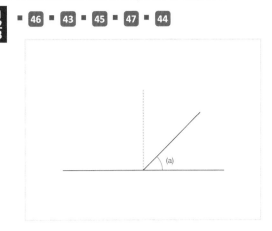

15. Which angle is the **odd one out**?

■ 195° ■ 231° ■ 175° ■ 335° ■ 206°

1/5

16. A **quadrilateral** has two angles which are **right angles** and one angle which measures **35 degrees**. What **type** of angle is the fourth angle?

a
b
c

■ Obtuse angle ■ An obtuse angle ■ Obtuse

17. Estimate the size of angle (b) in degrees.

1
2
3

■ 134 ■ 133 ■ 135 ■ 136 ■ 137

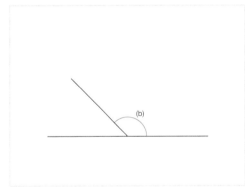

18. Which angle is the **odd one out**?

■ 27° ■ 79° ■ 81° ■ 95° ■ 50°

1/5

Level 3: Reasoning - Comparing and estimating measurements of angles.

✿ **Required:** 5/5   ✿ **Student Navigation:** on
✿ **Randomised:** off

19. Put the angles in order, starting with the **smallest**.

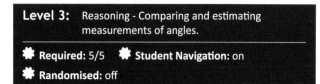

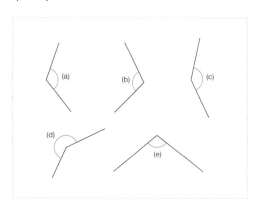

20. Which of these angles is the **odd one out?** Explain your answer.

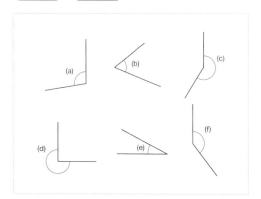

21. Winston says, "Angle (a) is an obtuse angle." Is he correct? Explain your answer.

22. The shapes are all **regular polygons. Estimate** the size of each angle. Which angle measures **120 degrees?**

1/4   ▪ Angle (a) ▪ Angle (b) ▪ Angle (c) ▪ Angle (d)

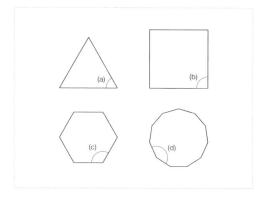

23. Wendel says, "When you add two acute angles together, they always make an obtuse angle." Is Wendel correct? Explain your answer.

Level 4: Problem Solving - Comparing and estimating angles of shapes.

✿ **Required:** 5/5   ✿ **Student Navigation:** on
✿ **Randomised:** off

24. What is the **minimum** number of 35 degree angles that you would need to construct a single **reflex** angle?

▪ 6

25. Which one of these **regular polygons** has internal angles that each measure **approximately** 130 degrees?

1/4   ▪ Pentagon ▪ Hexagon ▪ Heptagon ▪ Octagon

name	sides	sum of interior angles
pentagon	5	540°
hexagon	6	720°
heptagon	7	900°
octagon	8	1080°

Level 4: *cont.*

26. **Estimate** the size of the **obtuse angle** in this
shape.

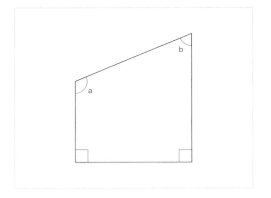

118	116	117	120	107	110	109
119	100	101	112	105	115	108
103	106	114	113	102	111	104

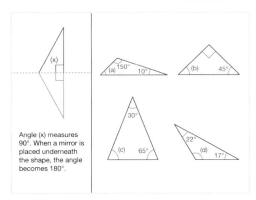

27. When a mirror is placed directly underneath each
shape, it creates a new shape as shown in the
example image. Which of the angles will become a
reflex angle when a mirror is placed below the
1/4   shape?

■ Angle (a) ■ Angle (b) ■ Angle (c) ■ Angle (d)

Angle (x) measures
90°. When a mirror is
placed underneath
the shape, the angle
becomes 180°.

(a) 150° 10°
(b) 45°
(c) 30° 65°
(d) 22° 17°

28. What is the **maximum** number of 88 degree
angles you could use to construct a **single reflex**
angle?

■ 4

Identify angles at different points

Competency: Identify angles at a point and one whole turn (total 360°), angles at a point on a straight line and half a turn (total 180°) and other multiples of 90°.

Quick Search Ref: 10169

Correct: Correct.   **Wrong:** Incorrect, try again.   **Open:** Thank you.

1. How many degrees are in **one full turn**?

- 90 degrees ▪ 180 degrees ▪ [360 degrees] ▪ 720 degrees

1/4

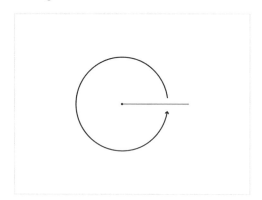

2. How many degrees are in a **half-turn**?

- 90 degrees ▪ [180 degrees] ▪ 360 degrees

1/3

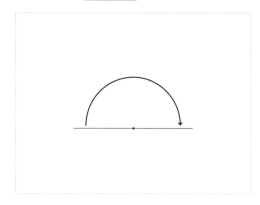

3. How many degrees are in a **quarter-turn**?

- [90 degrees] ▪ 180 degrees ▪ 360 degrees

1/3

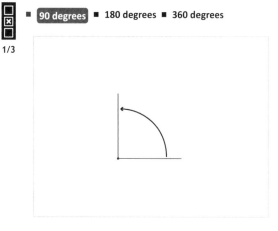

4. Angles around a point add up to:

- 90 degrees ▪ 180 degrees ▪ [360 degrees] ▪ 720 degrees

1/4

5. Angles on a straight line add up to:

- 90 degrees ▪ [180 degrees] ▪ 360 degrees

1/3

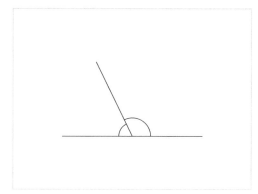

6. Which of these angles is the **smallest**?

- Angle (a) ▪ [Angle (b)] ▪ Angle (c) ▪ Angle (d)

1/4

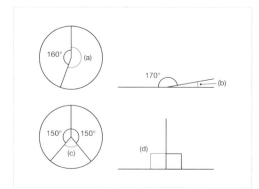

7. What is the size of angle (a)?

- 10 degrees ▪ 100 degrees ▪ 190 degrees
- 280 degrees

1/4

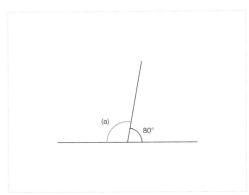

8. What is the size of angle (b)?

- 40 degrees ▪ 130 degrees ▪ 220 degrees

1/3

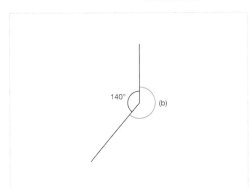

9. What is the size of angle (a)?

- 60 degrees ▪ 150 degrees ▪ 240 degrees
- 330 degrees

1/4

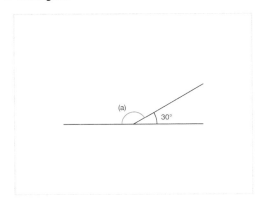

10. What is the size of angle (b)?

- 15 degrees ▪ 105 degrees ▪ 195 degrees

1/3

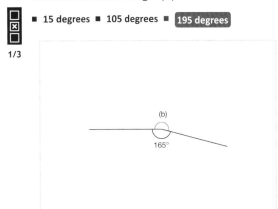

Level 2: Fluency - Calculating angles on a straight line and around a point.

✿ **Required:** 7/10   ✿ **Student Navigation:** on
✿ **Randomised:** off

11. Calculate the size of angle (a) in degrees.

1 2 3 ▪ 120

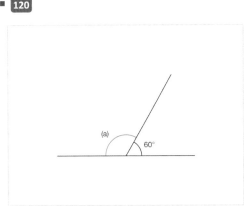

12. Calculate the size of angle (b) in degrees.

1 2 3 ▪ 244

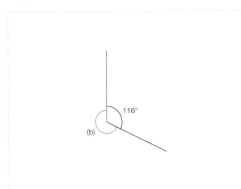

13. Terry is facing north. He turns **three right angles clockwise** to face west. How many degrees does he turn in total?

1
2
3

▪ 270

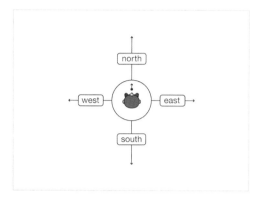

14. Calculate the size of angle (b) in degrees.

1
2
3

▪ 120

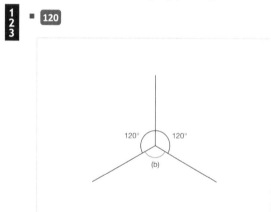

15. Calculate the size of angle (b) in degrees.

1
2
3

▪ 108

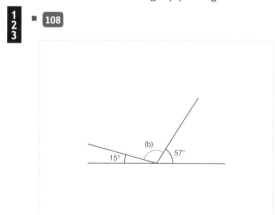

16. Adam cuts a cake into four equal-sized pieces. He takes one piece and cuts it in half again. In degrees, what is the **angle** of the small piece of cake left over?

1
2
3

▪ 45

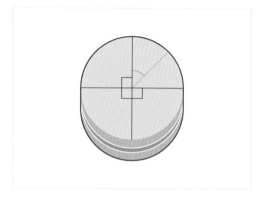

17. Calculate the size of angle (b) in degrees.

1
2
3

▪ 67

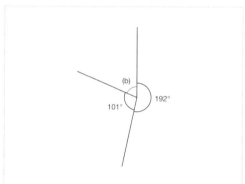

18. Calculate the size of angle (b) in degrees.

1
2
3

▪ 110

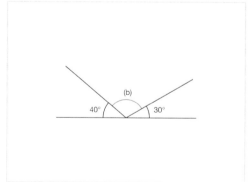

19. Calculate the size of angle (b) in degrees.

 ▪ 220

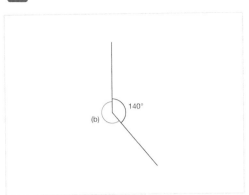

20. Calculate the size of angle (a) in degrees.

 ▪ 137

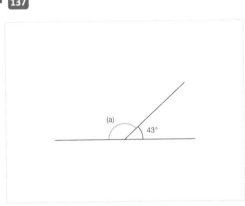

Level 3: Reasoning - Identify angles at different points.

✿ **Required:** 5/7   ✿ **Student Navigation:** on
✿ **Randomised:** off

21. Order the angles shown, starting with the **smallest** angle.

↑
↓   ▪ (e) ▪ (c) ▪ (a) ▪ (d) ▪ (b)

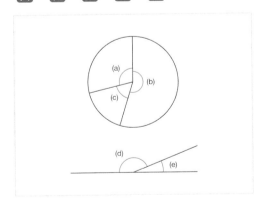

22. Kelly says, "If there are two angles on a straight line, I can calculate the size of each angle".

a
b
c

Is Kelly correct? Explain your answer.

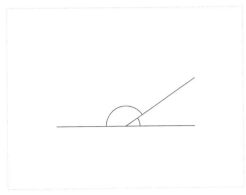

23. It's Peter's birthday and he has invited two friends to tea. He cuts a round cake into four pieces. One piece has an interior angle of **25 degrees**, one piece has an interior angle of **42 degrees** and one piece has an interior angle of **33 degrees**.
In degrees, what is the angle of the remaining piece of cake?

▪ 260

24. The figure is made up of **two intersecting lines**. Calculate the size of **angle (a)** in degrees.

▪ 108

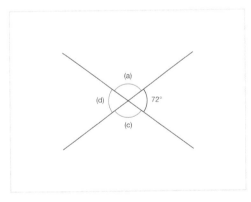

25. Order the angles shown, starting with the **largest** angle.

↑
↓   ▪ (b) ▪ (f) ▪ (g) ▪ (d) ▪ (e) ▪ (c) ▪ (a)

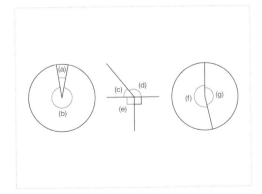

Level 3: cont.

26. The children in Year 5 are making masks using two paper plates and a square piece of paper. They need to colour in the section of each paper plate that **does not** overlap the square piece of paper. In degrees, what is the angle of the section that the children will colour in on each plate?

▪ 270

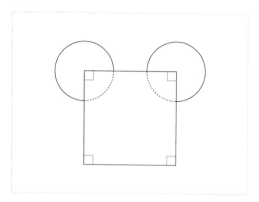

27. Two train tracks cross to create two **intersecting** **lines.** One angle at the intersection is 59 degrees. What is the size of angle (a) in degrees?

▪ 121

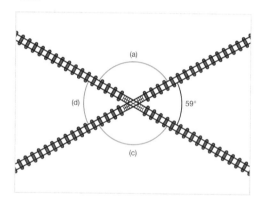

Level 4: Problem Solving - Identify angles at different points.

✸ **Required:** 5/5   ✸ **Student Navigation:** on
✸ **Randomised:** off

28. The composite shape is made up of three **regular** **pentagons**. What is the size of angle (a) in degrees?

▪ 36

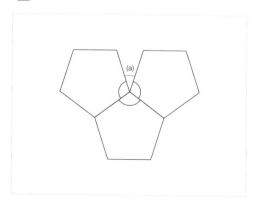

29. Use the secret code to spell out a message. For each letter, **start at A** and **turn clockwise** by the number of degrees given.

a
b
c

First word - 360, 540, 450, 135, 405, 270.
Second word - 720, 225, 45.
Third word - 45, 360, 630, 315.

▪ **ANGLES ARE EASY**

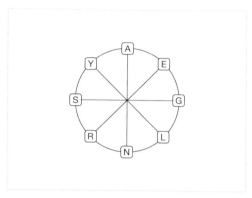

30. Gareth goes for a walk. He starts facing north. He makes a quarter-turn clockwise and walks for 2 miles. He then turns 135 degrees and walks for another mile. From his current position, how many degrees clockwise does he need to turn to face the end-point if the end-point is 2 miles **north-east**?

▪ 180

31. Turn each dial clockwise as instructed to crack the code and find the secret number:

Dial 1 - turn 180 degrees.
Dial 2 - turn 360 degrees.
Dial 3 - turn 450 degrees.
Dial 4 - turn 315 degrees.

■ `4027`

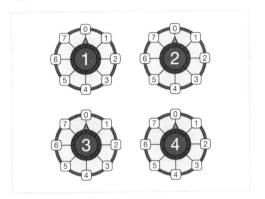

32. Two **regular hexagons** have been positioned next to each other. What is the size of angle (a) in degrees?

■ `120`

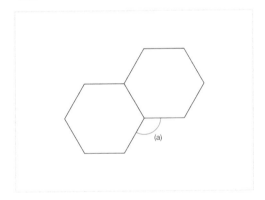

Understanding angles

Competency: Understand angles and know that angles are measured in degrees.

Quick Search Ref: 10203

Correct: Correct.   Wrong: Incorrect, try again.   Open: Thank you.

Level 1:   Understanding - Recognising angles.

✱ Required: 7/10   ✱ Student Navigation: on   ✱ Randomised: off

1. Which of the following describes an angle?

- An angle measures the amount of turn between two straight lines that meet each other.
- An angle is the length of a shape from one point to another.
- An angle is the straight line which passes through the centre of a circle.
- An angle is the distance from any point on the edge of a circle to its centre.

1/4

2. Angles are measured in:

- centimetres ▪ degrees ▪ millimetres
- degrees Celsius

1/4

3. What symbol is used to represent an angle?

- ° ▪ √ ▪ ∞ ▪ >

1/4

4. Which angle is the largest?

- Angle (a) ▪ Angle (b) ▪ Angle (c) ▪ Angle (d)
- All the angles are equal.

1/5

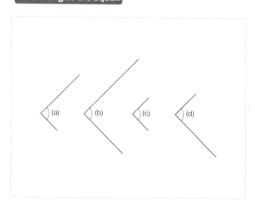

5. Which is the largest **angle**?

- green arc ▪ blue arc ▪ pink arc
- All the angles are equal.

1/4

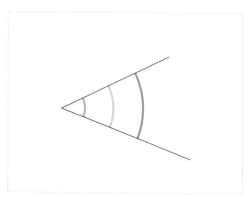

6. Which **three** options are types of angles?

- acute ▪ closed ▪ reflex ▪ extended ▪ retract
- obtuse

3/6

7. Which **two** options show angles that are **equal** in size?

- a and b ▪ a and c ▪ a and d ▪ b and c ▪ b and d
- c and d

2/6

8. Which piece of equipment would you use to measure an angle?

- compass ▪ protractor ▪ ruler ▪ scientific calculator

1/4

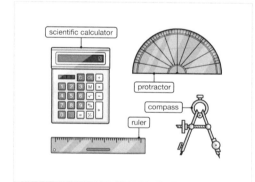

Level 1: *cont.*

9. How many angles are there within the hexagon?

 ▪ 6

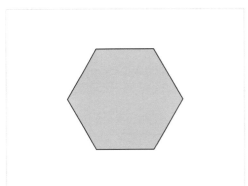

10. How many angles are there within the square?

 ▪ 4

Level 2: Fluency - Properties of angles.

✿ **Required:** 7/10   ✿ **Student Navigation:** on
✿ **Randomised:** off

11. How many degrees are in one **full** turn?

 ▪ 360

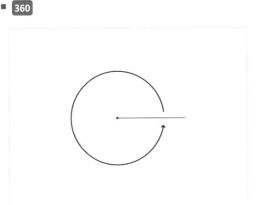

12. How many degrees are in a **half** turn?

 ▪ 180

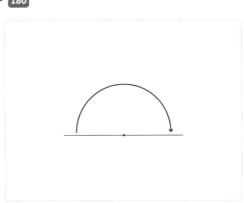

13. How many degrees are in a **quarter** turn?

 ▪ 90

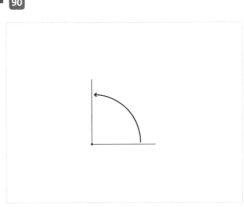

14. Put the following angle types in order, starting with the **smallest**.

▪ acute ▪ right angle ▪ obtuse ▪ reflex

15. What type of angle is (a)?

▪ acute ▪ obtuse ▪ reflex

1/3

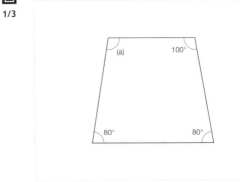

Level 2: *cont.*

16. What type of lines are shown in the diagram?

■ parallel lines ■ perpendicular lines ■ **intersecting lines**

1/3

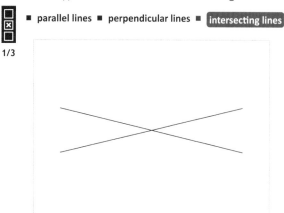

17. What type of lines are shown in the diagram?

■ parallel lines ■ **perpendicular lines** ■ intersecting lines

1/3

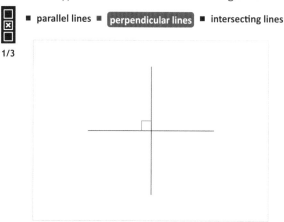

18. What type of lines are shown in the diagram?

■ **parallel lines** ■ perpendicular lines ■ intersecting lines

1/3

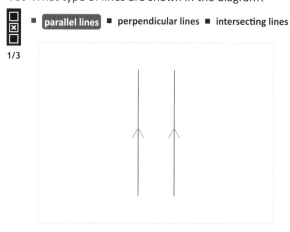

19. A 90 degree angle is known as a _____ angle.

■ **right** ■ **right angle**

20. Which of the following shapes only contains **right angles**?

1/4

■ triangle ■ **square** ■ pentagon ■ hexagon

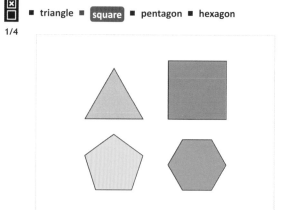

Level 3:   Reasoning - Find missing angles and add angles.

✿ **Required:** 4/5   ✿ **Student Navigation:** on
✿ **Randomised:** off

21. Orla and Archie are at the beach and want to look at Tokyo Island in the distance. To see the island they have to turn **one quarter** clockwise, plus an additional **15 degrees** clockwise.

How many **degrees** do they have to turn in **total** so that they're facing Tokyo Island?

■ **105**

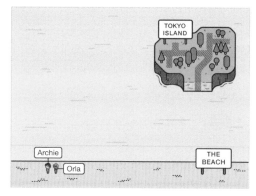

22. Joe says that the lines in the capital letter **L** are **perpendicular**. Is he correct? Explain your answer.

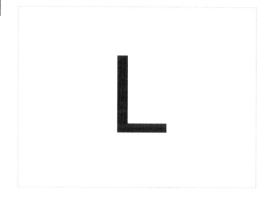

23. The angles of a regular **pentagon** are equal in size.

The sum of the angles is **540 degrees**. What does each angle measure?

▪ 108

24. It is quarter past eleven in the morning. The

minute hand will turn through **three right angles** to reach twelve o'clock.

How many **degrees** will the minute hand turn in total from its starting point?

▪ 270

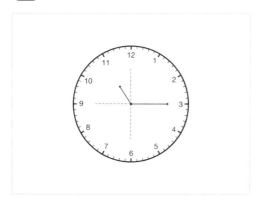

25. How many degrees does angle (a) measure? Remember that opposite angles on intersecting lines are equal.

▪ 120

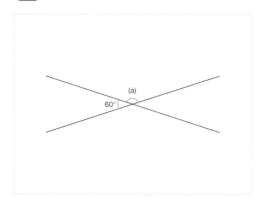

26. Franky, Sarah and Alberto share a cake for Franky's birthday. Sarah cuts a piece with an angle of 135 degrees. Alberto cuts a piece with an angle of 30 degrees.

What angle, in degrees, does Franky's piece of cake measure?

▪ 195

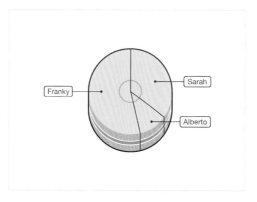

27. How many **degrees in total** does the **hour hand** on a clock turn between 12 o'clock and 4 o'clock?

▪ 120

Level 4: *cont.*

28. Find angle **(a)** using the clues below:

Angle (b) is acute.
Angle (a) is obtuse.
Angle (b) is greater than 45 degrees.
Both angles are divisible by 30.

▪ 120

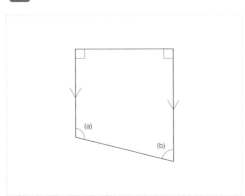

29. Adam covers some of the numbers on his dartboard to help him practise. All of the covered segments are next to each other. The sum of the angles of the covered segments is 198 degrees. How many numbers has Adam covered?

▪ 11

30. Majorton station is at the end of the main railway line. The lines from Lowell and Ashing also end at Majorton station, which covers an angle of 222 degrees.
The angle between the main line and the line to Ashing is **double** the angle between the main line and the line to Lowell.

In degrees, what is the angle between the main line and the line to Lowell?

▪ 46

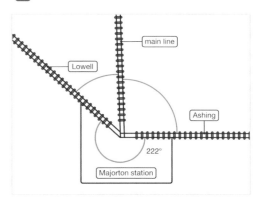

31. Find angle **(a)** using the clues below:

Angle (a) is acute.
Angle (b) is obtuse.
Both angles measure between 80 and 99 degrees.
Both angles are divisible by 5.

▪ 85

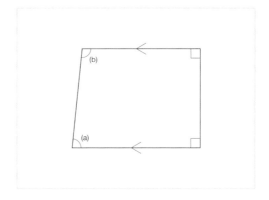

Identify, describe and represent reflection of a shape

Competency: Identify, describe and represent the position of a shape following a reflection or translation, using the appropriate language, and know that the shape has not changed.

Quick Search Ref: 10327

Correct: Correct.   **Wrong:** Incorrect, try again.   **Open:** Thank you.

Level 1: Understanding - Recognising lines of symmetry and reflective symmetry.

🌸 **Required:** 7/10   🌸 **Student Navigation:** on   🌸 **Randomised:** off

1. When reflecting a shape you:

1/3
- move the shape into a different position without flipping or rotating it.
- turn the shape around a central point.
- flip the shape over a mirror line to create a mirror image.

2. When reflecting a shape, the dimensions of the shape:

1/3
- never change - always change - sometimes change

3. What transformation is shown in the diagram?

1/3
- reflection - rotation - translation

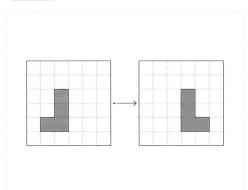

4. Does the dotted line represent a line of reflective symmetry?

1/2
- Yes - No

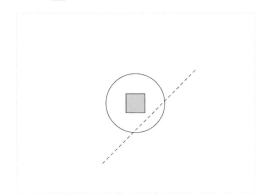

5. Which image shows a line of reflective symmetry?

1/4
- (i) - (ii) - (iii) - (iv)

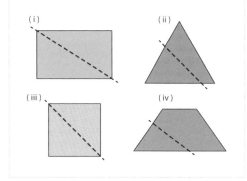
(i)   (ii)
(iii)   (iv)

6. What transformation is shown in the diagram?

1/3
- rotation - translation - reflection

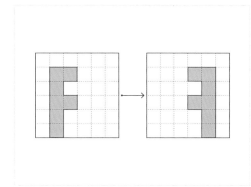

7. Which image shows a line of reflective symmetry?
1/4
- (i) - (ii) - (iii) - (iv)

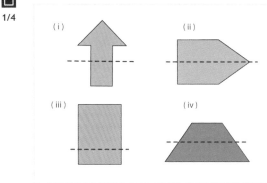
(i)   (ii)
(iii)   (iv)

8. Does the dotted line represent a line of reflective symmetry?

■ Yes ■ No

1/2

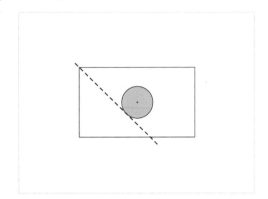

9. What transformation is shown in the diagram?

■ rotation ■ reflection ■ translation

1/3

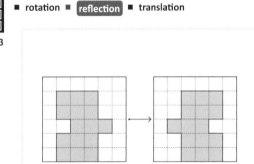

10. Which image shows a line of reflective symmetry?

■ (i) ■ (ii) ■ (iii) ■ (iv)

1/4

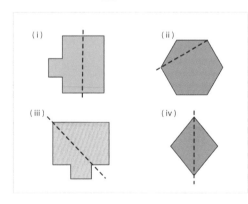

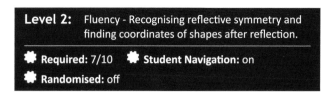**Level 2:** Fluency - Recognising reflective symmetry and finding coordinates of shapes after reflection.

✻ **Required:** 7/10   ✻ **Student Navigation:** on
✻ **Randomised:** off

11. Which diagram shows the original diagram reflected?

■ diagram (a) ■ diagram (b) ■ diagram (c)

1/3

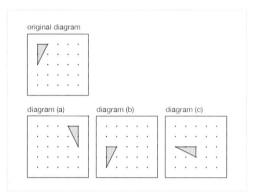

12. Which **two** shapes are a reflection of the original shape?

■ Shape A ■ Shape B ■ Shape C ■ Shape D

2/4

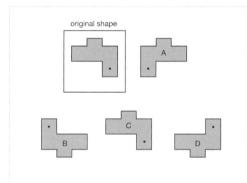

13. Which shape is a reflection of shape A?

■ Shape B ■ Shape C ■ Shape D ■ Shape E

1/4

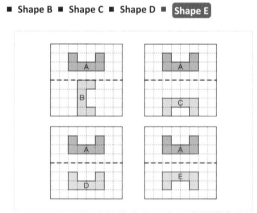

Level 2: *cont.*

14. If you reflect the shape over the mirror line, what are the new coordinates of point A?

- (4, 6) ■ (6, 6) ■ (9, 6) ■ (9, 3)

1/4

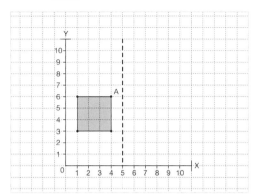

15. Which diagram shows a reflection of the original shape?

- diagram (a) ■ diagram (b) ■ diagram (c)

1/3

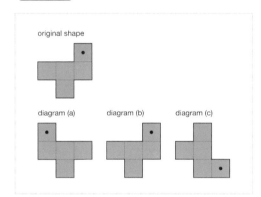

original shape

diagram (a)   diagram (b)   diagram (c)

16. Select the shape that is a reflection of shape L.

- Shape M ■ Shape N ■ Shape O ■ Shape P

1/4

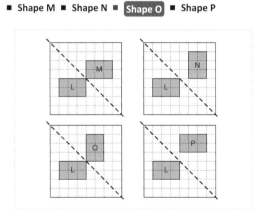

17. If you reflect the shape over the mirror line, what are the new coordinates of point A?

- (6, 9) ■ (5, 2) ■ (7, 2)

1/3

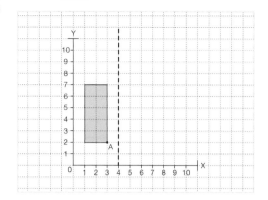

18. Which diagram shows the original diagram reflected?

- diagram (a) ■ diagram (b) ■ diagram (c)

1/3

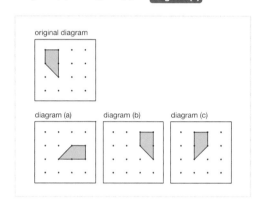

original diagram

diagram (a)   diagram (b)   diagram (c)

19. Which diagram shows a reflection of the original shape?

- diagram (a) ■ diagram (b) ■ diagram (c)

1/3

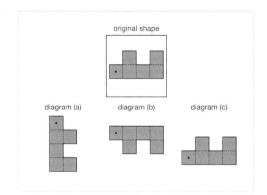

original shape

diagram (a)   diagram (b)   diagram (c)

Level 2: *cont.*

20. If you reflect the shape over the mirror line, what are the new coordinates of point A?

■ (6, 4) ■ (4, 8) ■ (4, 6)

1/3

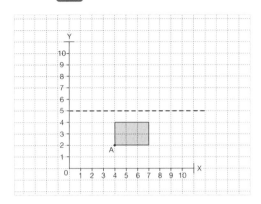

Level 3: Reasoning - Recognising transformation and finding coordinates after reflection.

✱ **Required:** 5/5   ✱ **Student Navigation:** on
✱ **Randomised:** off

21. What sequence of transformation is shown from shape 1 to shape 2 to shape 3 in the diagram?

■ rotation then reflection ■ reflection then translation
1/4 ■ translation then reflection ■ rotation then translation

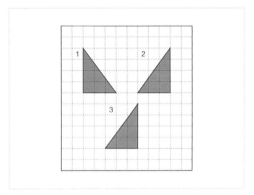

22. The blue rectangle is a reflection of the pink rectangle over the mirror line. What are the coordinates of point A?

■ (9, 1)

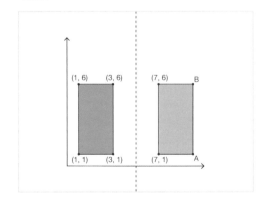

23. The green triangle is a reflection of the yellow triangle. What are the coordinates of the point A?

■ (9, 3)

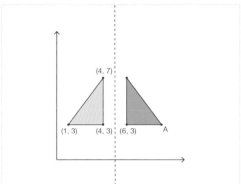

24. Mischa says, "When reflecting a shape on a grid, the coordinates of a point on the reflected shape will never be the same as the original shape". Is Mischa correct? Explain your answer.

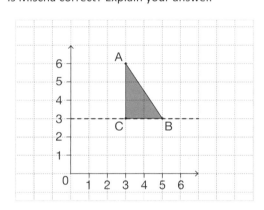

25. If the shape in each box is a reflection of the previous box, which boxes will contain the same shape as box 0?

3/6 ■ 1 ■ 2 ■ 3 ■ 4 ■ 5 ■ 6

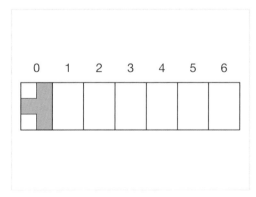

Level 4: Problem solving - Multi step problems with reflection of shapes.

✖ **Required:** 5/5   ✖ **Student Navigation:** on
✖ **Randomised:** off

26. When you fold along the mirror line, which numbers will be covered by shaded squares?

3/7   ▪ [1] ▪ 2 ▪ 3 ▪ [4] ▪ [5] ▪ 6 ▪ 7

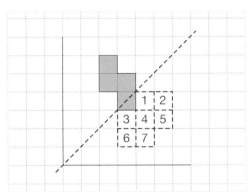

27. The coordinates of point A after it has been reflected are (9, 5). What are the coordinates of point B after it has been reflected?
Use brackets and a comma to represent your answer. For example, (1, 2).

▪ (13, 9)

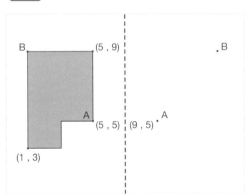

28. How many lines of reflective symmetry does a square have?

▪ 4

29. Which three numbers need to be shaded to make the pattern symmetrical in both mirror lines?

3/6   ▪ [1] ▪ 2 ▪ 3 ▪ [4] ▪ 5 ▪ [6]

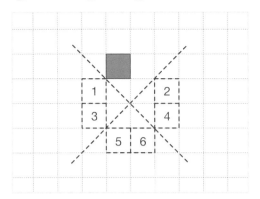

30. Point A has been reflected across the mirror line. What is the x-coordinate of any point on the reflective line of symmetry?

▪ 8

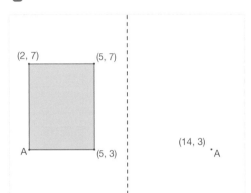

Identify, describe and represent rotation of a shape

Competency: Identify, describe and represent the position of a shape following a reflection or translation, using the appropriate language, and know that the shape has not changed.

Quick Search Ref: 10329

Correct: Correct.   **Wrong:** Incorrect, try again.   **Open:** Thank you.

Level 1: Understanding - Recognising rotation.

✿ **Required:** 7/10   ✿ **Student Navigation:** on   ✿ **Randomised:** off

1. When rotating a shape you:

   1/3
   - move the shape into a different position without flipping or rotating it.
   - turn the shape around a central point.
   - flip the shape over a mirror line to create a mirror image.

2. When rotating a shape, the dimensions of the shape:

   1/3
   - never change ■ always change ■ sometimes change

3. What transformation is shown in the diagram?

   1/3
   - reflection ■ rotation ■ translation

   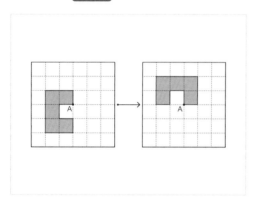

4. Is shape B a rotation of shape A?

   1/2
   - Yes ■ No

   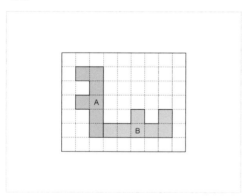

5. Which two shapes are a rotation of shape A?

   2/4
   - Shape B ■ Shape C ■ Shape D ■ Shape E

   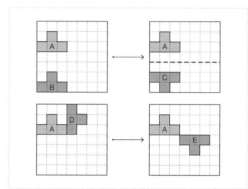

6. Shape Y is a rotation of shape X.

   1/2
   - True ■ False

   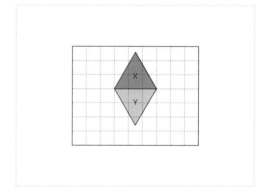

7. Which shape is a rotation of shape V?

   1/4
   - Shape W ■ Shape X ■ Shape Y ■ Shape Z

   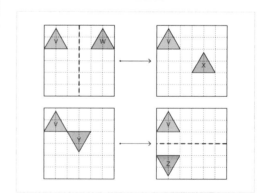

8. What transformation is shown in the diagram?

■ reflection ■ translation ■ rotation

1/3

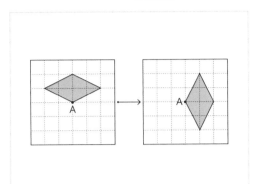

9. Which shape is a rotation of shape E?

■ Shape F ■ Shape G ■ Shape H ■ Shape I

1/4

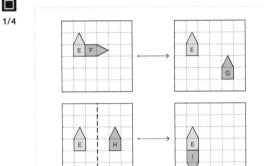

10. Is shape D a rotation of shape E?

■ Yes ■ No

1/2

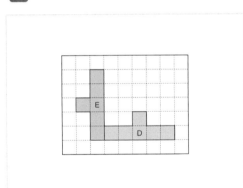

Level 2:   Fluency - Recognising degrees of rotation and finding coordinates of shapes after rotation.

✸ **Required:** 7/10   ✸ **Student Navigation:** on
✸ **Randomised:** off

11. Which diagram shows rotation of the shape in the original diagram?

■ diagram (a) ■ diagram (b) ■ diagram (c)

1/3

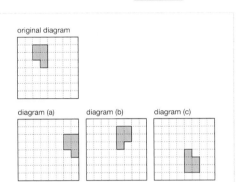

12. The triangle has been rotated around point C by how many degrees clockwise?

■ 90° ■ 180° ■ 270° ■ 360°

1/4

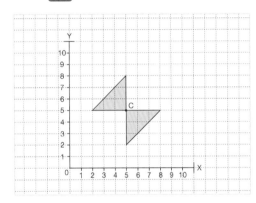

13. Which diagram shows rotation of the shape in the original diagram?

■ diagram (a) ■ diagram (b) ■ diagram (c)

1/3

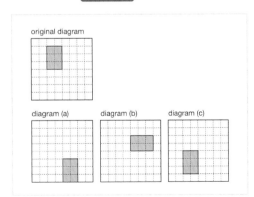

14. If you rotate the shape 90° clockwise around point B, what are the new coordinates of point C?

▪ (1, 5) ▪ (1, 9) ▪ (9, 1) ▪ (9, 9)

1/4

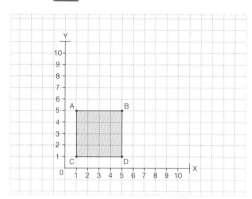

15. Which diagram shows rotation of the shape in the original diagram?

▪ diagram (a) ▪ diagram (b) ▪ diagram (c)

1/3

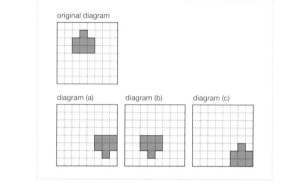

16. The blue shape has been rotated around point A by how many degrees clockwise?

▪ 90° ▪ 180° ▪ 270° ▪ 360°

1/4

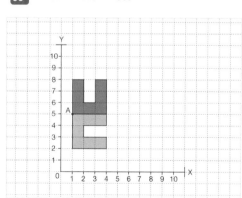

17. If you rotate the shape 90° clockwise around point C, what are the new coordinates of point B?

▪ (5, 10) ▪ (6, 1) ▪ (10, 5) ▪ (10, 9)

1/4

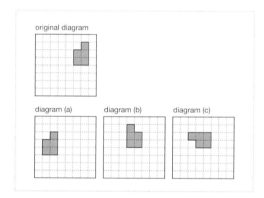

18. Which diagram shows rotation of the shape in the original diagram?

▪ diagram (a) ▪ diagram (b) ▪ diagram (c)

1/3

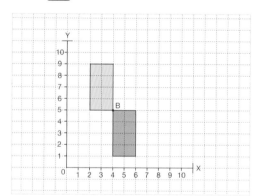

19. The yellow rectangle has been rotated around point B by how many degrees clockwise?

▪ 90° ▪ 180° ▪ 270° ▪ 360°

1/4

Level 2: *cont.*

20. If you rotate the shape 90° clockwise around point B, what are the new coordinates of point A?

1/4

■ (2, 9) ■ **(4, 9)** ■ (7, 6) ■ (9, 4)

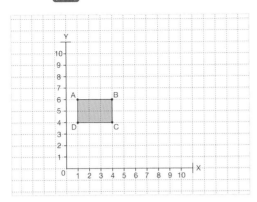

Level 3: Reasoning - Rotating shapes and finding coordinates after rotation.

🌼 **Required:** 5/5   🌼 **Student Navigation:** on
🌼 **Randomised:** off

21. Harry says, "Shape B is both a reflection and rotation of shape A".
Is Harry correct? Explain your answer.

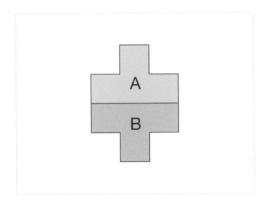

22. If you rotate the shape 270° clockwise around point C, what will the new coordinates of point G be?

1/5 ■ (2, 4) ■ **(4, 2)** ■ (8, 4) ■ (10, 0) ■ (12, 6)

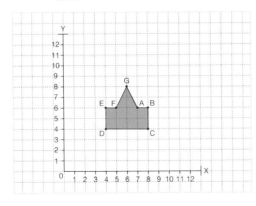

23. The blue triangle has been rotated around point C by how many degrees clockwise?

■ 45° ■ 135° ■ 180° ■ **225°** ■ 315°

1/5

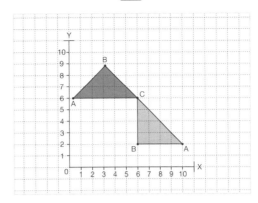

24. Rachel says, "If a shape is rotated, the original shape and the rotated shape will always have one coordinate which is the same in each".
Is Rachel correct? Explain your answer.

25. Jenny wants to create a pattern by rotating the rectangle three times around point D by 90°, 180° and 270° clockwise. After rotation, how many squares will her pattern contain in **total**?

■ **12**

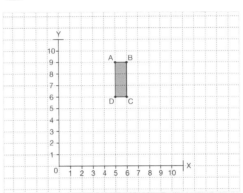

Level 4: Problem solving - Multi step problems involving rotation.

🌼 **Required:** 5/5   🌼 **Student Navigation:** on
🌼 **Randomised:** off

26. If you rotate the shape 180° clockwise around point B, what are the new coordinates of point D?
Give your answer in coordinate form. For example, (x, y).

■ **(7, 5)**

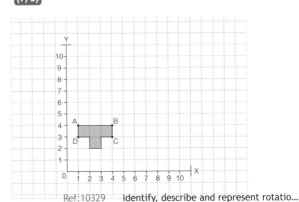

Ref:10329   Identify, describe and represent rotatio...

Level 4: *cont.*

27. If the rectangle is rotated 90°, 180° and 270° clockwise around point x, what three boxes will the letter C appear in?

3/7 ■ 1 ■ 2 ■ 3 ■ **4** ■ 5 ■ **6** ■ **7**

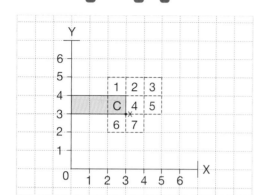

28. A and B are points on a square. If the square is rotated 180° clockwise around point B, what will the new coordinates of point A be?

a
b
c

■ **(7, 3)**

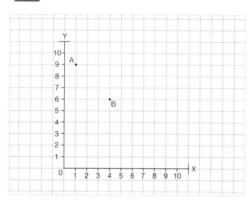

29. The square is rotated 90°, 180° and 270° clockwise around point a. What three boxes will the letter X appear in?

3/6 ■ **1** ■ 2 ■ 3 ■ **4** ■ 5 ■ **6**

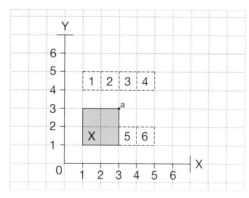

30. D and E are points on a rectangle. If the rectangle is rotated 90° clockwise around point E, what will the new coordinates of point D be?

a
b
c

■ **(8, 8)**

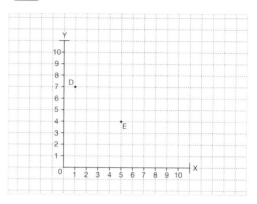

Identify, describe and represent translation of a shape

Competency: Describe movements between positions as translations of a given unit to the left/right and up/down.

Quick Search Ref: 10330

Correct: Correct.   **Wrong:** Incorrect, try again.   **Open:** Thank you.

Level 1: Understanding - Definitions and recognising transformations.

Required: 7/10   **Student Navigation:** on   **Randomised:** off

1. When translating a shape you:
   - ☐
   - ☒ **move the shape into a different position without flipping or rotating it.**
   - ☐
   1/3
   - flip the shape over a mirror line to create a mirror image.
   - turn the shape around a central point.

2. When translating a shape, the dimensions of the shape:
   - ☐
   - ☒
   - ☐
   1/3
   - **never change** - always change - sometimes change

3. What transformation is shown in the diagram?
   - ☐
   - ☒
   - ☐
   1/3
   - reflection - rotation - **translation**

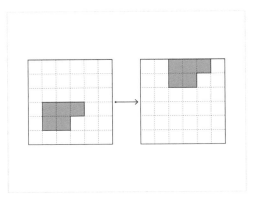

4. Is shape B a translation of shape A?
   - ☐
   - ☒
   - ☐
   1/2
   - Yes - **No**

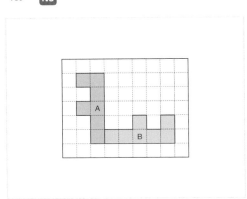

5. Which shape is a translation of shape A?
   - ☐
   - ☒
   - ☐
   1/4
   - **Shape B** - Shape C - Shape D - Shape E

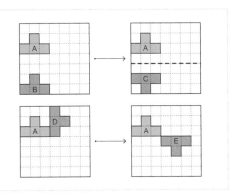

6. Shape Y is a translation of shape X.
   - ☐
   - ☒
   - ☐
   1/2
   - True - **False**

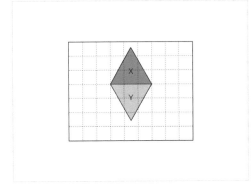

7. Which shape is a translation of shape V?
   - ☐
   - ☒
   - ☐
   1/4
   - Shape W - **Shape X** - Shape Y - Shape Z

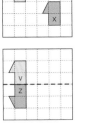

8. What transformation is shown in the diagram?

■ translation ■ reflection ■ rotation

1/3

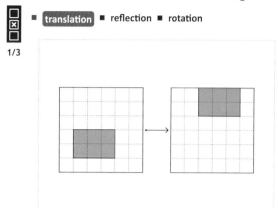

9. Which shape is a translation of shape E?

■ Shape F ■ Shape G ■ Shape H ■ Shape I

1/4

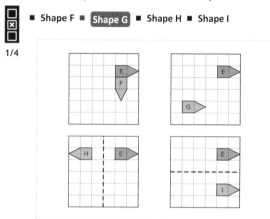

10. Is shape E a translation of shape D?

■ Yes ■ No

1/2

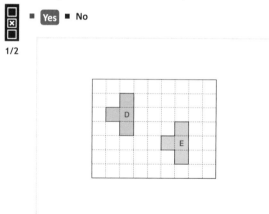

Level 2: Fluency - Recognising translation and finding coordinates of shapes after translation.

✱ Required: 7/10   ✱ Student Navigation: on
✱ Randomised: off

11. If you translate the shape 3 left and 2 up, what are the new coordinates of point B?

■ (3,5) ■ (3,7) ■ (7,3) ■ (9,7)

1/4

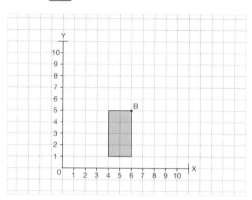

12. Describe the translation of shape A to shape B.

■ 3 right ■ 4 right ■ 5 right ■ 5 right, 2 up ■ 6 right

1/5

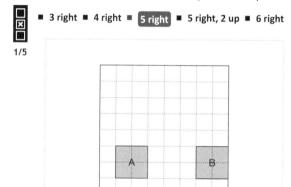

13. How would you describe the translation of the shape?

■ 4 right, 7 down ■ 4 right, 4 down ■ 5 right, 4 down

1/4 ■ 5 right, 7 down

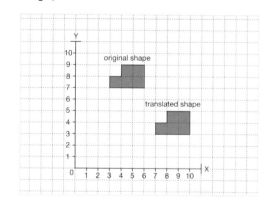

Level 2: cont.

14. Which diagram shows translation?

- diagram (a) ■ **diagram (b)** ■ diagram (c)

1/3

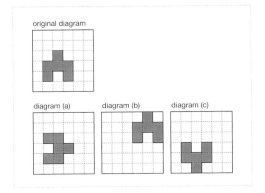

original diagram

diagram (a)   diagram (b)   diagram (c)

15. If you translate the shape 5 left and 1 down, what are the new coordinates of point A?

- **(3, 4)** ■ (3, 5) ■ (3, 6) ■ (4, 3)

1/4

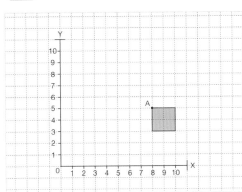

16. How would you describe the translation of the shape?

- 11 right, 2 down ■ **8 right, 2 down** ■ 9 right, 3 down

1/3

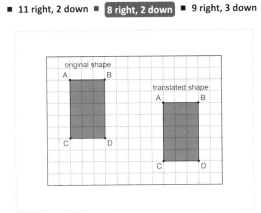

17. Which diagram shows translation of the shape in the original diagram?

- diagram (a) ■ diagram (b) ■ **diagram (c)**

1/3

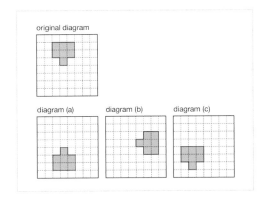

original diagram

diagram (a)   diagram (b)   diagram (c)

18. Describe the translation of shape X to shape Y.

- 1 right, 5 up ■ 5 down ■ **5 up** ■ 7 up

1/4

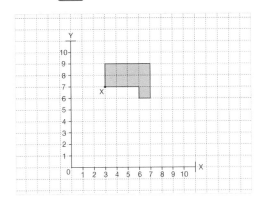

19. If you translate the shape 2 left and 6 down, what are the new coordinates of point X?

- (1, 7) ■ **(1, 1)** ■ (5, 1) ■ (3, 1)

1/4

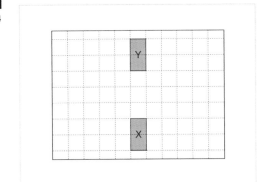

Level 2: *cont.*

20. How would you describe the translation of the shape?

- 3 left ■ 3 left, 4 up ■ 3 left, 6 up ■ 6 up

1/4

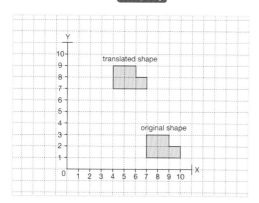

Level 3: Reasoning - Translating shapes and finding coordinates after translation.

🌼 **Required:** 5/5   🌼 **Student Navigation:** on

🌼 **Randomised:** off

21. Jerome says, "If the square is translated three down and one left, the coordinates of the translated square's point C will be (2, 6)."
Is he correct? Explain your answer.

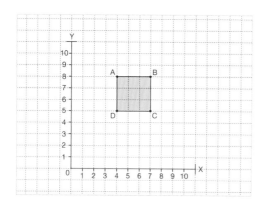

22. If you translate the shape so point D is at (0, 0), what will the new coordinates of point B be?

- (2, 4) ■ (4, 0) ■ (4, 2) ■ (8, 6)

1/4

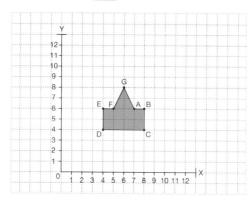

23. What sequence of transformation is shown from shape 1 to shape 2 to shape 3 in the diagram?

- rotation then reflection ■ reflection then translation
- translation then reflection ■ rotation then translation

1/4

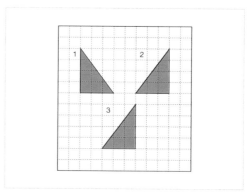

24. Tim says, "I can translate a square so that the translated shape is a reflection of the original shape. Therefore, I can do this with any shape".
Is Tim correct? Explain your answer.

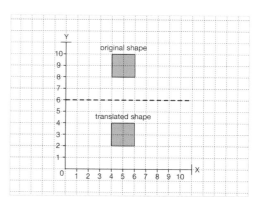

25. If you translate the shape so point F is at (0, 0), what will the new coordinates of point D be?

- (1, 3) ■ (2, 0) ■ (3, 1) ■ (6, 6)

1/4

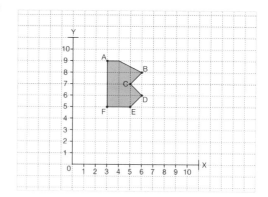

Level 4: Problem solving - Solve problems related to translation.

Required: 5/5   **Student Navigation:** on

Randomised: off

26. A triangle is translated four squares down and two squares right. The coordinates of the translated triangle are: (5, 8), (7, 9), (9, 6). What are the coordinates of the original triangle?

3/5

- (5, 13) ▪ (6, 13) ▪ (7, 10) ▪ (8, 10) ▪ (3, 12)

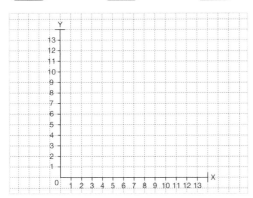

27. A parallelogram has been translated on a coordinate grid. What are the coordinates of point A, B and C?

3/5   ▪ (14, 2) ▪ (19, 5) ▪ (21, 2) ▪ (20, 2) ▪ (20, 5)

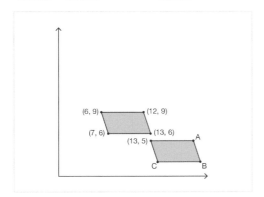

28. A rectangle is translated six squares up and three squares to the right. The coordinates of the translated rectangle are: (5, 7), (5, 10), (11, 10), (11, 7). What are the four coordinates of the original rectangle?

4/6

- (2, 1) ▪ (7, 5) ▪ (2, 4) ▪ (8, 4) ▪ (11, 9) ▪ (8, 1)

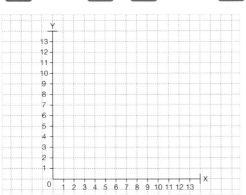

29. A rhombus has been translated on a coordinate grid. What are the coordinates of point A, B and C?

3/6

▪ (3, 6) ▪ (4, 5) ▪ (5, 4) ▪ (5, 8) ▪ (8, 5) ▪ (6, 3)

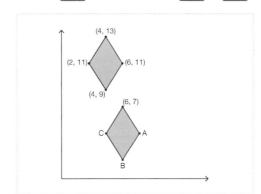

30. A triangle is translated five squares left and four squares up. The coordinates of the translated triangle are: (4, 4), (4, 7), (6, 4). What are the three coordinates of the original triangle?

3/6

▪ (0, 8) ▪ (0, 11) ▪ (3, 9) ▪ (9, 0) ▪ (9, 3) ▪ (11, 0)

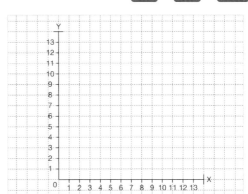

Reflection, rotation and translation of shapes

Competency: Identify, describe and represent the position of a shape following a reflection or translation, using the appropriate language, and know that the shape has not changed.

Quick Search Ref: 10019

Correct: Correct.　　Wrong: Incorrect, try again.　　Open: Thank you.

Level 1: Understanding - Definitions and recognising transformations.
❋ Required: 7/10　　❋ Student Navigation: on　　❋ Randomised: off

1. When **translating** a shape you:

- **move the shape into a different position without flipping or rotating it.**
- flip the shape over a mirror line to create a mirror image.
- turn the shape around a central point.

1/3

2. When **rotating** a shape you:

- move the shape into a different position without flipping or rotating it.
- **turn the shape around a central point.**
- flip the shape over a mirror line to create a mirror image.

1/3

3. When **reflecting** a shape you:

- move the shape into a different position without flipping or rotating it.
- turn the shape around a central point.
- **flip the shape over a mirror line to create a mirror image.**

1/3

4. When translating, rotating or reflecting a shape, the dimensions of the shape:

- **never change**
- always change
- sometimes change

1/3

5. Does the dotted line represent a line of reflective symmetry?

- Yes
- **No**

1/2

6. What transformation is shown in the diagram?

- reflection
- **rotation**
- translation

1/3

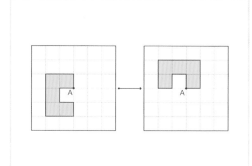

7. What transformation is shown in the diagram?

- **reflection**
- rotation
- translation

1/3

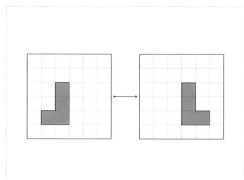

8. What transformation is shown in the diagram?

- reflection
- rotation
- **translation**

1/3

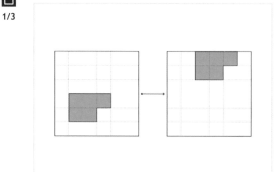

Level 1: *cont.*

9. What transformation is shown in the diagram?

■ reflection ■ rotation ■ translation

1/3

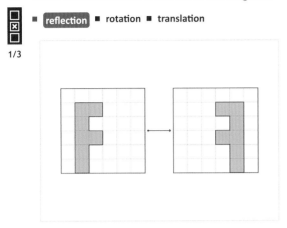

10. What transformation is shown in the diagram?

■ reflection ■ rotation ■ translation

1/3

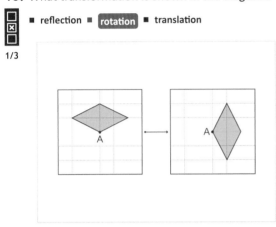

Level 2: Fluency - Recognising transformations and finding coordinates of shapes after transformation.

✿ **Required:** 7/10   ✿ **Student Navigation:** on
✿ **Randomised:** off

11. Which diagram shows the original diagram **reflected**?

■ diagram (a) ■ diagram (b) ■ diagram (c)

1/3

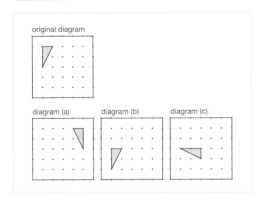

12. Describe the translation of shape A to shape B.

■ 4 right ■ 5 right ■ 5 right, 2 up ■ 6 right ■ 3 right

1/5

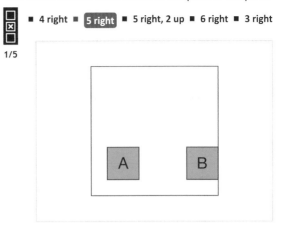

13. Which diagram shows **rotation**?

■ diagram (a) ■ diagram (b) ■ diagram (c)

1/3

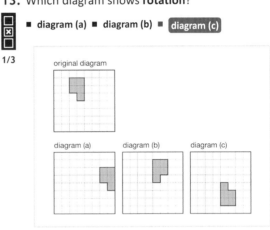

14. If you reflect the shape over the mirror line, what are the new coordinates of point A?

■ (4, 6) ■ (6, 6) ■ (9, 6) ■ (9, 3)

1/4

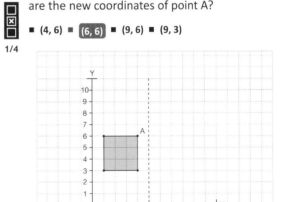

Level 2: *cont.*

15. The triangle has been rotated around point C by how many degrees clockwise?

■ 90° ■ **180°** ■ 270° ■ 360°

1/4

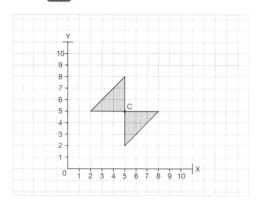

16. Which diagram shows translation?

■ diagram (a) ■ **diagram (b)** ■ diagram (c)

1/3

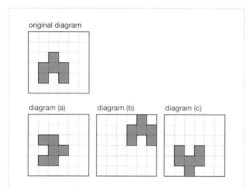

17. Which diagram shows a reflection of the original shape?

■ **diagram (a)** ■ diagram (b) ■ diagram (c)

1/3

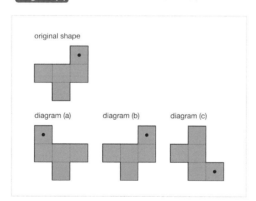

18. If you translate the shape 3 left and 2 up, what are the new coordinates of point B?

■ (3, 5) ■ **(3, 7)** ■ (7, 3) ■ (9, 7)

1/4

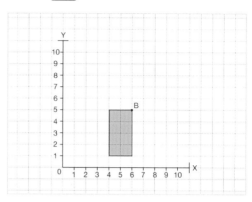

19. How would you describe the translation of the shape?

■ 11 right, 2 down ■ **8 right, 2 down** ■ 9 right, 3 down

1/3

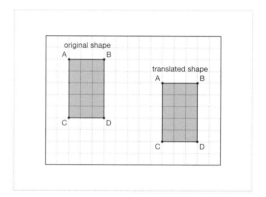

20. If you rotate the shape 90° clockwise around point B, what are the new coordinates of point C?

■ (1, 5) ■ **(1, 9)** ■ (9, 1) ■ (9, 9)

1/4

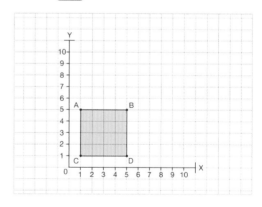

Level 3: Reasoning - Transforming shapes and finding coordinates after transformation.

✱ **Required:** 5/5   ✱ **Student Navigation:** on
✱ **Randomised:** off

21. What sequence of transformation is shown from shape 1 to shape 2 to shape 3 in the diagram?

1/4

- rotation then reflection ■ **reflection then translation**
- translation then reflection ■ rotation then translation

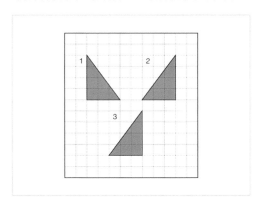

22. The blue rectangle is a reflection of the pink rectangle over the mirror line. What are the coordinates of point A?

■ **(9, 1)**

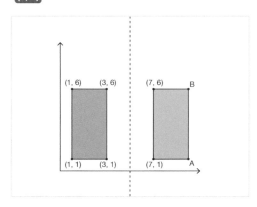

23. Jerome says, "If the square is translated three down and one left, the coordinates of the translated square's point C will be (2, 6)." Is he correct? Explain your answer.

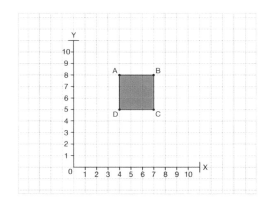

24. If you rotate the shape 270° clockwise around point C, what will the new coordinates of point G be?

1/5   ■ (2, 4) ■ **(4, 2)** ■ (8, 4) ■ (10, 0) ■ (12, 6)

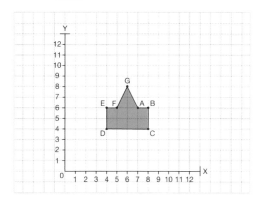

25. The green triangle is a reflection of the yellow triangle. What are the coordinates of the point A?

■ **(9, 3)**

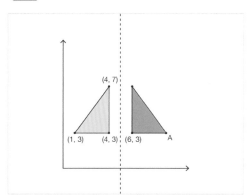

Level 4: Problem solving - Solve complex problems related to transformation.

✱ **Required:** 5/5   ✱ **Student Navigation:** on
✱ **Randomised:** off

26. A rectangle is translated six squares up and three squares to the right. The coordinates of the translated rectangle are: (5, 7), (5, 10), (11, 10), (11, 7). What are the four coordinates of the original rectangle?

4/6

■ **(2, 1)** ■ (7, 5) ■ **(2, 4)** ■ **(8, 4)** ■ (11, 9) ■ **(8, 1)**

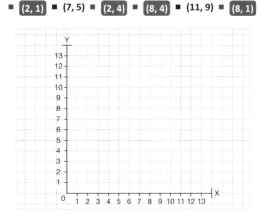

Level 4: *cont.*

27. A parallelogram has been translated on a coordinate grid. What are the coordinates of point A, B and C?

3/5 ▪ (14, 2) ▪ (19, 5) ▪ (21, 2) ▪ (20, 2) ▪ (20, 5)

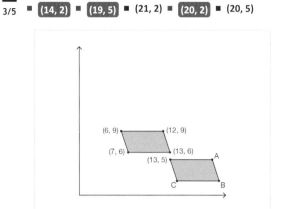

28. A triangle is translated four squares down and two squares right. The coordinates of the translated triangle are: (5, 8), (7, 9), (9, 6). What are the coordinates of the original triangle?

3/5

▪ (5, 13) ▪ (6, 13) ▪ (7, 10) ▪ (8, 10) ▪ (3, 12)

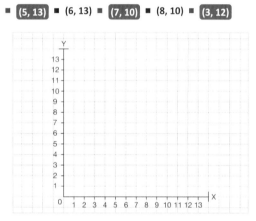

29. Which three numbers need to be shaded to make the pattern symmetrical in both mirror lines?

▪ 1 ▪ 2 ▪ 3 ▪ 4 ▪ 5 ▪ 6

3/6

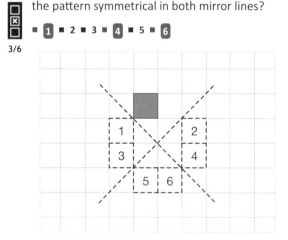

30. The square is rotated 90°, 180° and 270° clockwise around point a. What three boxes will the letter X appear in?

3/6 ▪ 1 ▪ 2 ▪ 3 ▪ 4 ▪ 5 ▪ 6

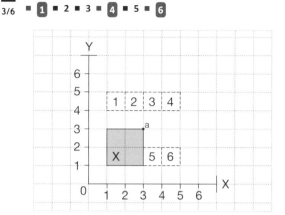

Mathematics

Y5

Statistics

Tables

Line Graphs

Complete, read and interpret information in tables

Competency: Complete, read and interpret information in tables including timetables.

Quick Search Ref: 10056

Correct: Correct.   **Wrong:** Incorrect, try again.   **Open:** Thank you.

Level 1:   Understanding - Read and compare data in a table with up to three columns.

✿ **Required:** 7/10   ✿ **Student Navigation:** on   ✿ **Randomised:** off

1. Which image shows data presented in a table?

▪ (a) ▪ (b) ▪ (c) ▪ (d)

1/4

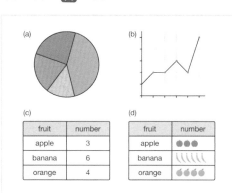

2. How many goals did Germany score at the World Cup in 2014?

▪ 18

	Argentina	England	Germany
2010	10	3	16
2014	8	2	18

3. A bus is travelling from Stopton to Canon. At what times does it stop at Yayville?
Select **two** options.

2/6   ▪ 10:20 ▪ 11:40 ▪ 10:05 ▪ 9:10 ▪ 11:25 ▪ 10:30

Bus Timetable

Stopton	09:10	10:30
Finetown	09:35	10:55
Yayville	10:05	11:25
Canon	10:20	11:40

4. How many pieces of fruit did the children in Year 1 eat in week 1?

▪ 132

class	week 1	week 2
Reception	121	113
Year 1	132	145
Year 2	127	125

5. Sort the number of goals scored, starting with the team and the year with the **smallest** number of goals scored.

▪ England 2014 ▪ England 2010 ▪ Argentina 2014
▪ Argentina 2010 ▪ Germany 2010 ▪ Germany 2014

team	2010	2014
Argentina	10	8
England	3	2
Germany	16	18

6. Which class ate 125 pieces of fruit in week 2?

▪ Reception ▪ Year 1 ▪ Year 2

1/3

	Reception	Year 1	Year 2
week 1	121	132	127
week 2	113	145	125

7. The bus is travelling from Stopton to Canon. At what times does the bus stop at Finetown? Select **two** options.

2/6 ▪ **10:55** ▪ 10:20 ▪ 11:40 ▪ 9:10 ▪ 10:30 ▪ **9:35**

Bus Timetable

Stopton	09:10	10:30
Finetown	09:35	10:55
Yayville	10:05	11:25
Canon	10:20	11:40

8. How many pieces of fruit did the children in Reception eat in week 1?

▪ **121**

class	week 1	week 2
Reception	121	113
Year 1	132	145
Year 2	127	125

9. Sort how much fruit was eaten by each class in each week, starting with the class and the week with the **smallest** amount of fruit eaten.

▪ **Reception, week 2** ▪ **Reception, week 1**
▪ **Year 2, week 2** ▪ **Year 2, week 1** ▪ **Year 1, week 1**
▪ **Year 1, week 2**

	Reception	Year 1	Year 2
week 1	121	132	127
week 2	113	145	125

10. Which team scored eight goals in the 2014 World Cup?

1/3 ▪ **Argentina** ▪ England ▪ Germany

team	2010	2014
Argentina	10	8
England	3	2
Germany	16	18

Level 2: Fluency - Read and compare data in a table with three columns.

✹ **Required:** 7/10 ✹ **Student Navigation:** on
✹ **Randomised:** off

11. Which sport is most popular in Year 6?

▪ Football ▪ **Rugby** ▪ Cricket ▪ Tennis

1/4

sport	Year 4	Year 5	Year 6
Football	10	12	7
Rugby	7	12	16
Cricket	5	7	1
Tennis	3	1	5

12. What time does train A arrive in Edgeton from Faceside?

▪ **12:27** ▪ 12:35 ▪ 12:52 ▪ 12:58 ▪ 13:07 ▪ 13:08

1/6

Train Timetable

	train A	train B	train C
Faceside	12:10	12:35	12:50
Edgeton	12:27	12:52	13:07
Vertiseas	12:46	13:08	13:21
Polytown	12:58	13:23	13:38

13. In 2015, how many more Christmas presents did Rachel receive than Bridget?

▪ 6

name	2014	2015	2016
Mark	15	13	8
Rachel	11	14	12
Bridget	9	8	14

14. How many more children prefer rugby in Year 6 than in Year 4?

▪ 9

sport	Year 4	Year 5	Year 6
Football	10	12	7
Rugby	7	12	16
Cricket	5	7	1
Tennis	3	1	5

15. How many minutes does train B take to get from Faceside to Vertiseas?

▪ 33

Train Timetable

	train A	train B	train C
Faceside	12:10	12:35	12:50
Edgeton	12:27	12:52	13:07
Vertiseas	12:46	13:08	13:21
Polytown	12:58	13:23	13:38

16. How many more Christmas presents did Bridget receive in 2016 than in 2014?

▪ 5

name	2014	2015	2016
Mark	15	13	8
Rachel	11	14	12
Bridget	9	8	14

17. At what time does train C arrive in Vertiseas?

1/6   ▪ 12:35 ▪ 12:46 ▪ 12:58 ▪ 13:08 ▪ 13:21 ▪ 13:38

Train Timetable

	train A	train B	train C
Faceside	12:10	12:35	12:50
Edgeton	12:27	12:52	13:07
Vertiseas	12:46	13:08	13:21
Polytown	12:58	13:23	13:38

18. Who received the most Christmas presents in 2015?

1/3   ▪ Mark ▪ Rachel ▪ Bridget

name	2014	2015	2016
Mark	15	13	8
Rachel	11	14	12
Bridget	9	8	14

19. How many minutes does the train A take to get from Faceside to Polytown.

▪ 48

20. How many more children prefer football to tennis in Year 4?

▪ 7

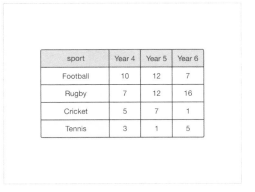

Level 3: Reasoning - Interpreting data in a timetable.

✹ **Required:** 5/7   ✹ **Student Navigation:** on
✹ **Randomised:** off

21. The 08:37 train from Pentley cannot set off until 08:46 because of a problem on the track. What time does it arrive at Hepburn?
Write your answer in digital time. For example, 08:00.

a
b
c

▪ 9:24 ▪ 09:24

22. Darren arrives at the train station in Brazley at 08:30. If he gets the next train, what time will he arrive in Coloton?

1/5 ▪ 09:05 ▪ 09:25 ▪ 09:35 ▪ 09:47 ▪ 10:21

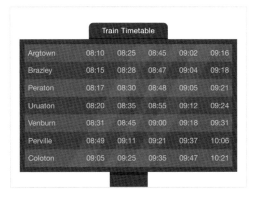

23. The 08:10 from Argtown does not depart until 08:23 because of engine problems. Joanie says this means that two trains will arrive at Peraton at the same time.
Is she correct? Explain your answer.

a
b
c

24. Katrina starts work in Hepburn at 09:30. What is the last train from Tryville she can catch to get to work on time?

1/5 ▪ 08:10 ▪ 08:25 ▪ 08:45 ▪ 09:02 ▪ 09:16

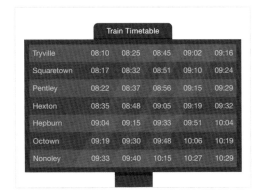

Level 3: *cont.*

25. Every morning when the train drivers start work, they must perform the following tasks before they can set off:

a
b
c

An inspection, which takes 40 minutes.
Fill the train with fuel, which takes 18 minutes.
Drive the train to the platform, which takes 27 minutes.

What time will the first driver begin work? Explain your reasoning.

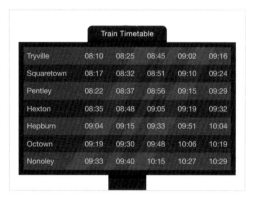

26. The 09:02 train from Argtown has mechanical problems and will not set off until 09:25. What time will it arrive at Venburn? Write your answer in digital time. For example, 08:00.

a
b
c

- `09:41`

27. Melissa arrives at Pentley train station at 09:00. She boards the next train to Nonoley. What time does she arrive?

1/5   - 09:33   - 09:40   - 10:15   - `10:27`   - 10:29

Level 4: Problem Solving - identifying data in a table with missing information.

✱ **Required:** 5/5   ✱ **Student Navigation:** on
✱ **Randomised:** off

28. A train arrives in Perville between 9:00 and 10:00. It takes this train **three minutes** to travel from Argtown to Brazley. How many minutes does it take the same train to get from Argtown to Perville?

1
2
3

- `46`

29. Mrs Halstead teaches Art. She plans the following activities, which she will use in all of her classes on Monday. According to her timetable, which is the **only class** that will be able to complete all four activities?

1/4

Activity 1 - 10 minutes
Activity 2 - 15 minutes
Activity 3 - 5 minutes
Activity 4 - 30 minutes

- Year 3 - Year 4 - `Year 5` - Year 6

time	class
09:00 - 09:45	Year 3
10:15 - 11:00	Year 4
12:30 - 13:30	Year 5
14:20 - 15:15	Year 6

30. The table shows the finishing times for runners in
a 5 km race.
How many **more** runners completed the race
between 20:00 and 29:59 minutes than runners
who completed the race between 15:00 and
19:59?

▪ 95

time (minutes)	number of runners
00:00 – 14:59	4
15:00 – 19:59	38
20:00 – 24:59	56
25:00 – 29:59	77
30:00 +	25

31. Mark arrives at Paperton bus stop at 8:48. How
many **minutes** will he have to wait for the next bus
to Pen Village?

▪ 53

Bus Timetable

	bus 1	bus 2	bus 3	bus 4	bus 5
Paperton	07:31	08:17	08:55	09:41	10:27
Stapleville	07:49	08:39			10:51
Pen Village		08:54		10:03	11:13
Markermont	08:11	09:09	09:32	10:22	11:25

32. How many minutes **longer** is the film than the
wildlife programme?

▪ 90

TV GUIDE

time	programme
17:30	cartoons
18:15	news
19:00	soaps
19:30	wildlife
20:45 - 23:30	film

Interpret information presented in a line graph

Competency: Solve comparison, sum and difference problems using information presented in a line graph.

Quick Search Ref: 10300

Correct: Correct.   **Wrong:** Incorrect, try again.   **Open:** Thank you.

Level 1:   Understanding - Read data in a line graph.

🌼 **Required:** 7/10   🌼 **Student Navigation:** on   🌼 **Randomised:** off

---

1.   A **line graph** is:

1/4

- a circular graph divided into segments, where each segment represents a fraction of the total amount.
- **a graph which uses lines to connect data points to show how something changes over time.**
- data presented in rows and columns.
- a chart that uses pictures to represent data.

2.   Which image shows data presented in a **line graph**?

1/4

- (a) ■ **(b)** ■ (c) ■ (d)

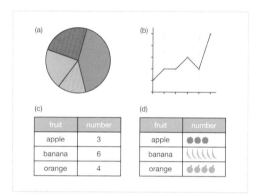

3.   On a line graph, the **x-axis** runs:

1/2

- **horizontally** ■ vertically

4.   What is the average temperature in Blackburn in April?

1/4

- 10°C ■ 8°C ■ **12°C** ■ 14°C

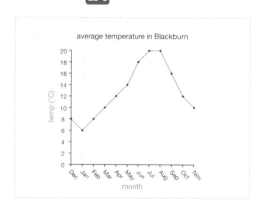

5.   How many birds did Keenan count on his bird table on Thursday?

- **6**

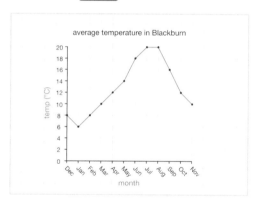

number of birds that have landed on Keenan's bird table

6.   In which **two** months was the average temperature in Blackburn 12°C?

2/7

- January ■ March ■ **April** ■ May ■ June
- September ■ **October**

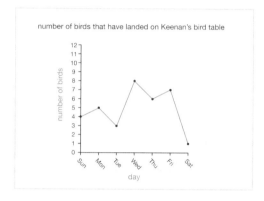

average temperature in Blackburn

7.   How tall was Chloe on her birthday in 2016?

- **117** ■ **117 cm** ■ **117 centimetres**

Chloe's height on her birthday each year

Level 1: *cont.*

8. In which month was the average temperature in Blackburn 16°C?

1/4

■ June ■ July ■ August ■ September

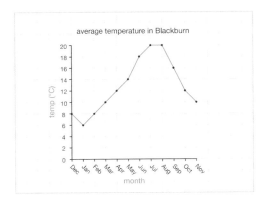

9. In which year was Chloe's average height 109 centimetres (cm)?

■ 2014

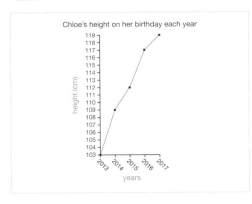

10. On what day did only one bird land on Keenan's bird table?

1/5

■ Wednesday ■ Thursday ■ Friday ■ Saturday
■ Sunday

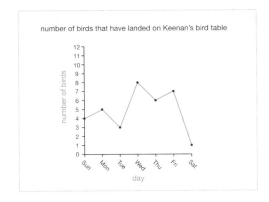

Level 2:   Fluency - Comparing data in a line graph.

✱ **Required:** 6/8   ✱ **Student Navigation:** on
✱ **Randomised:** off

11. The noise level at a football match is measured in decibels every ten minutes. From the 10th to the 50th minute sort the time of the noise level from lowest to highest volume.

■ 20 minutes ■ 10 minutes ■ 50 minutes
■ 30 minutes ■ 40 minutes

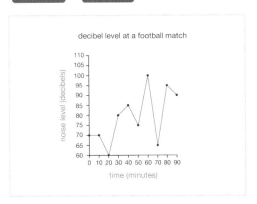

12. What is the difference in the number of birds between the day when the most birds landed on Keenan's bird table, and the day when the least amount of birds landed on the bird table.

■ 7

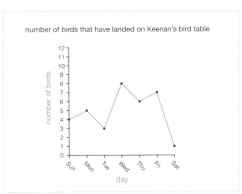

13. The noise level at a football match is measured in decibels every ten minutes. At what time in the first 50 minutes of the football match was the volume the loudest?

■ 40

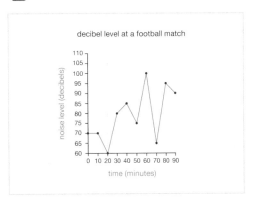

Level 2: *cont.*

14. Charlie records how many people visit his YouTube channel every hour. At what times did two people visit his channel.
Select **two** options.

2/5

■ `12:00` ■ 13:00 ■ 14:00 ■ `21:00` ■ 22:00

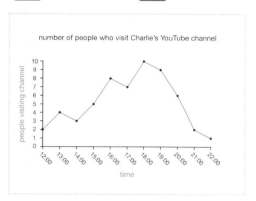

15. Between 12:00 and 17:00, Charlie's YouTube channel had the largest number of visitors at ___ o'clock.

■ `4`

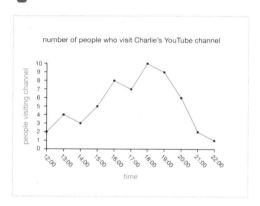

16. Find the noise level difference in decibels between the loudest point in the match and the quietest point.

■ `40`

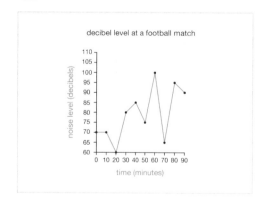

17. Order the days according to the number of birds that landed on Keenan's bird table, from the smallest to the largest number of birds.

■ `Saturday` ■ `Tuesday` ■ `Sunday` ■ `Monday`
■ `Thursday` ■ `Friday` ■ `Wednesday`

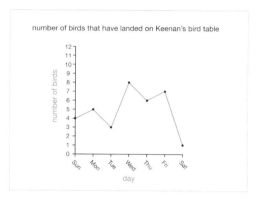

18. What is the difference in visitor numbers between the time when the **most** amount of people visited Charlie's YouTube channel, and the time when the **least** amount of people visited?

■ `9`

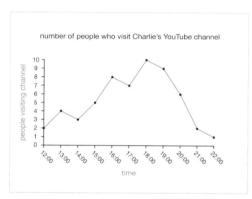

Level 3: Reasoning - Using multiple data points on a line graph.

✿ **Required:** 4/6   ✿ **Student Navigation:** on
✿ **Randomised:** off

19. John records how many eggs his hen lays each week. How many eggs does the hen lay in the first four weeks?

■ `16`

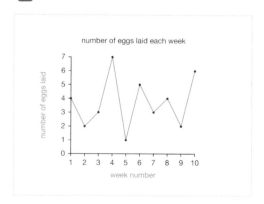

20. The temperature in Freetown was recorded every hour from 21:00 to 09:00. For how many hours was the temperature below 0°C?

1/5   ▪ **5 hours** ▪ **6 hours** ▪ **7 hours** ▪ **8 hours** ▪ **9 hours**

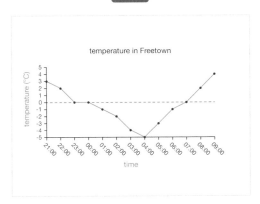

21. Hardcastle United played a home game against Bunchester City, which they won 1 - 0. The line graph shows the noise levels throughout the match. In what minute of the match do you think Hardcastle United scored their goal? Explain your answer.

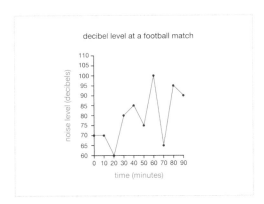

22. The speed of a steam train is recorded every 10 minutes on a two hour journey. For how many minutes did the train travel at 80 miles per hour (mph)?

▪ **20**

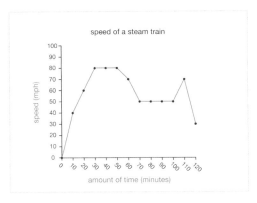

23. How many people visited Charlie's YouTube channel between 14:00 and 18:00?

▪ **30**

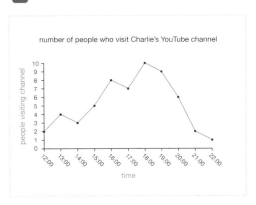

24. Mark sits at the side of the road and records data about the cars that drive past. He makes a note of the car model and colour. Should Mark use a line graph to record his data? Explain your answer.

Level 4:   Problem Solving - Using data from a line graph.

✳ **Required:** 3/5   ✳ **Student Navigation:** on
✳ **Randomised:** off

25. The speed of a train is recorded for the first 10 minutes of its journey. If the train continues to increase in speed at the same rate, how many miles per hour will it be travelling at after 25 minutes?

▪ **62.5**

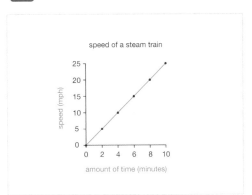

26. Frances works in a supermarket. Her boss asks her
to log how many customers are in the store each
hour. She forgets to include 24 customers who are
in the store cafe at 12:00, and also mistakenly
adds seven staff members to her count.
How many **customers** were actually in store at
12:00?

■ 52

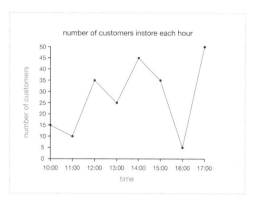

27. A children's event takes place at a theatre and the
stewards are told they are only allowed to let
people enter in 10 minute intervals. What is the
total number of people who enter the theatre
after 40 minutes?

■ 31

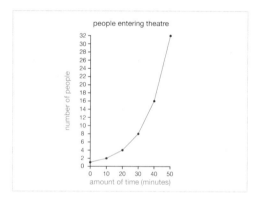

28. Jack's heart rate is checked every five minutes
during an exercise session. How many beats per
minute (bpm) has his heart rate risen by after 22
minutes?

■ 45

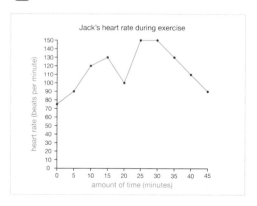

29. Phil's doctor told him to take a hot bath for **30
minutes** to help ease his sore back. The graph
shows the water level from the moment
Phil started to run the bath to after he got out and
emptied the bath.
Phil didn't get into the bath while it was running
and he emptied the water as soon as he got out.
How many minutes longer should Phil have stayed
in the bath?

■ 16

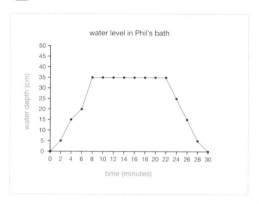

LbQ Super Deal
Class set of tablets and charging cabinet

Class charging & storage cabinet

\+ **32 x** Pupil 7" HD tablets with protective cover

\+ **1 x** Teacher 10" HD tablet with protective cover

*Special Offer Price

£1,100 per year on 3 years compliant operating lease

Subject to a £150 initial documentation fee

LbQ Question Set subscription required to be eligible

Min 1 LbQ subscription per set £200/year or £500/3 years

Learning by Questions App pre-loaded

Includes 3 years advanced replacement warranty on tablets (damage not covered)

Prices exclude VAT and delivery

Option to renew equipment or purchase at end of agreement

Available in United Kingdom and Republic of Ireland only

Product Code TC001

£1,100* per year for 3 years including warranty

Place your orders with our sales partner LEB who will organise the paperwork for you:

Email: orders@lbq.org
Tel: 01254 688060

Specifications

Charging & Storage Cabinet

- 32-bay up to 10" tablet charging cabinet
- 2 easy access sliding shelves – 16 bays on each shelf
- 4 efficient quiet fans for ventilation
- Locking Doors (4 keys)
- 4 castors / 2 x handling bars Overload, leakage and lightning surge protection
- CE / ROHS / FCC compliancy
- Warranty 3 years

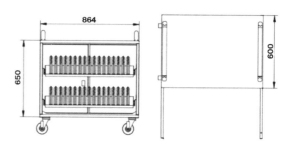

Student and Teacher tablets configuration

All tablets with LbQ Tablet Tasks App pre-loaded and installed in cabinet including charging cables and mains adapters for quick and easy deployment when onsite in classroom.

	7" Android Tablet with Protective Cover	10" Android Tablet with Protective Cover
Display		
1920 * 1200 IPS	✓	✓
16:10 Display ratio	✓	✓
Capacitive 5-touch	Capacitive 5-touch	Capacitive 10-touch
System		
Cortex 64bit Quad Core 1.5GHz CPU	✓	✓
2GB of RAM	✓	✓
16Gb of storage	✓	✓
Android 7.0	✓	✓
Front 2M and rear 5M Camera	✓	✓
Input / Output Ports		
1 x Micro SD Slot	✓	✓
1 x Micro USB (PC / device / charger)	✓	✓
Micro-HDMI output	✓	✓
1 x Earphone, 1 x Speaker, 1 x Mic	1 x Earphone, 1 x Speaker, 1 x Mic	1 x Earphone, 2 x Speaker, 1 x Mic
Communication		
Wifi – 802.11a/b/g/n	✓	✓
GPS module	✓	✓
Bluetooth	✓	✓
Power		
5V 2A	✓	✓
Battery	3000mAh battery	7000mAh battery
Physical		
Colour: Metal black	✓	✓
Weight:	230g	560g
Dimensions:	192 x 112 x 9mm (approx.)	263 x 164 x 9mm (approx.)
Warranty		
3 years Advanced Replacement for faulty tablets - does not cover damage CE / ROHS / FCC compliant	✓	✓

Learning by Questions